FINITE DIFFERENCES
FOR
ACTUARIAL STUDENTS

FINITE DIFFERENCES
FOR
ACTUARIAL STUDENTS

by

HARRY FREEMAN, C.M.G., M.A., F.I.A.

CAMBRIDGE

Published for the Institute of Actuaries

AT THE UNIVERSITY PRESS

1965

517
F85-1

PUBLISHED BY
THE SYNDICS OF THE CAMBRIDGE UNIVERSITY PRESS

Bentley House, 200 Euston Road, London, N.W.1
American Branch: 32 East 57th Street, New York, N.Y. 10022
West African Office: P.O. Box 33, Ibadan Nigeria

First Edition, published as
Mathematics for Actuarial

Students. Part II	1939
Reprinted	1940
	1945
	1946
	1947
	1948
	1949
	1952

Second Edition, published as
Finite Differences for

Actuarial Students	1960
Reprinted	1962
	1965

Printed in Great Britain at the University Printing House, Cambridge
(Brooke Crutchley, University Printer)

CONTENTS

CONTENTS   vii

PREFACE

In view of the recent alterations in the syllabus for the actuarial Examinations it was decided to publish separately the section of Part II of Mathematics for Actuarial Students relating to Finite Differences. The present book contains therefore the first nine chapters of the earlier book with only a few minor amendments.

The problems on Probabilities and Statistics which were originally included in the Miscellaneous Examples have been replaced by problems in Finite Differences.

H.F.

May 1959

NOTATION

$P_n(x)$ a polynomial (i.e., a rational integral function) of degree n in x.

$n_{(r)}$ $$\frac{n(n-1)(n-2)\ldots(n-r+1)}{r(r-1)(r-2)\ldots3.2.1}=\frac{n^{(r)}}{r!},$$ where n may be positive or negative, integral or fractional.

This is represented in other works by the symbols $\binom{n}{r}$ or n_r; see *J.I.A.* vol. LXIII, p. 58.

$n^{(r)}$ $n(n-1)(n-2)\ldots(n-r+1)$.

There seems to be no recognized symbol for the more general factorial $n(n-h)(n-2h)\ldots(n-\overline{r-1}h)$. It may sometimes be convenient to represent this by the same symbol $n^{(r)}$, but in that case the symbol must be specially defined and consistently used. Cf. *post*, p. 19.

$n^{(-r)}$ $$\frac{1}{(n+1)(n+2)\ldots(n+r)}=\frac{1}{(n+r)^{(r)}}.$$

A different notation is employed in certain other works—see *post*, p. 19.

$\triangle^t u_a$ ͖ₑ...   the divided difference of order t. This notation is explained and reference is made to other notations in Chapter III.

Paragraphs and examples marked with an asterisk, thus *, are intended for the advanced student only, and need not be read by students preparing for Part I of the Institute Examinations.

REFERENCES

J.I.A. *Journal of the Institute of Actuaries.*
T.F.A. *Transactions of the Faculty of Actuaries.*
J.S.S. *Journal of the Institute of Actuaries Students' Society.*

CHAPTER I

DEFINITIONS AND FUNDAMENTAL FORMULAE

1. The function $y = a + bx + cx^2 + \ldots + kx^n$ is a rational integral function of the nth degree in x, where the indices are positive integers, n being the greatest, and $a, b, c \ldots k$ are constants, of which $k \neq 0$ but the others are unrestricted.

A rational integral function is also called a polynomial, and it is convenient to represent a polynomial of the nth degree as $P_n(x)$.

Consider the simple polynomial $y = u_x = 1 + x + x^2$. It is quite easy to obtain the value of y corresponding to any value of x by substituting that value of x on the right-hand side of the equation. For example

x	0	1	2	3	4	5	6	7	8
y	1	3	7	13	21	31	43	57	73

It will be found that for successive integral values of x in the above table the values of y have interesting properties. If from each value of y the previous value of y be subtracted, we obtain a new set of figures:

(α) 2 4 6 8 10 12 14 16

and if the subtraction be performed on these figures in the same way the new differences are

(β) 2 2 2 2 2 2 2

The sequence of 2's in (β) is not a mere coincidence: it will be shown later that when y has the value supposed all the terms in (β) have the same value, 2, however far the series extends.

This leads us to another method of obtaining values of y. Suppose that we write down the original table in a different form, and include in the table the two sets of figures (α) and (β) thus:

x	y	(α)	(β)
0	1		
		2	
1	3		2
		4	
2	7		2
		6	
3	13		2
		8	
4	21		2
		10	
5	31		2
		12	
6	43		2
		14	
7	57		2
		16	
8	73		

We can now find any further value of y by extending the columns (α) and (β). We must however work from (β) to (α) and then to y instead of from y to (α) and then to (β) as has already been done. For example, to obtain the value of y when x has the value 9, i.e. to obtain u_9, a new 2 must be inserted in the (β) column: the new value in the (α) column will be $16+2=18$, and the required value of y will be $73+18=91$. To find u_{10} the process is continued. Any value of y corresponding to an integral value of x can be obtained in a similar manner.

2. The above is a particular instance of a far more general set of operations. We have used the simplest possible numerical values of x, namely the natural numbers, and we have evolved our example from a known quadratic function $y=u_x=1+x+x^2$. As a general rule the form of the function is not known and the given values of x are not necessarily consecutive integers.

3. Now suppose that instead of numerical values of x differing by unity we have the following consecutive values of x:

$$a,\ a+h,\ a+2h,\ a+3h,\ \dots,$$

where the values of x differ by a quantity h instead of by unity.

Then if the function be still $y = u_x$ the values of y corresponding to the above values of x will be

$$u_a, \ u_{a+h}, \ u_{a+2h}, \ u_{a+3h}, \ \dots.$$

In order to form a column similar to column (α) above we shall have to write down

$$u_{a+h} - u_a, \ u_{a+2h} - u_{a+h}, \ u_{a+3h} - u_{a+2h}, \ \dots.$$

These are called the *first differences* of the function $y = u_x$ and are denoted by

$$\Delta u_a, \ \Delta u_{a+h}, \ \Delta u_{a+2h}, \ \dots,$$

where Δ is not a quantity but a symbol representing an "operation".

Column (β), being the differences of column (α), will be

$$(u_{a+2h} - u_{a+h}) - (u_{a+h} - u_a),$$

$$(u_{a+3h} - u_{a+2h}) - (u_{a+2h} - u_{a+h}),$$

$$\dots\dots\dots\dots\dots\dots\dots\dots$$

or, more shortly,

$$\Delta u_{a+h} - \Delta u_a,$$

$$\Delta u_{a+2h} - \Delta u_{a+h},$$

$$\dots\dots\dots\dots\dots\dots\dots$$

These are called the *second differences* of u_x and are denoted by

$$\Delta^2 u_a, \ \Delta^2 u_{a+h}, \ \Delta^2 u_{a+2h} \ \dots,$$

where, it must be emphasized, the symbol Δ^2 does not represent the square of a quantity but denotes the repetition of the operation Δ.

Similarly, third, fourth, ... nth differences, formed in exactly the same way, are denoted by

$$\Delta^3 u_a, \ \Delta^4 u_a \ \dots \ \Delta^n u_a.$$

4. Before forming a *difference table* similar to that in paragraph 1, it is convenient to introduce alternative names for x and y in our equation $y = u_x$. Where our ultimate object is to obtain numerical values of x or y, the independent variable is often termed the *argument*, and the corresponding value of y the *entry*.

In a table of logarithms the number itself is the argument and the logarithm the entry. The converse holds in a table of antilogarithms, where the logarithm is the argument. Similarly in a table of sin α, α is the argument and the sine the entry, whereas α is the entry in a table of $\sin^{-1} \alpha$.

5. Our new difference table is therefore

Argument	Entry	First differences	Second differences	Third differences
a	u_a			
		Δu_a		
$a+h$	u_{a+h}		$\Delta^2 u_a$	
		Δu_{a+h}		$\Delta^3 u_a$
$a+2h$	u_{a+2h}		$\Delta^2 u_{a+h}$	
		Δu_{a+2h}		$\Delta^3 u_{a+h}$
$a+3h$	u_{a+3h}		$\Delta^2 u_{a+2h}$	
		Δu_{a+3h}		$\Delta^3 u_{a+2h}$
$a+4h$	u_{a+4h}		$\Delta^2 u_{a+3h}$	
		Δu_{a+4h}		
$a+5h$	u_{a+5h}			

The first term in the table (u_a) is called the *leading term*, and the differences which stand at the head of the respective columns, namely Δu_a, $\Delta^2 u_a$, $\Delta^3 u_a$ ..., are called the *leading differences*.

6. Although we have expressed the terms in the difference table by the use of Δ symbols, it is quite easy to obtain any difference in terms of the function alone.

For example, $\Delta^3 u_a$ is the difference between $\Delta^2 u_{a+h}$ and $\Delta^2 u_a$, or $\Delta^3 u_a = \Delta^2 u_{a+h} - \Delta^2 u_a$.

Again, $\Delta^2 u_a$ is the difference between Δu_{a+h} and Δu_a, or

$$\Delta^2 u_a = \Delta u_{a+h} - \Delta u_a,$$

and as $\Delta u_a = u_{a+h} - u_a,$

we have $\Delta^3 u_a = \Delta^2 u_{a+h} - \Delta^2 u_a$

$$= (\Delta u_{a+2h} - \Delta u_{a+h}) - (\Delta u_{a+h} - \Delta u_a)$$

$$= \Delta u_{a+2h} - 2\Delta u_{a+h} + \Delta u_a$$

$$= (u_{a+3h} - u_{a+2h}) - 2(u_{a+2h} - u_{a+h}) + (u_{a+h} - u_a)$$

$$= u_{a+3h} - 3u_{a+2h} + 3u_{a+h} - u_a.$$

7. It is a simple matter to construct a difference table from a given set of data.

Consider the following examples:

Example 1.

Construct a difference table from the following values, where y is a function of x:

x	y	Δy	$\Delta^2 y$	$\Delta^3 y$
1	1			
		7		
2	8		12	
		19		6
3	27		18	
		37		6
4	64		24	
		61		6
5	125		30	
		91		6
6	216		36	
		127		
7	343			

Example 2.

Show that, in the following table of annuity-values, third differences are practically constant:

Argument x	Entry a_x	Δa_x	$\Delta^2 a_x$	$\Delta^3 a_x$
35	14·298			
		−·154		
36	14·144		−·004	
		−·158		+·001
37	13·986		−·003	
		−·161		·000
38	13·825		−·003	
		−·164		+·001
39	13·661		−·002	
		−·166		+·001
40	13·495		−·001	
		−·167		
41	13·328			

It will be observed that in Ex. 1 third differences are invariably the same. In the second example, however, third differences are not quite constant, although the error in assuming them to be so is very small.

The difference in the two examples lies in the fact that, while the first function is $y = x^3$, the table of annuity-values from which the data in the second example have been taken does not conform to a simple mathematical law and, further, the values do not naturally terminate with the third decimal place, but are rounded off at that place.

Example 3.

Assuming third differences constant, find the values of u_2 and u_3 from the data:

x	4	5	6	7	8
u_x	·35	·88	1·71	2·90	4·51

Construct the difference table from the given values, and fill in the vacant spaces in the $\Delta^3 u_x$ column with the constant third difference, thus:

x	u_x	Δu_x	$\Delta^2 u_x$	$\Delta^3 u_x$
2	$-$ ·05			
		·11		
3	$+$ ·06		·18	
		·29		·06
4	$+$ ·35		·24	
		·53		·06
5	$+$ ·88		·30	
		·83		·06
6	$+1·71$		·36	
		1·19		·06
7	$+2·90$		·42	
		1·61		
8	$+4·51$			

8. Now it has been stated above that a convenient method for expressing the difference between two successive values of a function u_{a+h} and u_a is by the symbol Δ prefixed to u_a, so that $\Delta u_a = u_{a+h} - u_a$. It will be seen therefore that to find Δu_a we perform two operations: we change u_a to u_{a+h} and subtract u_a from it. The new function u_{a+h} resulting from the first of these operations is denoted symbolically by $E u_a$, and the double operation may be written

$$\Delta u_a = E u_a - u_a.$$

This gives

$$E u_a = u_a + \Delta u_a.$$

$E u_a$ may therefore otherwise be expressed as the sum of u_a and its first difference.

Suppose that in either of the above relations the u_a which occurs in each of the terms be omitted. Then we can state that the two operations denoted by "E" and "Δ" are connected by the symbolic identity

$$E \equiv 1 + \Delta.$$

It must be distinctly understood that we have not "factorized out" u_a in the relation $Eu_a = u_a + \Delta u_a$, and that we must relate the symbols to the functions on which they operate. If, therefore, we were using the equivalence $\Delta \equiv E - 1$, and we operated on the function sin x, it would be wrong to say that $\Delta \sin x = E \sin x - 1$. The correct statement is $\Delta \sin x = E \sin x - \sin x$. When we are dealing with symbols of operation we cannot treat any of them as quantities, and on forming the algebraic or trigonometrical identity the function must be included in all three terms. In other words, in the identity $E \equiv 1 + \Delta$ the 1 is a symbol of operation just as are E and Δ, and its meaning is that the function on which it operates is to be taken once without alteration.

9. In the same way as Δ^2 denotes, when operating on a function, the difference of the difference of the function, i.e. the second difference, so E^2 denotes the operation of repeating E. That is to say

$$E^2 u_x = E . E u_x = E u_{x+h} = u_{x+2h},$$

$$E^3 u_x = u_{x+3h},$$

$$\dots\dots\dots\dots\dots$$

and, generally, $E^n u_x = u_{x+nh}.$

Care must be taken not to confuse the expression $E^2 u_x$ with $(E u_x)^2$. For example,

$$E^2 (x^2) = (x + 2h)^2 = x^2 + 4hx + 4h^2,$$

but $(Ex)^2 = (x + h)^2 = x^2 + 2hx + h^2.$

10. It is evident that the first difference of a function of the form cx, where c is a constant, is constant: for $\Delta cx = c(x + h) - cx = ch$, which is constant.

Let us consider the effect of differencing a function of x of higher degree than the first.

Example 4.

Difference successively the functions (i) $y = bx^2$ and (ii) $y = ax^3$.

(i) $\Delta bx^2 = b\,(x+h)^2 - bx^2 = 2bhx + bh^2$,

$\Delta^2 bx^2 = \Delta\,(2bhx + bh^2) = 2bh\,(x+h) + bh^2 - 2bhx - bh^2 = 2bh^2$,

and since $2bh^2$ is constant all higher differences will be zero.

(ii) $\Delta ax^3 = a\,(x+h)^3 - ax^3 = 3ahx^2 + 3ah^2x + ah^3$,

$\Delta^2 ax^3 = 6ah^2x + 6ah^3$,

and $\Delta^3 ax^3 = 6ah^3$, higher differences vanishing.

Collating the above results, we have that

the first differences of functions of the form cx are constant,

the second   ,,   ,,   ,, bx^2 ,,

the third   ,,   ,,   ,, ax^3 ,,

It follows therefore that third differences of $ax^3 + bx^2 + cx + d$ are constant, for before we reach the third differences the terms bx^2, cx and d will have been eliminated.

11. The above considerations lead us to the following important proposition:

If u_x be a polynomial of the nth degree in x, then the nth difference of the function is constant.

Let the function be

$$u_x = ax^n + bx^{n-1} + cx^{n-2} + \ldots + s;$$

then $\Delta u_x = a\,(x+h)^n + b\,(x+h)^{n-1} + c\,(x+h)^{n-2} + \ldots + s$

$$- ax^n - bx^{n-1} - cx^{n-2} - \ldots - s$$

$$= anx^{n-1}h + b'x^{n-2} + c'x^{n-3} + \ldots + r',$$

where b', c', $\ldots$ r' are coefficients involving h but not x.

Similarly,

$$\Delta^2 u_x = an\,(n-1)\,x^{n-2}h^2 + b''x^{n-3} + c''x^{n-4} + \ldots + q'',$$

and so on.

Each time that we difference we lower the degree of the function by unity. After differencing n times no terms after the first will appear, and we shall be left with

$$\Delta^n u_x = an\,(n-1)\,(n-2)\,(n-3)\,...\,2\,.\,1\,.\,h^n \text{ or } an!\,h^n,$$

which is independent of x and is therefore constant.

As a corollary we may note that $\Delta^{n+1} u_x = 0$, a property of a polynomial of the nth degree which is of value in the practical application of the work.

The converse proposition is of importance: if the $(n+1)$th difference of a function is the first to become zero, the function is a polynomial of not more than the nth degree.

12. It should be remembered that we are dealing here with a particular form of function. Should the function be other than a polynomial the nth difference will not vanish however great n may be. Thus, we have

Example 5.

Find the nth difference of e^x.

$$\Delta e^x = e^{x+h} - e^x = e^x\,(e^h - 1),$$

$$\Delta^2 e^x = (e^h - 1)\,(e^{x+h} - e^x) = e^x\,(e^h - 1)^2.$$

Similarly, $\Delta^3 e^x = e^x\,(e^h - 1)^3,$

....

Generally, $\Delta^n e^x = e^x\,(e^h - 1)^n$, which is still a function of x, and is therefore not constant.

13. Although it has been said that the symbols Δ and E are in no sense algebraic quantities, our definitions, namely that Δ^n denotes the operation of differencing the function n times, and that E^n denotes the operation of obtaining a new function when the argument is increased by n unit differences, enable us to apply to these symbols the ordinary algebraic laws. For example,

$$\Delta\,(u_x + u_y) = u_{x+h} + u_{y+h} - u_x - u_y \text{ or } u_{x+h} - u_x + u_{y+h} - u_y,$$

which is $\Delta u_x + \Delta u_y$. This relation is exactly similar to the ordinary algebraic identity $3\,(x+y) = 3x + 3y$.

The three simple algebraic laws are the laws of (i) distribution, (ii) commutation, (iii) indices.

(i) $\Delta\,(u_x+v_x+w_x+\ldots)$

$$= (u_{x+h}+v_{x+h}+w_{x+h}+\ldots) - (u_x+v_x+w_x+\ldots)$$
$$= (u_{x+h}-u_x) + (v_{x+h}-v_x) + (w_{x+h}-w_x)$$
$$= \Delta u_x + \Delta v_x + \Delta w_x + \ldots.$$

Similarly,

$$E\,(u_x+v_x+w_x+\ldots) = Eu_x + Ev_x + Ew_x + \ldots.$$

(ii) The symbols Δ and E are commutative in their operation as regards constants. For if c be a constant,

$$\Delta cu_x = cu_{x+h} - cu_x = c\,(u_{x+h}-u_x) = c\Delta u_x,$$
and $\qquad\qquad Ecu_x = cu_{x+h} \qquad = cEu_x.$

(iii) The application of indices to the symbols Δ and E may be shown thus:

If m be a positive integer, then Δ^m represents the operation of differencing u_x m times.

$$\Delta^m u_x = (\Delta\Delta\Delta\Delta \ldots m \text{ times})\, u_x,$$
$$\Delta^n\,(\Delta^m u_x) = (\Delta\Delta\Delta\Delta \ldots n \text{ times})\,(\Delta\Delta\Delta\Delta \ldots m \text{ times})\, u_x$$
$$= (\Delta\Delta\Delta\Delta \ldots \overline{m+n} \text{ times})\, u_x$$
$$= \Delta^{m+n} u_x.$$

Similarly, $\qquad E^m u_x = u_{x+mh},$

$$E^n\,(E^m u_x) = E^n u_{x+mh} = u_{x+mh+nh} = E^{m+n} u_x.$$

14. In connection with the law of indices we must be careful to define Δ^m, Δ^n, E^m, ... when m and n are not positive integers. So far, the symbols Δ^m and E^m are intelligible only when we can actually perform the operations defined above and obtain the values of the new functions. We have not yet defined these symbols when the indices are negative. Consider for example the symbol Δ^{-1}. Since we have assumed that the symbol Δ obeys the ordinary algebraic laws, Δ^{-1} must be such that $\Delta\,(\Delta^{-1}u_x)$ gives $\Delta^0 u_x$, i.e. u_x.

Let m be a positive integer. Then we define $\Delta^{-m}u_x$ as a function such that if it be operated on by Δ^m the result will be $\Delta^{m-m}u_x,$

i.e. u_x. In the same way we have a meaning for $E^{-m}u_x$, namely, that E^m operating on $E^{-m}u_x$ produces u_x. But if m be a positive integer, E^m operating on u_{x-mh} produces $u_{x-mh+mh}$, i.e. u_x. Therefore the same result is obtained by operating with E^m on $E^{-m}u_x$ as on u_{x-mh}. In other words just as $E^m u_x$ gives u_{x+mh} so $E^{-m}u_x$ gives u_{x-mh}.

The symbols E and Δ may be manipulated in a manner similar to algebraic quantities provided that it is always remembered that they are operators and that they have no actual values. There are, however, two important points in which algebraic precedent cannot be safely followed. These are:

(1) Operators are not commutative with regard to variables. E.g., $\Delta(u_x v_x)$ does not as a rule equal $u_x \Delta v_x$.

(2) It is fundamental in algebra that if a function vanishes, then one of its factors must vanish. It is not true that if the result of a series of operations on u_x is equivalent to $0.u_x$ (i.e. zero), then some one of the operations on u_x must produce $0.u_x$. For example, if $x^2=0$, then $x=0$; it does not necessarily follow, however, that if $\Delta^2\equiv0$, then $\Delta\equiv0$.

In many problems it is convenient to use operators alone and to omit the functions on which they operate. Where this practice is followed the sign $\equiv$ (is equivalent to) should be adopted in place of $=$ (equals). Thus, $Eu_x=(1+\Delta)u_x$, but $E\equiv(1+\Delta)$.

For further information on the difficulties connected with the use of operators the student may refer to *J.S.S.* vol. II, pp. 237 *et seq.* (S. H. Alison).

15. Proceeding from the definition of differencing, it has been shown that

$$u_{x+h}=u_x+\Delta u_x,$$

$$u_{x+2h}=u_{x+h}+\Delta u_{x+h}$$
$$=u_x+\Delta u_x+\Delta(u_x+\Delta u_x)$$
$$=u_x+2\Delta u_x+\Delta^2 u_x,$$

$$u_{x+3h}=u_{x+2h}+\Delta u_{x+2h}$$
$$=u_x+2\Delta u_x+\Delta^2 u_x+\Delta(u_x+2\Delta u_x+\Delta^2 u_x)$$
$$=u_x+3\Delta u_x+3\Delta^2 u_x+\Delta^3 u_x.$$

The coefficients of the various terms in these expansions are the coefficients of x in the expansions of $(1+x)$, $(1+x)^2$, $(1+x)^3$ by the binomial theorem. If we assume, for positive integral values of n, that the general relation between u_{x+nh} and u_x and its differences follows the same law, we can prove the truth of the assumption by the method of mathematical induction.

Assume therefore that

$$u_{x+nh} = u_x + n_{(1)}\Delta u_x + n_{(2)}\Delta^2 u_x + \ldots + n_{(r)}\Delta^r u_x + \ldots + \Delta^n u_x$$

is true for the value n.

Then, since $\quad u_{x+(n+1)h} = u_{x+nh} + \Delta u_{x+nh}$,

we have

$$u_{x+(n+1)h} = u_x + n_{(1)}\Delta u_x + n_{(2)}\Delta^2 u_x + \ldots + n_{(r)}\Delta^r u_x + \ldots + \Delta^n u_x$$
$$+ \Delta\left(u_x + n_{(1)}\Delta u_x + n_{(2)}\Delta^2 u_x + \ldots + n_{(r)}\Delta^r u_x + \ldots + \Delta^n u_x\right)$$
$$= u_x + \Delta u_x\left(n_{(1)} + 1\right) + \Delta^2 u_x\left(n_{(2)} + n_{(1)}\right) + \ldots$$
$$+ \Delta^r u_x\left(n_{(r)} + n_{(r-1)}\right) + \ldots + \Delta^{n+1} u_x.$$

But $\qquad\qquad n_{(r)} + n_{(r-1)} = (n+1)_{(r)}$,

therefore

$$u_{x+(n+1)h} = u_x + (n+1)_{(1)}\Delta u_x + (n+1)_{(2)}\Delta^2 u_x + \ldots + (n+1)_{(r)}\Delta^r u_x$$
$$+ \ldots + \Delta^{n+1} u_x,$$

which is of the same form in $(n+1)$ as was the original expression in n.

Therefore if the assumption is true for n it is true for $n+1$.

But the theorem holds when $n = 1, 2, 3$.

Therefore it is true when $n = 4, 5, \ldots$ and for all positive integral values.

Therefore, for positive integral values of n,

$$u_{x+nh} = u_x + n_{(1)}\Delta u_x + n_{(2)}\Delta^2 u_x + n_{(3)}\Delta^3 u_x + \ldots + n_{(r)}\Delta^r u_x + \ldots + \Delta^n u_x.$$

16. When the relation between the operators Δ and E was discussed it was stated that our definition of these operations enables us to apply the ordinary algebraic laws to these symbols. We may therefore use the equivalent relation

$$E \equiv 1 + \Delta,$$

and if we operate on the function u_x we shall have

$$u_{x+nh} = E^n u_x = (1+\Delta)^n\, u_x$$
$$= (1 + n_{(1)}\Delta + n_{(2)}\Delta^2 + \dots + n_{(r)}\Delta^r + \dots + \Delta^n)\, u_x.$$

If we introduce the fact that the symbols follow the algebraic distributive law, we may write

$$u_{x+nh} = u_x + n_{(1)}\Delta u_x + n_{(2)}\Delta^2 u_x + \dots + n_{(r)}\Delta^r u_x + \dots + \Delta^n u_x,$$

which is the relation proved above for positive integral values of n.

This result is true whatever the form of the function so long as n is a positive integer. If n be other than a positive integer we cannot adopt the binomial expansion without further investigation. For the purposes of this chapter it will be sufficient to assume that the relation $E^n \equiv (1+\Delta)^n \equiv 1 + n_{(1)}\Delta + n_{(2)}\Delta^2 + n_{(3)}\Delta^3 + \dots$ holds without restriction. The conditions of the validity of the expansion will be discussed at a later stage (see Chap. II)

17. We are now in a position to state that if $n+1$ consecutive values of a polynomial of the nth degree are given, then, by the method of finite differences, we can obtain the actual function in the form

$$u_x = u_0 + x_{(1)}\Delta u_0 + x_{(2)}\Delta^2 u_0 + \dots + x_{(n)}\Delta^n u_0,$$

or $$u_x = A + Bx_{(1)} + Cx_{(2)} + \dots + Kx_{(n)},$$

where the coefficients A, B, C, ... K are obtained by inspection of a table of differences.

Now if we are given $n+1$ corresponding values of x and u_x it does not immediately follow that u_x is a polynomial of the nth degree.

For example, suppose that we have the following data:

x	0	1	2	3	4	5
u_x	1	4	9	16	25	36

Since six values are given there are the following possibilities:

(i) they may be actually given as values of the function $(1+x)^2$;

(ii) they may be given as values of a polynomial of the *second degree* in x, and it may be required to find the function;

(iii) they may be given as values of a polynomial of the *nth degree, where n is less than* 6, and it may be required to find the function;

(iv) they may be given as values of a polynomial without any information as to degree;

(v) no information regarding the nature of the function may be available.

The answer to (ii) and (iii) is obviously $u_x = (1+x)^2$.

The answer to (iv) is $u_x = (1+x)^2 + \dfrac{1}{6!} x(x-1) \ldots (x-5) F_x$ or $(1+x)^2 + x_{(6)} F_x$, where F_x is a polynomial in x which does not become infinite at any of the points 0, 1, 2, 3, 4, 5. The function

$$\frac{1}{6!} x(x-1) \ldots (x-5) F_x$$

will then obviously vanish for these values.

The answer to (v) is the same as to (iv) except that F_x need not be a polynomial.

It is of importance to realize that we can always find a value for F_x which will make the function $u_x = (1+x)^2 + x_{(6)} F_x$ agree with any additional value whatever. For example, if $u_{4.5} = 19 \cdot 75$ the function $u_x = (1+x)^2 + x_{(6)} 2^9$ will agree with the given values and also with the additional value which has been inserted at the point $x = 4 \cdot 5$.

Conversely we can say that whatever be the complete form of the function of which the six given values are samples, the value at any other point is the value of the function $(1+x)^2$ at that point with an error $x_{(6)} F_x$. Whether the value is a good approximation or not depends on the magnitude of F_x, and we may or may not have reason to suppose that F_x is so small that it can be neglected. It should be understood that we are not at liberty to say that $(1+x)^2$ gives an approximate value at the point in question unless we can give such a reason, based either on theory or on experience.

The matter is further investigated in later paragraphs, but it may be said that in most practical cases F_x is of the same order of magnitude as $\Delta^{n+1} u_x$ for some value of x in the range under consideration. It may in fact be shown that $F_x = \dfrac{d^6 u_\xi}{d\xi^6}$, where ξ is a quantity falling in the range which includes x and the given values of u. (See Chap. III, paragraph 17.)

18. If instead of writing $E^n \equiv (1 + \Delta)^n$ and expanding this by the binomial theorem, we write $\Delta^n \equiv (E - 1)^n$ and expand, a new series is obtained:

$$\Delta^n u_x = (E - 1)^n u_x$$
$$= [E^n - n_{(1)} E^{n-1} + n_{(2)} E^{n-2} - n_{(3)} E^{n-3} + \ldots + (-1)^r n_{(r)} E^{n-r}$$
$$+ \ldots + (-1)^n] u_x$$
$$= u_{x+nh} - n_{(1)} u_{x+(n-1)h} + n_{(2)} u_{x+(n-2)h} - \ldots$$
$$+ (-1)^r n_{(r)} u_{x+(n-r)h} + \ldots + (-1)^n u_x.$$

Just as the relation established in paragraph 15 enables us to obtain the value of u_{x+nh} in terms of u_x and its leading differences, so the above relation gives any required difference of the function u_x in terms of successive values of the function.

19. A few simple illustrations of the use of these two formulae are given below.

Example 6.

Find u_6, given $u_0 = -3$, $u_1 = 6$, $u_2 = 8$, $u_3 = 12$; third differences being constant.

The leading differences are easily found to be $\Delta u_0 = 9$; $\Delta^2 u_0 = -7$; $\Delta^3 u_0 = 9$.

$$u_6 = (1 + \Delta)^6 u_0 = (1 + 6\Delta + 15\Delta^2 + 20\Delta^3) u_0$$
$$= u_0 + 6\Delta u_0 + 15\Delta^2 u_0 + 20\Delta^3 u_0$$
$$= -3 + 54 - 105 + 180 = 126.$$

Note. There is no need to continue the expansion beyond third differences, as further differences are zero.

Example 7.

Find u_2, given $u_4 = 0$, $u_5 = 3$, $u_6 = 9$; second differences being constant.

Here the initial term of the known series is u_4, so that in order to find u_2 we must use the relation

$$u_2 = u_{4-2} = E^{-2} u_4 = (1 + \Delta)^{-2} u_4 = (1 - 2\Delta + 3\Delta^2) u_4,$$

as far as second differences.

$$u_2 = u_4 - 2\Delta u_4 + 3\Delta^2 u_4$$
$$= 0 - 6 + 9 = 3,$$

since $\quad\quad \Delta u_4 = 3 \quad$ and $\quad \Delta^2 u_4 = 3.$

Example 8.

From the following values of u_x, calculate $\Delta^5 u_0$:

$$u_0 = 3, \quad u_1 = 12, \quad u_2 = 81, \quad u_3 = 200, \quad u_4 = 100, \quad u_5 = 8.$$

Since we require only one value of $\Delta^5 u_x$, we do not need to form a difference table, but may write at once

$$\Delta^5 u_0 = (E - 1)^5 u_0$$
$$= (E^5 - 5E^4 + 10E^3 - 10E^2 + 5E - 1) u_0$$
$$= E^5 u_0 - 5E^4 u_0 + 10E^3 u_0 - 10E^2 u_0 + 5E u_0 - u_0$$
$$= u_5 - 5u_4 + 10u_3 - 10u_2 + 5u_1 - u_0$$
$$= 755.$$

Note. Before we can find the fifth difference six terms of the series must be given.

20. Separation of symbols.

In obtaining the value of $E^n u_x$ in terms of u_x and its differences we have used the symbolic relation $E \equiv 1 + \Delta$ and have expanded $(1 + \Delta)^n$ by the binomial theorem without introducing the function u_x until the last stage. This method, in which in fact u_x is omitted from both sides of the identity, is known as the method of *separation of symbols*, and enables many relations involving u_x and differences of u_x to be readily established. It must however be remembered that the operators cannot really stand alone and that the operand u_x is always understood.

Example 9.

Show that

$$u_0 + u_1 + u_2 + \ldots + u_n$$
$$= (n+1)_{(1)} u_0 + (n+1)_{(2)} \Delta u_0 + (n+1)_{(3)} \Delta^2 u_0 + \ldots + \Delta^n u_0.$$

$u_0 + u_1 + u_2 + \ldots + u_n$

$= u_0 + E u_0 + E^2 u_0 + \ldots + E^n u_0$

$= (1 + E + E^2 + \ldots + E^n)\, u_0$

$= \dfrac{E^{n+1} - 1}{E - 1}\, u_0$, or substituting $1 + \Delta$ for E,

$= \dfrac{(1 + \Delta)^{n+1} - 1}{\Delta}\, u_0$

$= \dfrac{1}{\Delta}\left[1 + (n+1)_{(1)}\Delta + (n+1)_{(2)}\Delta^2 + (n+1)_{(3)}\Delta^3 + \ldots + \Delta^{n+1} - 1 \right] u_0$

$= \left[(n+1)_{(1)} + (n+1)_{(2)}\Delta + (n+1)_{(3)}\Delta^2 + \ldots + \Delta^n \right] u_0$

$= (n+1)_{(1)} u_0 + (n+1)_{(2)}\Delta u_0 + (n+1)_{(3)}\Delta^2 u_0 + \ldots + \Delta^n u_0.$

Example 10.

Prove by the method of separation of symbols that

$$u_x = u_{x-1} + \Delta u_{x-2} + \Delta^2 u_{x-3} + \Delta^3 u_{x-4} + \ldots + \Delta^{n-1} u_{x-n} + \Delta^n u_{x-n}.$$

$u_x - \Delta^n u_{x-n} = u_x - \Delta^n E^{-n} u_x = \left\{ 1 - \left(\dfrac{\Delta}{E}\right)^n \right\} u_x = \dfrac{E^n - \Delta^n}{E^n}\, u_x$

$\qquad = \dfrac{1}{E^n}\left\{ \dfrac{E^n - \Delta^n}{E - \Delta} \right\} u_x,$ since $E - \Delta \equiv 1,$

$\qquad = E^{-n}\left(E^{n-1} + \Delta E^{n-2} + \Delta^2 E^{n-3} + \ldots + \Delta^{n-1} \right) u_x$

$\qquad = \left(E^{-1} + \Delta E^{-2} + \Delta^2 E^{-3} + \ldots + \Delta^{n-1} E^{-n} \right) u_x$

$\qquad = u_{x-1} + \Delta u_{x-2} + \Delta^2 u_{x-3} + \ldots + \Delta^{n-1} u_{x-n}.$

$\therefore \quad u_x = u_{x-1} + \Delta u_{x-2} + \Delta^2 u_{x-3} + \ldots + \Delta^{n-1} u_{x-n} + \Delta^n u_{x-n}.$

Since this is true for all values of n we have the convenient formulae

$\qquad u_x = u_{x-1} + \Delta u_{x-1}$ (which is otherwise evident),

$\qquad u_x = u_{x-1} + \Delta u_{x-2} + \Delta^2 u_{x-2},$

$\qquad u_x = u_{x-1} + \Delta u_{x-2} + \Delta^2 u_{x-3} + \Delta^3 u_{x-3},$

and so on.

Example 11.

Obtain a formula based on u_n similar to that given by the relation

$$E^x u_0 = (1 + \Delta)^x\, u_0.$$

$$E^x u_0 = u_x = E^{x-n} u_n = \left(\frac{1}{E}\right)^{n-x} u_n = \left(\frac{E-\Delta}{E}\right)^{n-x} u_n, \quad \text{since } E - \Delta \equiv 1,$$

$$= \left(1 - \frac{\Delta}{E}\right)^{n-x} u_n$$

$$= (1 - \Delta E^{-1})^{n-x} u_n$$

$$= [1 - (n-x)_{(1)} \Delta E^{-1} + (n-x)_{(2)} \Delta^2 E^{-2} - \ldots] u_n;$$

$$\therefore \quad u_x = u_n - (n-x)_{(1)} \Delta u_{n-1} + (n-x)_{(2)} \Delta^2 u_{n-2} - \ldots.$$

It will be found that this is an ordinary formula which could be obtained by using the values in the reverse order u_n, u_{n-1}, u_{n-2}, ... u_0. There is as much justification for using one order as the other. It should be noticed that the same numerical values appear in the table of differences, but that they are in the reverse order with a change of sign for the odd differences. This should be tested by a numerical example.

If $x > n$, we may use the general relation

$$(n-x)_{(t)} = (-1)^t (x-n+t-1)_{(t)}$$

and write the formula as

$$u_x = u_n + (x-n)_{(1)} \Delta u_{n-1} + (x-n+1)_{(2)} \Delta^2 u_{n-2} + \ldots,$$

where the coefficients are positive and are those in the expansion of $(1 - \Delta E^{-1})^{-(x-n)} u_x$.

Example 12.

Find the value of

$$\Delta x^m - \tfrac{1}{2} \Delta^2 x^m + \frac{1 \cdot 3}{2 \cdot 4} \Delta^3 x^m - \frac{1 \cdot 3 \cdot 5}{2 \cdot 4 \cdot 6} \Delta^4 x^m + \ldots \text{ to } m \text{ terms.}$$

Since $\Delta^{m+1} x^m$ and higher differences of x^m are zero, the sum of the series to m terms is the same as the sum to infinity.

Omitting the function x^m, and working on symbols alone, we have

$$\Delta - \tfrac{1}{2}\Delta^2 + \frac{1 \cdot 3}{2 \cdot 4}\Delta^3 - \frac{1 \cdot 3 \cdot 5}{2 \cdot 4 \cdot 6}\Delta^4 + \ldots \equiv \Delta \left(1 - \tfrac{1}{2}\Delta + \frac{1 \cdot 3}{2 \cdot 4}\Delta^2 - \frac{1 \cdot 3 \cdot 5}{2 \cdot 4 \cdot 6}\Delta^3 + \ldots\right)$$

$$\equiv \Delta \left(1 - \tfrac{1}{2}\Delta + \frac{\tfrac{1}{2} \cdot \tfrac{3}{2}}{2!}\Delta^2 - \frac{\tfrac{1}{2} \cdot \tfrac{3}{2} \cdot \tfrac{5}{2}}{3!}\Delta^3 + \ldots\right)$$

$$\equiv \Delta (1 + \Delta)^{-\frac{1}{2}} \equiv \Delta E^{-\frac{1}{2}}.$$

The value of the given series is therefore

$$\Delta E^{-\frac{1}{2}} x^m = \Delta (x - \tfrac{1}{2})^m = (x + \tfrac{1}{2})^m - (x - \tfrac{1}{2})^m,$$

if the interval of differencing be taken as unity.

Further examples of the application of the method of separation of symbols to the operators Δ and E and to other operators will be found in Chapters VI and VII.

21. Factorial notation.

For many purposes it is useful to use a notation for the product of m factors of which the first is x and the successive factors decrease by a constant difference.

Generally,

$$x^{(m)} \equiv x(x-h)(x-2h)(x-3h)\dots(x-\overline{m-1}h).$$

For convenience in working we shall take $h = 1$. Then, if

$$x^{(m)} = x(x-1)(x-2)(x-3)\dots(x-\overline{m-1}),$$

$$\Delta x^{(m)} = (x+1)x(x-1)\dots(x-\overline{m-2})-x(x-1)(x-2)\dots(x-\overline{m-1})$$

$$= mx(x-1)\dots(x-\overline{m-2})$$

$$= mx^{(m-1)}.$$

Similarly $\Delta^2 x^{(m)} = m(m-1)x^{(m-2)}$,

and, eventually, $\Delta^m x^{(m)} = m!$.

Again, from the definition of $x^{(m)}$,

$$x^{(m)} = (x-m+1)x^{(m-1)}.$$

$$\therefore \text{ when } m = 0, \quad x^{(0)} = (x+1)x^{(-1)}.$$

By convention, $x^{(0)} = 1$.

$$\therefore \quad 1 = (x+1)x^{(-1)}$$

or

$$x^{(-1)} = \frac{1}{x+1}.$$

When $m = -1$

$$x^{(-1)} = (x+2)x^{(-2)},$$

so that

$$x^{(-2)} = \frac{x^{(-1)}}{x+2} = \frac{1}{(x+1)(x+2)}.$$

Generally $x^{(-m)} = \dfrac{1}{(x+1)(x+2)\dots(x+m)} = \dfrac{1}{(x+m)^{(m)}}.$

This notation, adopted by Aitken and Milne-Thomson, differs from that used in Boole's *Finite Differences*, Steffensen's *Interpolation* and Freeman's *Actuarial Mathematics*. It has the advantage that, for any value of x, the relation $x^{(r)}(x-r)^{(m)} = x^{(m+r)}$

is valid for all integral values of r and m, whether negative, zero or positive, provided that division by zero is not involved.

By proceeding as above it can be shown that

$$\Delta x^{(-m)} = -mx^{(-\overline{m+1})}; \quad \Delta^2 x^{(-m)} = m\,(m+1)\,x^{(-\overline{m+2})},$$

and so on.

It should be noted that the result of differencing $x^{(-m)}$ is to increase the degree of the denominator, and that, as a result, $\Delta^m x^{(-m)}$ is not constant.

A special case of $x^{(m)}$ is where x is a positive integer. We have then that
$$x^{(m)} = x\,(x-1)\,(x-2)\,...\,(x-m+1) = x!/(x-m)! \quad \text{or} \quad {}^xP_m.$$

It is also of interest to note that the result of differencing $x^{(m)}$ is analogous to that of differentiating x^m. We have

$$\Delta x^{(m)} = mx^{(m-1)} \quad \text{and} \quad Dx^m = mx^{m-1},$$

$$\Delta^m x^{(m)} = m! \qquad \text{and} \quad D^m x^m = m!.$$

Similarly we have

$$\Delta^r x_{(m)} = x_{(m-r)} \quad \text{and} \quad \Delta^m x_{(m)} = 1.$$

These relations are very important.

Note. In the demonstrations above Δx has been taken as unity. If $\Delta x = h$, then $\Delta x^{(m)} = mh\,x^{(m-1)}$, $\Delta^2 x^{(m)} = m\,(m-1)\,h^2 x^{(m-1)}$, and so on. The general principles are the same.

Example 13.

Express $2x^3 - 3x^2 + 3x - 10$ and its differences in factorial notation.

Let

$$u_x = 2x^3 - 3x^2 + 3x - 10 = Ax\,(x-1)\,(x-2) + Bx\,(x-1) + Cx + D.$$

Putting $x = 0,\,1,\,2$ in succession, we obtain easily that

$$D = -10; \quad C = 2; \quad B = 3.$$

By equating coefficients of x^3 on both sides of the identity we find that $A = 2$.

$$\therefore \quad 2x^3 - 3x^2 + 3x - 10 = 2x^{(3)} + 3x^{(2)} + 2x^{(1)} - 10.$$

$$\Delta u_x = 6x^{(2)} + 6x^{(1)} + 2,$$

$$\Delta^2 u_x = 12x^{(1)} + 6,$$

and $$\Delta^3 u_x = 12.$$

22. An alternative method for expressing $P_n(x)$ in the factorial notation is by use of *detached coefficients*. By this method any such function can be written down in the form

$$Ax^{(n)} + Bx^{(n-1)} + Cx^{(n-2)} + \ldots + K$$

with very little trouble.

The principle can best be illustrated by an example.

Example 14.

Write down $11x^4 + 5x^3 + 2x^2 + x - 15$ in factorial notation.
Let

$$u_x = 11x^4 + 5x^3 + 2x^2 + x - 15 = Ax^{(4)} + Bx^{(3)} + Cx^{(2)} + Dx^{(1)} + E$$
$$= Ax\,(x-1)\,(x-2)\,(x-3) + Bx\,(x-1)\,(x-2)$$
$$+ Cx\,(x-1) + Dx + E.$$

If we divide u_x by x, the quotient will be

$$11x^3 + 5x^2 + 2x + 1$$

and the remainder $\qquad\qquad -15 \qquad\qquad\qquad = E.$

Divide $11x^3 + 5x^2 + 2x + 1$ by $x - 1$:

$$
\begin{array}{r|l|l}
x-1 & 11x^3 + 5x^2 + 2x + 1 & 11x^2 + 16x + 18 \\
 & 11x^3 - 11x^2 & \\
 \cline{2-2}
 & 16x^2 + 2x & \\
 & 16x^2 - 16x & \\
 \cline{2-2}
 & 18x + 1 & \\
 & 18x - 18 & \\
 \cline{2-2}
 & 19 &
\end{array}
$$

$\qquad\qquad\qquad = D.$

Divide $11x^2 + 16x + 18$ by $x - 2$:

$$
\begin{array}{r|l|l}
x-2 & 11x^2 + 16x + 18 & 11x + 38 \\
 & 11x^2 - 22x & \\
 \cline{2-2}
 & 38x + 18 & \\
 & 38x - 76 & \\
 \cline{2-2}
 & 94 &
\end{array}
$$

$\qquad\qquad\qquad = C,$

and so on.

The above processes may be appreciably shortened by adopting the following procedure:

(i) omit the x^4, x^3, x^2, ... and work on coefficients alone;

(ii) change the sign of the constant term in $x - 1$, $x - 2$, $x - 3$, ..., so that addition takes the place of subtraction.

The required remainders can then be easily obtained. Thus:

$$
\begin{array}{c|cccc}
1 & 11 & 5 & 2 & 1 & -15 \\
  & 0 & 11 & 16 & 18 \\
\hline
2 & 11 & 16 & 18 & 19 \\
  & 0 & 22 & 76 \\
\hline
3 & 11 & 38 & 94 \\
  & 0 & 33 \\
\hline
4 & 11 & 71 \\
  & 0 \\
\hline
  & 11
\end{array}
$$

$\therefore\ u_x = 11x^4 + 5x^3 + 2x^2 + x - 15 = 11x^{(4)} + 71x^{(3)} + 94x^{(2)} + 19x^{(1)} - 15.$

This short method is the method of detached coefficients and is of particular advantage in solving certain problems in summation of series (see Chap. VI).

23. It is often simpler, and in some cases more practically useful, to express $P_n(x)$ in terms of $x_{(r)}$, $x_{(r-1)}$ ... rather than in terms of $x^{(r)}$, $x^{(r-1)}$ .... This can easily be done by evaluating u_0, u_1, u_2, ..., forming a difference table and then using the formula given in paragraph 15. Thus, using the polynomial in Example 14, we have

x	u_x	Δu_x	$\Delta^2 u_x$	$\Delta^3 u_x$	$\Delta^4 u_x$
0	-15				
		19			
1	4		188		
		207		426	
2	211		614		264
		821		690	
3	1032		1304		
		2125			
4	3157				

whence $u_x = 264x_{(4)} + 426x_{(3)} + 188x_{(2)} + 19x_{(1)} - 15$. The arithmetic can be made even simpler by using $...u_{-2}$, u_{-1}, u_0, u_1, u_2 ... and inserting the constant difference for the purpose of obtaining the leading differences of u_0. In the case of the polynomial considered above, the constant difference will be $\Delta^4 u_x$, and it is instructive for the student to rework the example on these lines.

EXAMPLES 1

By constructing difference tables, find:

1. The sixth term of the series 8, 12, 19, 29, 42, ...

2. The seventh and eighth terms of the series 0, 0, 2, 6, 12, 20, ...

3. The first term of the series whose second and subsequent terms are 8, 3, 0, -1, 0, ...

4. The entry corresponding to the argument 3 from the table:

x (argument)	5	6	7	8	9	10
y (entry)	10·1	18·1	29·5	44·9	64·9	90·1

5. The tenth term of the series 3, 14, 39, 84, 155, 258, ...

6. Given that $y = x^3 - x^2 + x + 10$, verify by constructing a difference table that the value of y when $x = 10$ is 920. Use the following values of x: 1, 2, 3, 4, 5, 6 and the corresponding values of y.

7. Prove that $u_4 = u_3 + \Delta u_2 + \Delta^2 u_1 + \Delta^3 u_1$.

8. Find $\Delta^3 u_x$, where $u_x = ax^3 + bx^2 + cx + d$ and the interval of differencing is h.

9. u_x is a polynomial in x, the following values of which are known: $u_2 = u_3 = 27$; $u_4 = 78$; $u_5 = 169$. Find the function u_x.

10. Obtain $\Delta^{10} [(1 - ax)(1 - bx^2)(1 - cx^3)(1 - dx^4)]$.

11. Find Δab^{cx} and $\Delta^2 ab^{cx}$. Hence sum the first ten differences of ab^{cx}.

12. What are the functions whose first differences are (1) x; (2) c^x; (3) $9x^2 + 3$?

13. $u_x = (5x + 12)/(x^2 + 5x + 6)$. Find Δu_x and $\Delta^2 u_x$.

14. $u_x = -(x - 1)^{-1}(x - 2)^{-1}$. Find Δu_x.

15. $u_1 = (12 - x)(4 + x)$; $u_2 = (5 - x)(4 - x)$; $u_3 = (x + 18)(x + 6)$; $u_4 = 94$. Obtain a value of x, assuming second differences constant.

16. Find $\Delta^n u_x$, where u_x is (1) $ax^n + bx^{n-1}$, (2) e^{ax+b}.

17. Show that $u_4 = u_0 + 4\Delta u_0 + 6\Delta^2 u_{-1} + 10\Delta^3 u_{-1}$ as far as third differences.

18. The first four terms of a series are 0, 5, 16, 30. Find the sixth term, using the relation in Qu. 17.

19. Find the value of $\Delta^2 \left[\dfrac{a^{2x} + a^{4x}}{(a^2 - 1)^2} \right]$.

20. Obtain the function whose first difference is

$$x^3 + 3x^2 + 5x + 12.$$

By means of the relation $u_x = (1 + \Delta)^x u_0$, find

21. u_{12} given $u_0 = 3$; $u_1 = 14$; $u_2 = 40$; $u_3 = 86$; $u_4 = 157$; $u_5 = 258$.

22. u_6 given $u_0 = 25$; $u_1 = 25$; $u_2 = 22$; $u_3 = 18$; $u_4 = 15$; $u_5 = 15$.

23. u_9 given $u_0 = 1$; $u_1 = 11$; $u_2 = 21$; $u_3 = 28$; $u_4 = 29$.

24. The tenth term of the series $1, 37, 61, 77, \ldots$.

25. The eleventh term of the series $1, 4, 13, 36, 81, 156, 269, \ldots$.

26. Prove that the rth difference of a polynomial of the nth degree is a polynomial of the $(n-r)$th degree if $r < n$. What happens when (1) $r = n$, (2) $r > n$?

27. Define the functions $x^{(m)}$ and $x^{(-m)}$. Obtain their nth differences, distinguishing between the cases when $n \lessgtr m$.

28. Represent the function $x^4 - 12x^3 + 42x^2 - 30x + 9$ and its successive differences in factorial notation.

29. Find $\Delta^n u_x$ where u_x is

(i) $(ax+b)(a.\overline{x+1}+b)(a.\overline{x+2}+b) \ldots (a.\overline{x+m}+b)$ given $m > n$.

(ii) $[(ax+b)(a.\overline{x+1}+b)(a.\overline{x+2}+b) \ldots (a.\overline{x+m}+b)]^{-1}$.

30. Obtain $\Delta \sin x$, $\Delta \tan x$ and $\Delta (x + \cos x)$ where the interval of differencing is α.

31. Explain the difference between $\left(\dfrac{\Delta^2}{E}\right) u_x$ and $\dfrac{\Delta^2 u_x}{E u_x}$ and find the values of these functions when $u_x = x^3$.

32. $u_x = \sin x$. Show that $\Delta^2 u_x = k E u_x$ where k is constant.

33. Prove that $\Delta (\tan^{-1} x) = \tan^{-1} \left\{ \dfrac{h}{1 + xh + x^2} \right\}$, where h is the interval of differencing.

Use the method of separation of symbols to prove the following identities:

34. $u_1 x + u_2 x^2 + u_3 x^3 + \ldots$

$$= \frac{x}{1-x} u_1 + \frac{x^2}{(1-x)^2} \Delta u_1 + \frac{x^3}{(1-x)^3} \Delta^2 u_1 + \ldots.$$

35. $\Delta^n u_{x-n} = u_x - n_{(1)} u_{x-1} + n_{(2)} u_{x-2} - n_{(3)} u_{x-3} + \ldots$.

36. $u_{x+n} = u_n + x_{(1)} \Delta u_{n-1} + (x+1)_{(2)} \Delta^2 u_{n-2} + (x+2)_{(3)} \Delta^3 u_{n-3} + \ldots$.

37. $u_0 + x_{(1)}\Delta u_1 + x_{(2)}\Delta^2 u_2 + x_{(3)}\Delta^3 u_3 + \ldots$

$$= u_x + x_{(1)}\Delta^2 u_{x-1} + x_{(2)}\Delta^4 u_{x-2} + \ldots.$$

38. $u_0 + \dfrac{u_1 x}{1!} + \dfrac{u_2 x^2}{2!} + \dfrac{u_3 x^3}{3!} + \ldots$

$$= e^x \left[u_0 + x\Delta u_0 + \dfrac{x^2}{2!}\Delta^2 u_0 + \dfrac{x^3}{3!}\Delta^3 u_0 + \ldots \right].$$

39. $u_x - u_{x+1} + u_{x+2} - u_{x+3} + \ldots = \dfrac{1}{2}\left[u_{x-\frac12} - \dfrac{1}{8}\Delta^2 u_{x-\frac32} \right.$

$$\left. + \dfrac{1\cdot 3}{2!}\left(\dfrac{1}{8}\right)^2 \Delta^4 u_{x-\frac52} - \dfrac{1\cdot 3\cdot 5}{3!}\left(\dfrac{1}{8}\right)^3 \Delta^6 u_{x-\frac72} + \ldots \right].$$

40. $u_{2n} - n_{(1)}\cdot 2u_{2n-1} + n_{(2)}\cdot 2^2 u_{2n-2} - \ldots + (-2)^n u_n = (-1)^n (c - 2an)$,
where $u_x = ax^2 + bx + c$.

41. $u_x - \dfrac{1}{8}\Delta^2 u_{x-1} + \dfrac{1\cdot 3}{8\cdot 16}\Delta^4 u_{x-2} - \dfrac{1\cdot 3\cdot 5}{8\cdot 16\cdot 24}\Delta^6 u_{x-3} + \ldots$

$$= u_{x+\frac12} - \tfrac12\Delta u_{x+\frac12} + \tfrac14\Delta^2 u_{x+\frac12} - \tfrac18\Delta^3 u_{x+\frac12} + \ldots.$$

42. Find the relation between α, β, γ in order that $\alpha + \beta x + \gamma x^2$ may be expressible in one term in factorial notation.

43. Sum to n terms

$$1\cdot 2\Delta x^n - 2\cdot 3\Delta^2 x^n + 3\cdot 4\Delta^3 x^n - 4\cdot 5\Delta^4 x^n + \ldots.$$

44. If u_x be a polynomial in x of the third degree and $\Delta x = 1$, prove that

$$u_x = u_0 + x\Delta u_0 + \dfrac{x^{(2)}}{2!}\Delta^2 u_0 + \dfrac{x^{(3)}}{3!}\Delta^3 u_0.$$

45. Prove that

$u_0 + n_{(1)} u_1 x + n_{(2)} u_2 x^2 + n_{(3)} u_3 x^3 + \ldots$

$$= (1+x)^n u_0 + n_{(1)}(1+x)^{n-1} x\Delta u_0 + n_{(2)}(1+x)^{n-2} x^2\Delta^2 u_0 + \ldots.$$

46. If n be a positive integer, prove that u_n is the difference between the two series:

$$n_{(1)} u_1 + (n+1)_{(3)}\Delta^2 u_0 + (n+2)_{(5)}\Delta^4 u_{-1} + \ldots$$

and $\qquad (n-1)_{(1)} u_0 + n_{(3)}\Delta^2 u_{-1} + (n+1)_{(5)}\Delta^4 u_{-2} + \ldots.$

CHAPTER II

INTERPOLATION WITH EQUAL INTERVALS

1. Interpolation may be defined as the operation of obtaining the value of a function for any intermediate value of the argument, being given the values of the functions for certain values of the argument. The process has been picturesquely described by Thiele as "the art of reading between the lines of a table". Where the form of the function $y = u_x$ is known or can be deduced from the given values, the ordinary algebraic process of substitution can be used and the required value obtained with little difficulty. In actuarial work the relation connecting the function and the independent variable is seldom simple or evident, and it is then that recourse must be had to finite difference methods.

2. Before proceeding to examine the practical aspect of interpolation the question of negative and fractional values of n in the expression $(1 + \Delta)^n u_x$ must be considered. The proof of the identity $u_{x+nh} = (1 + \Delta)^n u_x$ by means of operators or by induction, as in the previous chapter, ceases to have a meaning if n is negative or fractional, since the reasoning assumes that the argument x advances by steps of h at a time. The assumption that, so long as the ordinary algebraic rules are followed, the expansion is true for all values of the quantities involved and not only for certain specified values, is not necessarily true, and an analogy can be drawn between the application of the binomial theorem to algebraic quantities and to operators. For example, the expansion $(1 + x)^n$ is only convergent, i.e. is arithmetically intelligible, for negative values of n, provided that x is numerically less than unity.

Thus $(1 - x)^{-2} = 1 + 2x + 3x^2 + 4x^3 + \ldots + rx^{r-1} + \ldots$ leads to an absurd result if we put $x = 2$, for then we should have

$$(-1)^{-2} = 1 + 4 + 12 + 32 + \ldots$$

which is impossible, since

$$(-1)^{-2} = 1/(-1)^2 = 1.$$

Similarly, in some cases there is no possibility of expanding $(1+\Delta)^n u_x$ by the use of the binomial theorem.

Consider the two following series of corresponding values of x and u_x:

(i)

x	0	1	2	3	4	5
u_x	1	4	9	16	25	36

Then to find the value of, say, $u_{\frac{1}{2}}$ we shall have

$$u_{\frac{1}{2}} = E^{\frac{1}{2}}u_0 = (1+\Delta)^{\frac{1}{2}} u_0$$

$$= u_0 + \tfrac{1}{2}\Delta u_0 + \frac{\frac{1}{2}\left(\frac{1}{2}-1\right)}{2!} \Delta^2 u_0 + \dots.$$

The leading differences are $\Delta u_0 = 3$ and $\Delta^2 u_0 = 2$, higher differences being zero.

$$\therefore \ u_{\frac{1}{2}} = 1 + \tfrac{1}{2}.3 + \frac{\frac{1}{2}\left(\frac{1}{2}-1\right)}{2!}.2$$

$$= 1 + \tfrac{3}{2} - \tfrac{1}{4} = \tfrac{9}{4},$$

which is otherwise evident, since u_x is $(1+x)^2$, and, for the value $x = \tfrac{1}{2}, u_x = \left(\tfrac{3}{2}\right)^2 = \tfrac{9}{4}$.

(ii)

x	0	1	2	3	4	5
u_x	1	5	25	125	625	3125

This is evidently a geometrical progression and the function from which the values are derived is $y = u_x = 5^x$. If we attempted to express u_x as a polynomial in x so that

$$u_x = a + bx + cx^2 + dx^3 + \dots,$$

and then applied the relation $E^n u_0 = (1+\Delta)^n u_0$ for the value $n = \tfrac{1}{2}$, we should obtain as above

$$u_{\frac{1}{2}} = E^{\frac{1}{2}}u_0 = (1+\Delta)^{\frac{1}{2}} u_0$$

$$= u_0 + \tfrac{1}{2}\Delta u_0 + \frac{\frac{1}{2}\left(\frac{1}{2}-1\right)}{2!} \Delta^2 u_0 + \dots.$$

Here the leading differences are 1, 4, 16, 64, 256, ... and tend to become successively larger. But $u_{\frac{1}{2}} = 5^{\frac{1}{2}} = 2 \cdot 24$ approximately, and this cannot be the same as the divergent series found by expanding $(1+\Delta)^{\frac{1}{2}}u_0$.

Hence unless the function is capable of being expressed as a polynomial in x we cannot use the relation $E^n \equiv (1+\Delta)^n$ for the value $n = \frac{1}{2}$.

3. Let us now consider the problem more generally. If u_x be a polynomial of degree k in x, we may write

$$u_x = a + bx + cx^2 + \dots + px^k.$$

If we adopt the binomial expansion of $(1+\Delta)^n$ for expressing u_x in terms of u_0 and the leading differences of u_0, namely,

$$u_x = u_0 + x_{(1)}\Delta u_0 + x_{(2)}\Delta^2 u_0 + \dots + x_{(r)}\Delta^r u_0 + \dots$$

we have two series for u_x which are equivalent for more than k values of the variable, since they are true for all positive integral values of x.

Hence by a well-known algebraic theorem, they are true for all values of x, positive or negative, integral or fractional.

Therefore so long as u_x is a polynomial in x the binomial expansion is valid for all values of x. It is not necessarily valid for other forms of function, and we are led to the conclusion that we can expand u_{x+nh} in terms of Δu_x, $\Delta^2 u_x \dots \Delta^r u_x \dots$ for all forms of the function if n be a positive integer, but for other values of n only if u_{x+nh} is a polynomial. (Cf. Chap. I, paragraph 17.)

4. All finite difference formulae which are employed for the purpose of interpolation are based on the hypothesis that the functions in question can be represented by polynomials, i.e. by rational integral functions, with sufficient accuracy for the purpose in hand. This assumption is the justification for extending the formulae to fractional intervals: the processes to be explained in this and subsequent chapters are simply various methods of carrying out the calculations based on these assumptions. One special advantage of these methods is that it is unnecessary to fix in advance the degree (n) of the polynomial; the interpolation formulae will be in such a form that to increase n will merely involve the introduction of a fresh term without affecting the other terms. The introduction of additional terms however will not necessarily improve the approximation or justify the assumption, although it will generally do so. Fortunately, in actuarial work the functions with which we deal are usually such that the assumption is sufficiently accurate for our purpose.

5. In applying the formula in paragraph 3 to a given set of data the following points should be noted:

(*a*) If the basic curve is $y = a + bx + cx^2 + \ldots + kx^{n-1}$ there will be n constants, and in order to determine these constants n equations are necessary. For there to be n equations, values of y corresponding to n values of x must be given. Therefore either n points on the curve, or n other corresponding relations between x and y, must be known. In that event the curve will be of degree $n - 1$, and nth and higher differences are zero.

(*b*) Our investigation has been confined to equidistant values of the argument. If the given values are not equidistant a formula slightly different in form from the expansion $(1 + \Delta)^x u_0$ can be developed with a modified method of differencing (see Chap. III).

With regard to the statement (*a*) above that for a curve of degree $n - 1$ there must be n facts given, it is not essential that n points on the assumed curve must be known. We may have given, for example, three points and two values of the differential coefficient $\dfrac{du_x}{dx}$. Here we have five facts; we assume therefore a fourth degree curve, so that fifth and higher differences are zero.

6. Newton's formula.

The formula $u_{x+nh} = u_x + n_{(1)} \Delta u_x + n_{(2)} \Delta^2 u_x + \ldots$ is known as Newton's formula, and is the fundamental formula for interpolation when the given values are at equidistant intervals. The expansion can be applied to solve many forms of the problem of interpolation.

The following variations of the problem may arise:

(i) Where there are n equidistant terms and it is required to find an intermediate term.

(ii) Where there are n equidistant terms of which $n-1$ are known and it is required to find the missing term.

(iii) Where there are n equidistant terms of which $n-r$ are known and it is required to find the r missing terms.

Note. Some modern writers have adopted the name "Newton-Gregory formula" for the above expansion, as the first publication appears to have occurred in a letter from James Gregory to John Collins on 23 Nov. 1670. The letter is given and the question of Newton's priority is fully discussed by D. C. Fraser in *J.I.A.* vol. LII, pp. 117–35.

7. Examples of the variations referred to above are given below: they are all solved by assuming the last difference constant.

Example 1.

The values of annuities by a certain table are given for the following ages:

Age	x	25	26	27	28	29
Annuity-value	a_x	16·195	15·919	15·630	15·326	15·006

Determine the value of the annuity at age $27\frac{1}{2}$.

Five values are given: we must therefore assume that fourth differences are constant. The difference table is

x	a_x	Δa_x	$\Delta^2 a_x$	$\Delta^3 a_x$	$\Delta^4 a_x$
25	16·195				
		−·276			
26	15·919		−·013		
		−·289		−·002	
27	15·630		−·015		+·001
		−·304		−·001	
28	15·326		−·016		
		−·320			
29	15·006				

The leading differences correspond to the argument $x=25$ and we require the entry for age $27\frac{1}{2}$. Our formula is therefore

$$a_{27\frac{1}{2}} = E^{2\frac{1}{2}} a_{25} = (1+\Delta)^{2\frac{1}{2}} a_{25}$$

$$= \left[1 + 2\cdot5\Delta + \frac{2\cdot5 \times 1\cdot5}{2}\Delta^2 + \frac{2\cdot5 \times 1\cdot5 \times \cdot5}{6}\Delta^3 \right.$$

$$\left. + \frac{2\cdot5 \times 1\cdot5 \times \cdot5 \times (-\cdot5)}{24}\Delta^4 \right] a_{25}$$

$$= a_{25} + 2\cdot5\Delta a_{25} + 1\cdot875\Delta^2 a_{25} + \cdot3125\Delta^3 a_{25} - \cdot03906\Delta^4 a_{25}$$

$$= 16\cdot195 - \cdot6900 - \cdot0244 - \cdot0006 - \cdot00004$$

$$= 15\cdot480.$$

Note. Since the data are given to three places of decimals, sufficient figures have been used to give three places only in the result. Since our interpolation is based on an assumption, namely, that fourth differences are constant, a result to more than this number of decimal places would be unjustifiable.

Example 2.

From the following data find the value of u_{47}:

$$u_{46} = 19 \cdot 2884; \quad u_{48} = 19 \cdot 5356; \quad u_{49} = 19 \cdot 6513; \quad u_{50} = 19 \cdot 7620.$$

We cannot form a difference table, since the given terms are not equidistant. As however four terms are available we may assume that third differences are constant, and that as a consequence fourth differences are zero.

If the function is $y = u_x$ we assume therefore that $\Delta^4 u_x = 0$ whatever the value of x. We may write

$$\Delta^4 u_{46} = 0,$$

i.e. $$(E-1)^4 \, u_{46} = 0,$$

or $$(E^4 - 4E^3 + 6E^2 - 4E + 1) \, u_{46} = 0,$$

i.e. $$u_{50} - 4u_{49} + 6u_{48} - 4u_{47} + u_{46} = 0,$$

so that $$19 \cdot 7620 - 78 \cdot 6052 + 117 \cdot 2136 - 4u_{47} + 19 \cdot 2884 = 0,$$

from which $$u_{47} = 19 \cdot 4147.$$

Note. As mentioned above, all the given terms are not equidistant. The method however depends upon the fact that the term required makes up in all five equidistant terms.

Example 3.

Complete the following table:

x	2·0	2·1	2·2	2·3	2·4	2·5	2·6
u_x	·135		·111	·100		·082	·074

This is similar to Ex. 2. Instead of using the assumption once that $\Delta^5 u_x = 0$, we write down two equations of the same form, thus

$$\Delta^5 u_{2 \cdot 0} = 0, \quad \text{so that} \quad (E-1)^5 \, u_{2 \cdot 0} = 0,$$

and $$\Delta^5 u_{2 \cdot 1} = 0, \quad \text{,,} \quad (E-1)^5 \, u_{2 \cdot 1} = 0.$$

Our two equations then become

$$u_{2 \cdot 5} - 5u_{2 \cdot 4} + 10u_{2 \cdot 3} - 10u_{2 \cdot 2} + 5u_{2 \cdot 1} - u_{2 \cdot 0} = 0,$$

and $$u_{2 \cdot 6} - 5u_{2 \cdot 5} + 10u_{2 \cdot 4} - 10u_{2 \cdot 3} + 5u_{2 \cdot 2} - u_{2 \cdot 1} = 0,$$

since the interval of differencing is 0·1.

Inserting the known values of u_x and solving, the required values are easily found to be $u_{2.1} = \cdot 123$ and $u_{2.4} = \cdot 090$.

Note. The function in this question is $y = e^{-x}$ and the tabular value of $u_{2.4}$ is $\cdot 091$ correct to three decimal places. This difference is due to the fact that our assumption that the curve $y = u_x$ is a polynomial of the fourth degree in x is only approximately true.

8. Change of origin and scale.

If we had plotted the curve $y = u_x$ on which the values of u_x in, say, Example 2 were assumed to lie, we should have had values of y corresponding to values of x at 46, 48, 49, 50. Precisely the same curve would result, however, if we changed the origin of our co-ordinates so that 46 was represented by the value $x = 0$, 48 by $x = 2$, 49 by $x = 3$ and so on, the unit of x being unaltered. This process of changing the origin simplifies our notation considerably. In the examples above we could have changed the origin alone, or both the origin and scale, and could have altered the questions to read:

Ex. 1.　Origin at age 25　　　　　　　　Given u_0, u_1, u_2, u_3, u_4
　　　　　Unit of differencing 1 year of age　Required $u_{2\frac{1}{4}}$.

Ex. 2.　Origin at $x = 46$　　　　　　　　Given u_0, u_2, u_3, u_4
　　　　　Unit of differencing $x = 1$　　　Required u_1.

Ex. 3.　Origin at $x = 2 \cdot 0$　　　　　　Given u_0, u_2, u_3, u_5, u_6
　　　　　Unit of differencing $x = 1$　　　Required u_1 and u_4.

9. If in Newton's formula

$$u_{x+nh} = u_x + n_{(1)}\Delta u_x + n_{(2)}\Delta^2 u_x + n_{(3)}\Delta^3 u_x + \ldots$$

we put $h = 1$, $x = 0$, and replace n by x, we obtain the series

$$u_x = u_0 + x_{(1)}\Delta u_0 + x_{(2)}\Delta^2 u_0 + x_{(3)}\Delta^3 u_0 + \ldots.$$

This is generally called the *advancing difference* formula, and gives u_x in terms of u_0 and its leading differences, where the interval of tabulation is treated as the unit abscissa.

If, however, we wish to obtain u_x in terms of u_{-m} and its leading differences, we may write the formula

$$u_x = u_{-m+(m+x)} = E^{m+x}u_{-m} = (1 + \Delta)^{m+x} u_{-m}$$
$$= u_{-m} + (m+x)_{(1)}\Delta u_{-m} + (m+x)_{(2)}\Delta^2 u_{-m} + \ldots$$
$$+ (m+x)_{(r)}\Delta^r u_{-m} + \ldots.$$

It is often more convenient to use this formula than to obtain u_x in terms of u_0 and differences of u_0, the advantage being that thereby we can make use of values of the argument on either side of x.

In some cases, particularly when dealing with the summation of certain series, it is expedient to represent the first term by u_1 rather than by u_0. If in Newton's formula we put $h=1$, $x=1$ we have

$$u_x=u_1+(x-1)_{(1)}\Delta u_1+(x-1)_{(2)}\Delta^2 u_1+\dots$$

or $$u_{1+x}=u_1+x_{(1)}\Delta u_1+x_{(2)}\Delta^2 u_1+\dots,$$

and these formulae can be used for the summation of the series $u_1+u_2+u_3+\dots$. (See Chap. VI, paragraph 2.)

10. Subdivision of intervals.

A frequent problem in actuarial work is the interpolation for values of u_x at intervening points given every fifth or tenth value of the function. For example, the problem may be to complete the series u_0, u_1, u_2, u_3, ... from the known values u_0, u_5, u_{10}, u_{15}, ... or from u_0, u_{10}, u_{20}, u_{30}, ...

A simple method for obtaining the intervening values where quinquennial values are known is given below.

Let δu_x denote the difference for *unit* intervals of x and Δu_x denote the difference for *quinquennial* intervals.

Then u_{x+5} may be expressed as either $(1+\delta)^5 u_x$ or as $(1+\Delta) u_x$.

Symbolically $$(1+\delta)^5 \equiv 1+\Delta,$$

i.e. $$(1+\delta) \equiv (1+\Delta)^{\frac{1}{5}},$$

or $$\delta \equiv (1+\Delta)^{\frac{1}{5}}-1.$$

From this relation we can find easily that

$$\delta u_x = (\cdot 2\Delta - \cdot 08\Delta^2 + \cdot 048\Delta^3 - \dots) u_x.$$

Hence $$\delta^2 u_x = (\cdot 2\Delta - \cdot 08\Delta^2 + \cdot 048\Delta^3 - \dots)^2 u_x$$
$$= (\cdot 04\Delta^2 - \cdot 032\Delta^3 + \dots) u_x.$$

Similarly $$\delta^3 u_x = (\cdot 008\Delta^3 - \dots) u_x.$$

The same principle can be adopted if decennial values are known. In that event Δu_x, $\Delta^2 u_x$, ... will represent differences for decennial intervals, and the individual differences will be found from the identity $\delta \equiv (1+\Delta)^{\frac{1}{10}} - 1$.

An example will show the application of the method.

Example 4.

From the following table of yearly premiums for policies maturing at quinquennial ages, estimate the premium for policies maturing at all ages from 45 to 50 inclusive:

Age x	45	50	55	60	65
Premium	2·871	2·404	2·083	1·862	1·712

The leading differences for quinquennial intervals are

Δu_x	$\Delta^2 u_x$	$\Delta^3 u_x$	$\Delta^4 u_x$
$-\cdot467$	$+\cdot146$	$-\cdot046$	$+\cdot017$

The formulae required are

$$\delta u_x = (\cdot2\Delta - \cdot08\Delta^2 + \cdot048\Delta^3 - \cdot0336\Delta^4)\, u_x = -\cdot1078592,$$

$$\delta^2 u_x = (\cdot04\Delta^2 - \cdot032\Delta^3 + \cdot0256\Delta^4)\, u_x = +\cdot0077472,$$

$$\delta^3 u_x = (\cdot008\Delta^3 - \cdot0096\Delta^4)\, u_x = -\cdot0005312,$$

$$\delta^4 u_x = \cdot0016\Delta^4 u_x = +\cdot0000272,$$

assuming fourth differences constant.

We have therefore by completing the table of differences,

Age	u_x	δu_x	$\delta^2 u_x$	$\delta^3 u_x$	$\delta^4 u_x$
45	2·871				
		$-\cdot10786$			
46	2·763		$+\cdot007747$		
		$-\cdot10011$		$-\cdot0005312$	
47	2·663		$+\cdot007216$		$+\cdot0000272$
		$-\cdot09290$		$-\cdot0005040$	
48	2·570		$+\cdot006712$		$+\cdot0000272$
		$-\cdot08618$		$-\cdot0004768$	
49	2·484		$+\cdot006235$		
		$-\cdot07995$			
50	2·404				

Note. Since we require the value of the premium to the nearest penny, three decimal places will be required in the u_x column. In this example, for results correct to three figures, four decimal places will be needed: δu_x must therefore be given to five decimal places, $\delta^2 u_x$ to six and $\delta^3 u_x$ to seven, since errors in higher differences accumulate rapidly.

EXAMPLES 2

Given the following data (*a*), find the missing term or terms (*b*):

1. (*a*) $u_0 = 580$, $u_1 = 556$, $u_2 = 520$, $u_4 = 385$; (*b*) u_3.

2. (*a*) $u_1 = 386$, $u_3 = 530$, $u_5 = 810$; (*b*) u_2; u_4.

3. (*a*) $u_0 = 150$, $u_1 = 192$, $u_2 = 241$, $u_4 = 374$; (*b*) u_3.

4. (*a*) $u_1 = 94$, $u_3 = 265$, $u_5 = 415$; (*b*) u_2; u_4.

5. (*a*) $u_0 = 6021$, $u_1 = 5229$, $u_2 = 4559$, $u_3 = 3979$; (*b*) $u_{\frac{3}{4}}$.

6. (*a*) $u_{50} = 92345$, $u_{51} = 91556$, $u_{52} = 90748$, $u_{55} = 88204$; (*b*) u_{53}; u_{54}.

7. (*a*) $u_{-1} = 202$, $u_0 = 175$, $u_1 = 82$, $u_2 = 55$; (*b*) $u_{\frac{1}{2}}$.

8. (*a*) $u_0 = 0$, $u_1 = 3$, $u_2 = 10$, $u_3 = 34$, $u_5 = 209$, $u_8 = 1002$; (*b*) u_4; u_6; u_7.

9. (*a*) $u_0 = 192 \cdot 1$, $u_1 = 187 \cdot 5$, $u_2 = 184 \cdot 7$, $u_3 = 184 \cdot 6$, $u_4 = 194 \cdot 6$, $u_5 = 199 \cdot 4$, $u_7 = 212 \cdot 7$, $u_9 = 224 \cdot 3$; (*b*) u_6; u_8.

10. (*a*) $u_0 = 98203$, $u_1 = 97843$, $u_2 = 97459$, $u_3 = 97034$; (*b*) $u_{2 \cdot 25}$.

11. The numbers of members of a certain Society are as given in the following table:

Year	Number	
1910	845	
1911	867	
1912		Make the best estimate
1913	846	you can of the
1914	821	numbers in 1912 and
1915	772	1916
1916		
1917	757	
1918	761	
1919	796	

12. Find p_{53} if $p_{50} = \cdot 98428$, $p_{51} = \cdot 98335$, $p_{54} = \cdot 98008$, $p_{55} = \cdot 97877$.

13. If u_0, u_1, u_2, ... u_6 be consecutive terms of a series, prove that, if fifth differences are constant,

$$u_3 = \cdot 05 u_0 - \cdot 3 u_1 + \cdot 75 u_2 + \cdot 75 u_4 - \cdot 3 u_5 + \cdot 05 u_6.$$

Supply the missing term:

$$u_0 = 72795 \qquad u_4 = 67919$$
$$u_1 = 71651 \qquad u_5 = 66566$$
$$u_2 = 70458 \qquad u_6 = 65152.$$

14. $u_{235}=2\cdot37107$ $u_{237}=2\cdot37474$

          $u_{236}=2\cdot37291$ $u_{238}=2\cdot37658.$

Find $u_{235\cdot63}$.

15. Given $u_0=-\cdot5$, $u_1=-\cdot484$, $u_5=0$, $u_6=\cdot256$, find the missing terms.

16. Given the following data: $u_0=0$, $u_{10}=15$, $u_{20}=50$; estimate u_{15}. If you were given in addition $u_5=35$, how would your estimate be revised? Illustrate your answer by a diagram.

17. Find the value of an annuity at $5\frac{3}{8}$ per cent. given the following table:

Rate per cent.	Annuity-value
4	17·29203
$4\frac{1}{2}$	16·28889
5	15·37245
$5\frac{1}{2}$	14·53375
6	13·76483

18. Obtain approximations to the missing values:

x	50	51	52	53	54	55	56
$f(x)$	3·684			3·756	3·780	3·803	3·826

19. The area A of a circle diameter d is given for the following values:

d	80	85	90	95	100
A	5026	5674	6362	7088	7854

Find approximate values for the areas of circles of diameters 82 and 91 respectively.

20. Calculate the value of sin 33° 13′ 30″ from the following table of sines:

angle $x°$	30	31	32	33	34
sin $x°$	·5000	·5150	·5299	·5446	·5592

21. $u_{75}=2459$; $u_{80}=2018$; $u_{85}=1180$; $u_{90}=402$. Calculate the values of u_{82} and u_{79}.

22. From the data in Qu. 21 complete the table for values of u_x corresponding to individual values of x from 75 to 85.

23. Four values of a function at decennial points are given. Express δu_x, $\delta^2 u_x$, $\delta^3 u_x$ (the differences for unit intervals) in terms of the differences of the function for decennial intervals.

Find the values u_1 to u_9 inclusive, given $u_0=0$, $u_{10}=\cdot174$, $u_{20}=\cdot347$, $u_{30}=\cdot518$.

24. $u_0 = 23 \cdot 1234$; $u_6 = 23 \cdot 7234$; $u_{12} = 24 \cdot 6834$; $u_{18} = 26 \cdot 1330$. Complete the series u_0 to u_6.

25. If you were asked at very short notice to obtain approximate values for the complete series $f(0)$, $f(1)$, $f(2)$, ... $f(20)$, being given that $f(0) = \cdot 013$, $f(10) = \cdot 248$, $f(15) = \cdot 578$, and $f(20) = \cdot 983$, what methods would you adopt, and what value would you obtain for $f(9)$?

26.

$$u_0 + u_8 = 1 \cdot 9243 \qquad\qquad u_2 + u_6 = 1 \cdot 9823$$
$$u_1 + u_7 = 1 \cdot 9590 \qquad\qquad u_3 + u_5 = 1 \cdot 9956.$$

Find u_4.

27. Tables are available giving premiums at age 40 at the following rates per cent.:

Rate per cent.	3	$3\frac{1}{2}$	4	$4\frac{1}{2}$	5	6
P_{40}	$\cdot 025891$	$\cdot 024654$	$\cdot 023517$	$\cdot 022470$	$\cdot 021509$	$\cdot 019811$

It is desired to obtain P_{40} at $5\frac{1}{2}$ per cent. Obtain this, using

(α) two of the above values; (β) four of the above values; (γ) six of the above values.

28. Given

$$\sum_1^{10} f(x) = 500426, \; \sum_4^{10} f(x) = 329240, \; \sum_7^{10} f(x) = 175212 \text{ and } f(10) = 40365,$$

find $f(1)$.

29. $u_1 = 1$; $u_2 + u_3 = 5 \cdot 41$; $u_4 + u_5 + u_6 = 18 \cdot 47$;

$$u_7 + u_8 + u_9 + u_{10} + u_{11} + u_{12} = 90 \cdot 36.$$

Find the value of u_x for all values of x from 1 to 12 inclusive.

30. If you were given u_0, u_1, u_2 and $\sum\limits_{x=1}^{x=10} u_x$ how would you complete the table of u_x up to u_{10}?

31. Given $u_0 = 117 \cdot 7$; $u_2 = 110 \cdot 5$; $u_4 = 102 \cdot 7$; $u_{10} = 75 \cdot 4$, obtain the values of u_x for all integral values of x from 0 to 10.

32. Obtain the following relation between nine terms of the series represented by u_1, u_2, ... u_9:

$$u_5 = \tfrac{4}{5}(u_4 + u_6) - \tfrac{2}{5}(u_3 + u_7) + \tfrac{4}{35}(u_2 + u_8) - \tfrac{1}{70}(u_1 + u_9),$$

and find u_5, given

$$u_1 = \cdot 74556; \quad u_2 = \cdot 55938; \quad u_3 = \cdot 42796; \quad u_4 = \cdot 32788; \quad u_6 = \cdot 18432;$$
$$u_7 = \cdot 13165; \quad u_8 = \cdot 08828; \quad u_9 = 0.$$

33. It is asserted that a quantity, which varies from day to day, is a rational and integral function of the day of the month, of less than the fifth degree, and that its values on the first seven days of the month are

$$30, \quad 30, \quad 28, \quad 25, \quad 22, \quad 20, \quad 20.$$

Examine whether these assertions are consistent. If so, assume them to be true, and find (1) the degree of the function, (2) its value on the sixteenth of the month.

34. Extrapolation may be defined as the process of obtaining further terms of a series as opposed to interpolation, which is the process of finding intermediate terms.

The values of a certain function, corresponding to the values 4, 6, 8, 10 of the argument are 914, 742, 605, 500 respectively. Extrapolate to calculate the value of the function corresponding to the value 11 of the argument.

35. Given $u_0 = 1876$, $u_1 = 777$, $u_3 = 19$, $u_6 = -218$, interpolate the values of u_2, u_4 and u_5, and find the form of the function, assuming it to be a rational integral function.

36. Show that Newton's formula

$$u_x = u_0 + x_{(1)}\Delta u_0 + x_{(2)}\Delta^2 u_0 + x_{(3)}\Delta^3 u_0 + x_{(4)}\Delta^4 u_0 + \ldots$$

can be put into the form

$$u_x = u_0 + x\Delta u_0 - xa\Delta^2 u_0 + xab\Delta^3 u_0 - xabc\Delta^4 u_0 + \ldots,$$

where $a = 1 - \frac{1}{2}(x+1)$, $b = 1 - \frac{1}{3}(x+1)$, $c = 1 - \frac{1}{4}(x+1)$ etc.

Hence show that the successive coefficients converge slowly and tend eventually to numerical equality.

CHAPTER III

INTERPOLATION WITH UNEQUAL INTERVALS

1. In the previous chapter formulae have been developed on the assumption that the argument proceeded by equal intervals. Although in actuarial problems the data are generally given at equidistant intervals of the independent variable, it sometimes happens that we are required to interpolate when values of the function are known for unequal intervals. In other words, instead of values of u_x for arguments $x+h$, $x+2h$, $x+3h$, ... being given, the known values correspond to the arguments a, b, c, ..., where $a-b$, $b-c$, ... are not necessarily equal.

2. Divided differences.

Since we cannot use the differences as hitherto defined, we adopt a special process involving the argument as well as the entry. The differences obtained by this process are called "divided" differences, and are found in the following manner.

Let $f(x) \equiv u_x$ be given for the values $x=a$, $x=b$, $x=c$, $x=d$ ..., where the intervals need not be equal.

Then we have

    (i) First divided differences:

$$\frac{u_b-u_a}{b-a}; \quad \frac{u_c-u_b}{c-b}; \quad \frac{u_d-u_c}{d-c}; \quad ...$$

which may be written as

$$f(b, a); \quad f(c, b); \quad f(d, c); \quad ....$$

    (ii) Second divided differences:

$$\frac{f(c, b)-f(b, a)}{c-a}; \quad \frac{f(d, c)-f(c, b)}{d-b}; \quad ...$$

or
$$f(c, b, a); \quad f(d, c, b); \quad ....$$

(iii) Third divided differences:

$$\frac{f(d, c, b) - f(c, b, a)}{d-a}; \ \dots \ \text{ or } \ f(d, c, b, a); \ \dots.$$

3. Notation for divided differences.

There seems to be at present no universally recognized notation for divided differences. There are objections to the many forms in practice. For example, $\Delta' u_a$, representing $(u_b - u_a)/(b-a)$ (Freeman's *Actuarial Mathematics*, p. 57, and Henry's *Calculus and Probability*, Chap. VIII), has the disadvantage that the dash is apt to be confused with the index (cf. $\Delta'^2 u_a$ and $\Delta^{12} u_a$). A preferable form $\Delta(a, b)$, $\Delta^2(a, b, c) \dots$ is clearer, but departs from the recognized symbolical notation in that the function u_x on which the divided difference symbol operates is not present; this renders the notation unsuitable for elementary work. The method adopted in paragraph 2 above is simple, and where there is no ambiguity with $f(x, y)$, representing a function of two variables, there is no objection to its use. This notation does not, however, conform with the Δ notation for differencing when the intervals are equal and to that extent it is hardly satisfactory.

The following are some alternative notations that have been used:

	Arguments	Function	Divided differences
(1)	$a, b, c \dots$	$u_a, u_b, u_c \dots$	$\Delta(a, b), \Delta(b, c), \Delta^2(a, b, c) \dots$
(2)	$a, b, c \dots$	$u_a, u_b, u_c \dots$	$(a, b), (b, c), (a, b, c) \dots$
(3)	$x_0, x_1, x_2 \dots$	$f(x_0), f(x_1), f(x_2) \dots$	$f(x_0, x_1), f(x_1, x_2), f(x_0, x_1, x_2) \dots$
(4)	$x_0, x_1, x_2 \dots$	$f(x_0), f(x_1), f(x_2) \dots$	$[x_0, x_1], [x_1, x_2], [x_0, x_1, x_2] \dots$
(5)	$a_0, a_1, a_2 \dots$	$A_0, A_1, A_2 \dots$	$\theta A_0, \theta A_1, \theta^2 A_0 \dots$

(1) D. C. Fraser, (2) W. F. Sheppard, (3) J. F. Steffensen, (4) Milne-Thomson, (5) De Morgan.

The notation that we shall adopt is due to Dr A. C. Aitken (*Proc. Roy. Soc. Edin.* vol. LVIII, pp. 169 and 175) and has all the advantages possessed by the ordinary difference symbol.

The convention and definition are

$$\underset{b}{\triangle}u_a=(u_a-u_b)/(a-b)$$

$$=\frac{u_a}{a-b}+\frac{u_b}{b-a}.$$

$$\underset{bc}{\triangle^2}u_a=\underset{c}{\triangle}\left(\underset{b}{\triangle}u_a\right)$$

$$=\frac{1}{a-c}\left\{\frac{u_a}{a-b}+\frac{u_b}{b-a}\right\}+\frac{1}{c-a}\left\{\frac{u_c}{c-b}+\frac{u_b}{b-c}\right\}$$

$$=\frac{u_a}{(a-b)\,(a-c)}+\frac{u_b}{(b-c)\,(b-a)}+\frac{u_c}{(c-a)\,(c-b)}.$$

Similarly it may be shown that

$$\underset{bcd}{\triangle^3}u_a=\frac{u_a}{(a-b)\,(a-c)\,(a-d)}+\frac{u_b}{(b-c)\,(b-d)\,(b-a)}$$

$$+\frac{u_c}{(c-d)\,(c-a)\,(c-b)}+\frac{u_d}{(d-a)\,(d-b)\,(d-c)}.$$

The symmetry of these differences is apparent and suggests that the property holds for a divided difference of any order. This is in fact true and the general proposition may be proved in many different ways.

It may be proved by induction, by actually arranging the co-efficients or, incidentally, in establishing another important proposition, namely that if u_x is of the form $P_n(x)$ then $\triangle^n u_x$ is constant (see paragraph 6).

An elegant and succinct proof, based on the permutability of the arguments, is due to Dr Aitken, and is given below.

*4. By definition

$$\underset{a}{\triangle}u_x=(u_x-u_a)/(x-a)$$

$$=(u_a-u_x)/(a-x)=\underset{x}{\triangle}u_a.$$

The suffix of the operator and the argument of the operand are therefore interchangeable. Also, if u_x is of the form $P_n(x)$, by the remainder theorem $x-a$ is a factor of u_x-u_a and it follows that $\underset{a}{\triangle}u_x$ is of the form $P_{n-1}(x)$.

For divided differences of higher orders the definitions are

$$\underset{b}{\triangle} \left(\underset{a}{\triangle} u_x \right) = \underset{ab}{\triangle^2} u_x$$

$$\underset{c}{\triangle} \left(\underset{ba}{\triangle^2} u_x \right) = \underset{abc}{\triangle^3} u_x,$$

and so on.

A divided difference of any order, e.g. $\underset{abc}{\triangle^3} u_x$, is unaltered by any permutation of the arguments. For, since the suffix of any $\triangle$ operator and the argument of the operand are interchangeable, we have such interchanges as

$$\underset{b}{\triangle} \left(\underset{a}{\triangle} u_x \right) = \underset{b}{\triangle} \left(\underset{x}{\triangle} u_a \right) = \underset{a}{\triangle} \left(\underset{x}{\triangle} u_b \right)$$

$$= \underset{a}{\triangle} \left(\underset{b}{\triangle} u_x \right) = \underset{x}{\triangle} \left(\underset{b}{\triangle} u_a \right)$$

$$= \underset{x}{\triangle} \left(\underset{a}{\triangle} u_b \right).$$

All permutations can be obtained by successive single interchanges. Thus, in the illustration above,

$$bax \to bxa \to axb \to abx \to xba \to xab.$$

These interchanges are obviously possible for divided differences of any order and it follows therefore that a divided difference is a symmetrical function of all the arguments involved.

Note. The proof given above depends entirely on the symmetrical property of the differences. It does not follow that if $u_x = v_y$ then $\underset{a}{\triangle} u_x = \underset{a}{\triangle} v_y$. In passing from, say, $\underset{a}{\triangle} \left(\underset{b}{\triangle} u_x \right)$ to $\underset{a}{\triangle} \left(\underset{x}{\triangle} u_b \right)$ the student should satisfy himself that the equivalence holds by writing down

$$\underset{a}{\triangle} \left(\underset{b}{\triangle} u_x \right) = \frac{1}{x-a} \left\{ \frac{u_x - u_b}{x-b} - \frac{u_a - u_b}{a-b} \right\}$$

$$= \frac{u_x}{(x-a)(x-b)} + \frac{u_b}{(b-x)(b-a)} + \frac{u_a}{(a-b)(a-x)},$$

$$\underset{a}{\triangle} \left(\underset{x}{\triangle} u_b \right) = \frac{1}{b-a} \left\{ \frac{u_b - u_x}{b-x} - \frac{u_a - u_x}{a-x} \right\}$$

$$= \frac{u_b}{(b-x)(b-a)} + \frac{u_x}{(x-a)(x-b)} + \frac{u_a}{(a-b)(a-x)}.$$

5. The method of forming a divided difference table is best illustrated by an actual example.

Example 1.

Take out the divided differences of u_x given the following table:

x	1	2	4	7	12
u_x	22	30	82	106	206

The table is

x	u_x	$\triangle u_x$	$\triangle^2 u_x$	$\triangle^3 u_x$	$\triangle^4 u_x$
1	22				
		$\dfrac{30-22}{2-1}=8$			
2	30		$\dfrac{26-8}{4-1}=6$		
		$\dfrac{82-30}{4-2}=26$		$\dfrac{-3\cdot6-6}{7-1}=-1\cdot6$	
4	82		$\dfrac{8-26}{7-2}=-3\cdot6$		$\dfrac{\cdot51-(-1\cdot6)}{12-1}=\cdot192\ldots$
		$\dfrac{106-82}{7-4}=8$		$\dfrac{1\cdot5-(-3\cdot6)}{12-2}=\cdot51$	
7	106		$\dfrac{20-8}{12-4}=1\cdot5$		
		$\dfrac{206-106}{12-7}=20$			
12	206				

Note. When the arguments and their order are fixed, we may use the shortened notation $\triangle u_x$, $\triangle^2 u_x$, $\triangle^3 u_x$ ... for the leading divided differences of u_x, as in the example above.

It is essential to arrange the work systematically if error is to be avoided. The numerators and denominators must be set out, either in parallel columns or in the form of fractions. Where there is ample space the columnar arrangement is better, especially where the divisors are cumbrous. It should be noted that while the numerators are the first ordinary differences of the preceding divided differences, the denominators are all formed directly from the arguments, differencing first in the ordinary way, then in pairs, then in triplets, and so on. It will also be seen that the divisor is always the difference between the values of x for the last and first u_x involved in the difference.

6. Newton's divided difference formula.

Let the given values of u_x be

$$u_a,\ u_b,\ u_c \ \ldots\ u_k,\ u_l.$$

Then, by definition, $\quad u_x = u_a + (x-a) \underset{x}{\triangle} u_a,$

$$\underset{x}{\triangle} u_a = \underset{b}{\triangle} u_a + (x-b) \underset{bx}{\triangle^2} u_a,$$

$$\underset{bx}{\triangle^2} u_a = \underset{bc}{\triangle^2} u_a + (x-c) \underset{bcx}{\triangle^3} u_a,$$

$$\cdots\cdots\cdots\cdots\cdots$$

$$\underset{bc\ldots kx}{\triangle^n} u_a = \underset{bc\ldots kl}{\triangle^n} u_a + (x-l) \underset{bc\ldots lx}{\triangle^{n+1}} u_a.$$

Hence, by successive substitution of each identity in the one preceding it, we have

$$u_x = u_a + (x-a) \underset{b}{\triangle} u_a + (x-a)(x-b) \underset{bc}{\triangle^2} u_a + \ldots$$

$$+ (x-a)(x-b)\ldots(x-k) \underset{bc\ldots l}{\triangle^n} u_a + (x-a)(x-b)\ldots(x-l) \underset{bc\ldots lx}{\triangle^{n+1}} u_a.$$

Thus $\qquad\qquad u_x = U_x + R_{n+1}(x),$

where U_x represents the sum of all the terms except the last and $R_{n+1}(x)$ the last.

$R_{n+1}(x)$ may be written as

$$(x-a)(x-b)\ldots(x-l) \underset{abc\ldots l}{\triangle^{n+1}} u_x$$

by permuting the arguments of the divided difference.

It should be noted that the term preceding R is

$$(x-a)(x-b)\ldots(x-k) \underset{bc\ldots l}{\triangle^n} u_a,$$

involving n factors in the coefficient. In R there is an additional factor $x-l$.

If we put x equal to $a, b, c \ldots$ in succession, the R term vanishes and we have the following results which are identities, analogous to those obtained for equal intervals in Chapter I:

$$[U_x]_{x=b} = u_b = u_a + (b-a) \underset{b}{\triangle} u_a,$$

$$[U_x]_{x=c} = u_c = u_a + (c-a) \underset{b}{\triangle} u_a + (c-a)(c-b) \underset{bc}{\triangle^2} u_a,$$

$$[U_x]_{x=d} = u_d = u_a + (d-a) \underset{b}{\triangle} u_a + (d-a)(d-b) \underset{bc}{\triangle^2} u_a$$

$$+ (d-a)(d-b)(d-c) \underset{bcd}{\triangle^3} u_a.$$

$$\cdots\cdots\cdots\cdots\cdots$$

It is seen that R is the only term involving u_x; it vanishes if x takes any of the values $a, b, c \ldots l$, or for any value of x if $\triangle^{n+1} u_a = 0$.

It follows therefore that U_x is that polynomial of the nth degree in x which takes the $(n+1)$ given values u_a, u_b, u_c ... u_l, when $x = a$, b, c ... l respectively. If therefore u_x is itself a polynomial of the nth degree in x it must be the polynomial U_x; i.e. R vanishes for all values of x. We have therefore that

$$\underset{abc\ldots l}{\triangle^{n+1}} u_x = 0 \quad \text{and} \quad \underset{bc\ldots l}{\triangle^{n}} u_x \text{ is constant.}$$

U_x is thus the *unique* polynomial of degree n which represents u_a, u_b, ... Therefore the coefficient of x^n does not depend on the order in which a, b, c, ... are taken. Since this coefficient is $\triangle^n u_x$, it follows that the divided difference is a symmetrical function of all the arguments involved. (See paragraph 3 above.)

If u_x is not a polynomial of the nth degree in x, we have only the relation
$$u_x = U_x + R_{n+1}(x),$$
where the R term itself involves u_x, and if the expression $U_x + R_{n+1}(x)$ be worked out by expanding the coefficients all that we obtain is the identity $u_x = u_x$. Thus our results do not help us to find u_x unless we have some knowledge of or may make some assumption with regard to the value of $R_{n+1}(x)$. It may be said in fact that $R_{n+1}(x)$ plays the same part as does F_x in Chap. I, paragraph 17. As in the case of ordinary differences it is assumed that $R_{n+1}(x)$ is negligible and may be put equal to zero, giving finally

$$u_x = U_x$$
$$= u_a + (x - a) \underset{b}{\triangle} u_a + (x - a)(x - b) \underset{bc}{\triangle^2} u_a + \ldots$$
$$+ (x - a)(x - b) \ldots (x - k) \underset{bc\ldots l}{\triangle^n} u_a,$$

which is Newton's formula for interpolation with divided differences.

For the method of obtaining the limits between which $R_{n+1}(x)$ lies, see paragraphs 16 and 17 below.

7. Sheppard's rules.

If, as in the paragraph above, the arguments are x, a, b, c ... k, l, where u_x is to be found and the $n+1$ values u_a, u_b, u_c... u_k, u_l are given, we may put Newton's formula into a more compact form by the use of a notation due to Mr D. C. Fraser. This notation is as follows:

$$x - a \equiv A,$$
$$x - b \equiv B,$$
$$x - c \equiv C,$$
$$\cdots\cdots\cdots$$

The arguments a, b, c ... involved in the divided differences and the factors A, B, C ... are in the same order, with the exception that the small letters are always one in advance of the capitals, thus:

Arguments,	a	ab	abc	$abcd$	$abcde$ ....
Capitals,	1	A	AB	ABC	$ABCD$ ....

Newton's formula thus reads

$$u_x = u_a + A \underset{b}{\triangle} u_a + AB \underset{bc}{\triangle^2} u_a + ABC \underset{bcd}{\triangle^3} u_a + \dots + ABCD \dots K \underset{bc \dots l}{\triangle^n} u_a.$$

Dr W. F. Sheppard has given very convenient rules, embodying the same principle, and by means of these rules formulae may be written down at sight for any intervals. As expanded by Mr G. J. Lidstone [*J.I.A.* vol. LVIII, p. 65 and references there given] these rules are as follows:

"(i) We start with any tabulated value of u.

(ii) We pass to the successive differences by steps, each of which may be either upward or downward";

[each step involving a new u whose subscript will be numerically the next lower/higher if the step is up/down, and the u's are arranged in the numerical sequence of the variables.]

"(iii) The new suffix [of u] which is introduced at each step determines the new factor (involving x) for use in the next term."

[That is, each divided difference of the nth order has for its coefficient the product of n factors of the form $(x - a_k)$ where a_k represents a value of the variable, and has to be given all the n values that were involved in the last preceding difference.

These rules apply whether the intervals are equal or unequal; if they are equal the divided differences are of the form $\Delta^n u / n!$.]

These rules are familiarly known as the "zig-zag rules" for reasons which will now be explained. If we are given a set of u's and their differences as in the following scheme

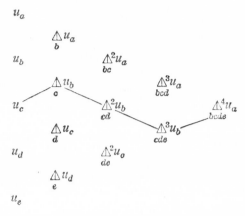

u_a

$\triangle u_a \atop b$

u_b $\qquad \triangle^2 u_a \atop bc$

$\triangle u_b \atop c$ $\qquad \triangle^3 u_a \atop bcd$

u_c $\qquad \triangle^2 u_b \atop cd$ $\qquad \triangle^4 u_a \atop bcde$

$\triangle u_c \atop d$ $\qquad \triangle^3 u_b \atop cde$

u_d $\qquad \triangle^2 u_c \atop de$

$\triangle u_d \atop e$

u_e

and use them to interpolate for u_x, it is not necessary to use the formula involving u_a and its leading differences. We may begin with *any* of the u's and at each step move either upwards or downwards in proceeding to the next column in the difference table, so that we may if we like follow a "zig-zag" route; in fact with n values we have a choice of 2^{n-1} different routes. [Cf. Sheppard, *J.I.A.* vol. L, p. 89.]

Suppose we wish to begin with u_c. The next term may be either $\triangle u_b \atop c$ or $\triangle u_c \atop d$, since both of these involve u_c: let us take $\triangle u_b \atop c$ involving u_c and u_b. We may next take either $\triangle^2 u_a \atop bc$ or $\triangle^2 u_b \atop cd$, since both of these also involve u_c and u_b: let us take $\triangle^2 u_b \atop cd$. We may then move to $\triangle^3 u_a \atop bcd$ or $\triangle^3 u_b \atop cde$ and we select the latter. We then have no further choice and we move to $\triangle^4 u_a \atop bcde$. Our formula thus brings in the small letters in the order

$$c, \ b, \ d, \ e, \ a$$

and therefore the factors of the coefficients will enter in the order

$$\text{I}, \ C, \ B, \ D, \ E.$$

Thus we may write down at once the required formula

$$u_x = u_c + C \underset{c}{\triangle} u_b + BC \underset{cd}{\triangle^2} u_b + BCD \underset{cde}{\triangle^3} u_b + BCDE \underset{bcde}{\triangle^4} u_a$$

or

$$u_x = u_c + (x-c) \underset{c}{\triangle} u_b + (x-b)(x-c) \underset{cd}{\triangle^2} u_b + (x-b)(x-c)(x-d) \underset{cde}{\triangle^3} u_b$$

$$+ (x-b)(x-c)(x-d)(x-e) \underset{bcde}{\triangle^4} u_a.$$

Sheppard's rules are of the utmost importance, and a clear understanding of them will save the student much trouble.

8. The following is an alternative proof of the property of divided differences which was established in paragraph 6.

If u_x be a polynomial of the nth degree in x, then the nth divided difference of u_x is constant.

It will be sufficient to consider the function $y = x^n$. Then, if the values of the argument x be $a, b, c \ldots$, the first divided difference $\underset{b}{\triangle} a^n$ is

$$(b^n - a^n)/(b-a) = b^{n-1} + b^{n-2} a + b^{n-3} a^2 + \ldots + a^{n-1}.$$

This is a symmetrical function of the $(n-1)$th degree in a and b, and is the coefficient of x^{n-1} in the expansion of

$$(1 + bx + b^2 x^2 + \ldots)(1 + ax + a^2 x^2 + \ldots),$$

i.e. in the expansion of $\dfrac{1}{1-bx} \cdot \dfrac{1}{1-ax}$.

Thus $\underset{c}{\triangle} b^n$ is the coefficient of x^{n-1} in $\dfrac{1}{1-cx} \cdot \dfrac{1}{1-bx}$ and therefore $\underset{bc}{\triangle^2} a^n$ is the coefficient of x^{n-1} in

$$\frac{1}{c-a} \left(\frac{1}{1-cx} \cdot \frac{1}{1-bx} - \frac{1}{1-bx} \cdot \frac{1}{1-ax} \right),$$

i.e. in $x \left(\dfrac{1}{1-cx} \cdot \dfrac{1}{1-bx} \cdot \dfrac{1}{1-ax} \right)$, or the coefficient of x^{n-2} in

$$\frac{1}{1-ax} \cdot \frac{1}{1-bx} \cdot \frac{1}{1-cx}.$$

Proceeding in this way, we find that $\underset{bc\ldots}{\triangle^r} a^n$ is the coefficient of

x^{n-r} in $\dfrac{1}{1-ax} \cdot \dfrac{1}{1-bx} \cdot \dfrac{1}{1-cx} \ldots$, where there are r factors in the product. This coefficient is evidently symmetrical in $a, b, c \ldots$.

Finally, $\underset{bc\ldots}{\triangle^n}a^n$ is the coefficient of x^0 in a similar expression, and this coefficient is unity.

Thus, the nth divided difference of a polynomial of the nth degree in x is constant and equal to the coefficient of the highest power of x; and higher divided differences vanish. Also, it has been proved incidentally that a divided difference is a symmetrical function of the variables involved; for the expression obtained for $\underset{bcd\ldots}{\triangle^r}a^n$ is symmetrical in $a, b, c \ldots$.

9. Newton's divided difference formula is quite easy to apply in practice, as the following example will show.

Example 2.

From the data in Ex. 1, find u_8.

Assuming fourth divided differences constant, the formula gives

$$u_8 = u_1 + (8-1)\ \triangle u_1 + (8-1)(8-2)\ \triangle^2 u_1$$
$$+ (8-1)(8-2)(8-4)\ \triangle^3 u_1 + (8-1)(8-2)(8-4)(8-7)\ \triangle^4 u_1$$
$$= u_1 + 7\ \triangle u_1 + 42\ \triangle^2 u_1 + 168\ \triangle^3 u_1 + 168\ \triangle^4 u_1$$
$$= 22 + 56 + 252 - 268\cdot8 + 32\cdot3$$
$$= 93 \text{ to the nearest integer.}$$

10. Relation between divided differences and ordinary differences.

If the arguments $a, b, c \ldots k, l$ are spaced at equal intervals h, we shall have
$$h = b - a = c - b = d - c = \ldots = l - k.$$

Hence in forming $\triangle u$ the divisors will all be equal to h.

Thus
$$\underset{b}{\triangle} u_a = \Delta u_a / h \text{ etc.}$$

Similarly in forming $\triangle^2 u$ the divisors $c-a$, $d-b \ldots$ will all be equal to $2h$.

$\therefore$
$$\underset{bc}{\triangle^2} u_a = \Delta^2 u_a / 2!\ h^2.$$

In forming $\triangle^3 u$ the divisors $d-a$, $e-b \ldots$ will all be equal to $3h$.

$$\therefore \quad \underset{bcd}{\triangle^3} u_a = \Delta^3 u_a / 3! \; h^3.$$

In general

$$\underset{bcd\dots}{\triangle^n} u_a = \Delta^n u_a / n! \; h^n.$$

If therefore the common interval $h \gtrless$ unity, the divided differences will diminish much more rapidly than the ordinary differences. In interpolation formulae this is counterbalanced by the denominators of the form $n!$ which appear in the coefficients of the ordinary differences but not in the coefficients of the divided differences.

The formula for u_x in terms of u_a and its leading divided differences is

$$u_x = u_a + (x-a) \underset{b}{\triangle} u_a + (x-a)(x-b) \underset{bc}{\triangle^2} u_a + \dots$$
$$+ (x-a)(x-b) \dots (x-k) \underset{bc\dots l}{\triangle^n} u_a.$$

This becomes, on putting $x - a = nh$,

$$u_{a+nh} = u_a + nh \underset{b}{\triangle} u_a + nh\,[nh - (b-a)] \underset{bc}{\triangle^2} u_a + \dots.$$

If now $b - a = h, \; c - a = 2h \dots$

$$u_{a+nh} = u_a + \frac{nh\Delta u_a}{h} + \frac{nh\,(nh-h)\,\Delta^2 u_a}{2!\;h^2}$$
$$+ \frac{nh\,(nh-h)\,(nh-2h)\,\Delta^3 u_a}{3!\;h^3} + \dots$$

from the relations proved above;

i.e. $$u_{a+nh} = u_a + n_{(1)}\Delta u_a + n_{(2)}\Delta^2 u_a + n_{(3)}\Delta^3 u_a + \dots,$$

which is Newton's formula for advancing differences.

It is easily seen therefore that in order to pass from the divided difference formula

$$u_x = u_a + (x-a) \underset{b}{\triangle} u_a + (x-a)(x-b) \underset{bc}{\triangle^2} u_a + \dots$$

to the advancing difference formula (when the intervals are the same) we may replace $\triangle$ by Δ, drop the subscripts and insert factorial denominators thus:

$$u_x = u_a + (x-a)\,\Delta u_a + \frac{(x-a)(x-a-1)}{2!}\,\Delta^2 u_a + \dots.$$

11. Lagrange's interpolation formula.

On the same assumption as has been made hitherto, namely that the function concerned is a polynomial in x, an interpolation formula can be evolved which is equivalent to the process of splitting up an algebraic fraction into its partial fractions.

Let n values of the function $y = u_x$ be given, so that u_x is supposed to be a polynomial of the $(n-1)$th degree in x, and let the given values of x be $a, b, c, ..., j, k$.

Then we may write

$$u_x = A (x-b) (x-c) ... (x-k) + B (x-a) (x-c) ... (x-k) + ...$$
$$+ K (x-a) (x-b) ... (x-j),$$

where there are n terms each of degree $n-1$ in x.

This is true for all values of x involved. Put therefore $x = a$.

Then
$$u_a = A (a-b) (a-c) ... (a-k),$$

$$\therefore A = \frac{u_a}{(a-b)(a-c) ... (a-k)}.$$

Similarly, by putting $x = b$,

$$B = \frac{u_b}{(b-a)(b-c) ... (b-k)}.$$

In like manner all the coefficients can be found.

$$\therefore u_x = u_a \frac{(x-b)(x-c) ... (x-k)}{(a-b)(a-c) ... (a-k)} + u_b \frac{(x-a)(x-c) ... (x-k)}{(b-a)(b-c) ... (b-k)} + ...$$
$$+ u_k \frac{(x-a)(x-b)(x-c) ...}{(k-a)(k-b)(k-c) ...},$$

or otherwise

$$\frac{u_x}{(x-a)(x-b) ... (x-k)} = \frac{u_a}{(a-b)(a-c) ... (a-k)} \cdot \frac{1}{x-a}$$
$$+ \frac{u_b}{(b-a)(b-c) ... (b-k)} \cdot \frac{1}{x-b} + ...$$

It is evident that this is exactly the same as splitting the fraction

$$\frac{u_x}{(x-a)(x-b) ... (x-k)}$$

into partial fractions.

This alternative expression is due to Euler and was given earlier than Lagrange's formula.

It is interesting to note that Euler's form, when written as

$$\frac{u_x}{(x-a)\,(x-b)\,\ldots} + \frac{u_a}{(a-x)\,(a-b)\,\ldots} + \frac{u_b}{(b-x)\,(b-a)\,\ldots} + \ldots = 0$$

is an expression for the divided difference $\underset{abc\ldots}{\triangle^n} u_x$. It follows therefore that Euler's formula (and consequently Lagrange's) can be evolved from the divided difference formula by equating the nth divided difference to zero. Also, since the expansion is symmetrical in x, a, b, c ... k, the divided difference is independent of the order in which the arguments are taken, as stated in paragraph 3 above.

12. Lagrange's formula is usually laborious to apply in practice and requires close attention to sign; it is generally simpler to employ other finite difference methods. Where the intervals are equal an advancing difference formula may be used, and for unequal intervals it is preferable to use divided differences.

The principles on which this formula has been developed are the same as those assumed for the difference formulae, namely that n values of the function being given, nth differences are assumed zero. The following examples show the application of the formula:

Example 3.

Given the data in Ex. 1, obtain u_8 by the use of Lagrange's formula.

$$\frac{u_8}{(8-1)(8-2)(8-4)(8-7)(8-12)} = \frac{u_1}{(1-2)(1-4)(1-7)(1-12)} \cdot \frac{1}{(8-1)}$$

$$+ \frac{u_2}{(2-1)\,(2-4)\,(2-7)\,(2-12)} \cdot \frac{1}{(8-2)}$$

$$+ \frac{u_4}{(4-1)\,(4-2)\,(4-7)\,(4-12)} \cdot \frac{1}{(8-4)} + \ldots,$$

i.e.
$$\frac{u_8}{7.6.4.1.(-4)} = \frac{22}{(-1)(-3)(-6)(-11).7} + \frac{30}{1.(-2)(-5)(-10).6}$$

$$+ \frac{82}{3.2.(-3)\,(-8).4} + \frac{106}{6.5.3.(-5).1}$$

$$+ \frac{206}{11.10.8.5.(-4)}.$$

$\therefore\quad u_8 = -10{\cdot}666 \ldots + 33{\cdot}6 - 95{\cdot}666 \ldots + 158{\cdot}293 \ldots + 7{\cdot}865$

$\qquad = 93$ (to the nearest integer) as in Ex. 2.

Example 4.

Find the form of the function $y = u_x$ given that

$$u_0 = 8, \quad u_1 = 11, \quad u_4 = 68, \quad u_5 = 123.$$

By Lagrange's formula:

$$\frac{u_x}{x\,(x-1)\,(x-4)\,(x-5)} = \frac{8}{(-1)\,(-4)\,(-5)}\cdot\frac{1}{x} + \frac{11}{1\,(-3)\,(-4)}\cdot\frac{1}{x-1}$$

$$+ \frac{68}{4\cdot3\,(-1)}\cdot\frac{1}{x-4} + \frac{123}{5\cdot4\cdot1}\cdot\frac{1}{x-5}$$

$$= -\frac{2}{5}\cdot\frac{1}{x} + \frac{11}{12}\cdot\frac{1}{x-1} - \frac{68}{12}\cdot\frac{1}{x-4} + \frac{123}{20}\cdot\frac{1}{x-5}$$

$$= \frac{1}{20}\,\frac{115x+40}{x\,(x-5)} - \frac{1}{12}\,\frac{57x-24}{(x-1)\,(x-4)}$$

$$= \frac{23x+8}{4x\,(x-5)} - \frac{19x-8}{4\,(x-1)\,(x-4)}.$$

$$\therefore \quad u_x = \tfrac{1}{4}\,[(23x+8)\,(x^2-5x+4) - (19x-8)\,(x^2-5x)]$$
$$= x^3 - x^2 + 3x + 8.$$

It is useful to work out this example by divided differences, adopting two different orders for the values of x, thus illustrating the principle that, if the same u's are involved, the order is indifferent.

(a)

x	u_x	$\triangle u_x$	$\triangle^2 u_x$	$\triangle^3 u_x$
0	8			
		$3 \div 1 = 3$		
1	11		$16 \div 4 = 4$	
		$57 \div 3 = 19$		$5 \div 5 = 1$
4	68		$36 \div 4 = 9$	
		$55 \div 1 = 55$		
5	123			

$$\therefore \quad u_x = 8 + 3x + 4x\,(x-1) + 1x\,(x-1)\,(x-4) = x^3 - x^2 + 3x + 8.$$

(b)

x	u_x	$\triangle u_x$	$\triangle^2 u_x$	$\triangle^3 u_x$
5	123			
		$-115 \div -5 = 23$		
0	8		$-8 \div -1 = 8$	
		$+ 60 \div +4 = 15$		$-4 \div -4 = 1$
4	68		$+4 \div +1 = 4$	
		$- 57 \div -3 = 19$		
1	11			

5

$$\therefore \quad u_x = 123 + 23\,(x-5) + 8\,(x-5)\,x + 1\,(x-5)\,x\,(x-4)$$
$$= 123 + 23x - 115 + 8x^2 - 40x + x^3 - 9x^2 + 20x$$
$$= x^3 - x^2 + 3x + 8.$$

Here, for example,

$$\underset{4}{\triangle} u_1 = \underset{1}{\triangle} u_4 = 19,$$

$$\underset{1,4,5}{\triangle^3} u_0 = \underset{0,4,1}{\triangle^3} u_5 = 1.$$

13. The following examples are instructive:

Example 5.

$u_0 = -18,\ u_1 = 0,\ u_3 = 0,\ u_5 = -248,\ u_6 = 0,\ u_9 = 13104.$

Find the form of u_x, assuming it to be a polynomial in x.

Now since $u_1 = 0,\ u_3 = 0,\ u_6 = 0$, the function must be of the form $(x-1)\,(x-3)\,(x-6)\,\phi\,(x)$, where $\phi\,(x)$ is a polynomial in x of the second degree.

$$\therefore \quad \frac{u_x}{(x-1)\,(x-3)\,(x-6)} = \phi\,(x).$$

I.e. $\qquad \dfrac{u_0}{(-1)\,(-3)\,(-6)} = \phi\,(0) \quad \therefore \quad \phi\,(0) = 1,\ \text{since}\ u_0 = -\quad 18$

$$\frac{u_5}{4.2\,(-1)} = \phi\,(5) \quad \therefore \quad \phi\,(5) = 31,\ \text{,,}\ u_5 = -\quad 248$$

and $\qquad \dfrac{u_9}{8.6.3} = \phi\,(9) \quad \therefore \quad \phi\,(9) = 91,\ \text{,,}\ u_9 = \quad 13104$

Whence, from the divided difference table,

x	$\phi\,(x)$	$\triangle \phi\,(x)$	$\triangle^2 \phi\,(x)$
0	1		
		6	
5	31		1
		15	
9	91		

$$\phi\,(x) = \phi\,(0) + x\triangle\phi\,(x) + x\,(x-5)\,\triangle^2\phi\,(x)$$
$$= 1 + 6x + x\,(x-5)$$
$$= x^2 + x + 1;$$

$$\therefore \quad u_x = (x-1)\,(x-3)\,(x-6)\,(x^2 + x + 1)$$
$$= x^5 - 9x^4 + 18x^3 - x^2 + 9x - 18.$$

Example 6.

Given $u_5 = 23$, $u_{11} = 899$, $u_{27} = 17315$, $u_{34} = 35606$, $u_{42} = 68510$, construct a table of divided differences and extend the table to include arguments $x = 3$ repeated as many times as may be necessary to find u_x in powers of $(x-3)$.

From the data we have

x	u_x	$\triangle u_x$	$\triangle^2 u_x$	$\triangle^3 u_x$
5	23			
		146		
11	899		40	
		1026		1
27	17315		69	
		2613		1
34	35606		100	
		4113		1
42	68510		a	
		b		1
3	c		d	
		e		1
			f	
				1

Now

$$a = 100 - 24 \times 1 = 76$$
$$b = 4113 - 31 \times a = 1757$$
$$c = 68510 - 39 \times b = -13$$
$$d = a - 31 \times 1 = 45$$
$$e = b - 39 \times d = 2$$
$$f = d - 39 \times 1 = 6$$

$$\therefore \quad u_x = c + (x-3)\,e + (x-3)^2 f + (x-3)^3 \times 1$$
$$= -13 + 2\,(x-3) + 6\,(x-3)^2 + (x-3)^3.$$

14. Newton's formula with divided differences may be considered as the basic formula in finite differences. It has been shown that, by making the intervals equal, the ordinary advancing difference formula follows, and that Lagrange's formula can be evolved from the divided difference formula by equating the nth divided difference to zero. Moreover, by taking the limiting values when the intervals tend to zero, Taylor's theorem can be obtained.

The formula is of the utmost importance analytically and

historically, and the advanced student may be recommended to read Mr D. C. Fraser's "Newton's Interpolation Formulas" (*J.I.A.* vol. LI, pp. 77–106 and pp. 211–32, and vol. LVIII, pp. 53–95) and the same author's "Newton and Interpolation" (an article in *Newton,* 1727–1927, a memorial volume published by the Mathematical Association).

*15. Adjusted differences.

There is a system of differences which may be considered as the connecting link between ordinary differences and divided differences. These differences, which are called *adjusted differences,* were used by Newton and re-discovered by Sheppard.

When the successive arguments are $a, b, c \ldots$ the relation between adjusted differences and ordinary differences is as follows:

Order of differences	Divisor of difference for divided differences	Divisor of difference for adjusted differences
First	$a-b$	$a-b$
Second	$a-c$	$\frac{1}{2}(a-c)$
Third	$a-d$	$\frac{1}{3}(a-d)$
Fourth	$a-e$	$\frac{1}{4}(a-e)$
$\vdots$	$\vdots$	$\vdots$

Ordinary differences are adjusted differences and both sets can be used in the same scheme.

An interesting account of the Newton-Sheppard system of adjusted differences will be found in *J.I.A.* vol. LVIII, pp. 60–74 (D. C. Fraser).

*16. An expression for the nth divided difference.

The results of paragraph 5 may be written in the form

$$R_{n+1}(x) = u_x - U_x,$$

where $R_{n+1}(x)$ vanishes for $n+1$ values of x, say $a, b, c \ldots l$. Hence, by repeated application of Rolle's Theorem, it follows that, in the interval which includes these values, the first differential coefficient of R with respect to x vanishes at least n times, the second differential coefficient vanishes at least $n-1$ times, and finally, the nth differential coefficient vanishes at least once, say where $x = \xi$.

$$\therefore \quad 0 = \left[\frac{d^n}{dx^n} R_{n+1}(x) \right]_{x=\xi}$$

$$= \left[\frac{d^n}{dx^n} (u_x - U_x) \right]_{x=\xi}.$$

Now U_x is of the form $P_n(x)$, and since the nth differential coefficient of $P_n(x)$ with respect to x is $n!$ times the coefficient of x^n, it follows that

$$\frac{d^n}{dx^n} U_x = n! \underset{bc\ldots l}{\triangle^n} u_a.$$

$$\therefore \quad 0 = \left[\frac{d^n}{dx^n} u_x \right]_{x=\xi} - n! \underset{bc\ldots l}{\triangle^n} u_a,$$

or
$$\underset{bc\ldots l}{\triangle^n} u_a = \frac{1}{n!} \left[\frac{d^n}{dx^n} u_x \right]$$

for some value of x (ξ) within the range which includes $a, b, c \ldots l$, and x.

*17. Remainder term in the divided difference formula.

If in the proof above we bring in another term u_x, we have

$$\underset{bcl\ldots x}{\triangle^{n+1}} u_a = \left[\frac{d^{n+1}}{d\xi^{n+1}} u_\xi \right] \Big/ (n+1)!,$$

where $\dfrac{d^{n+1}}{d\xi^{n+1}} u_\xi$ is written for $\left[\dfrac{d^{n+1}}{dx^{n+1}} u_x \right]_{x=\xi}$.

This is the divided difference involved in $R_{n+1}(x)$.

$$\therefore \quad R_{n+1}(x) = \left[(x-a)(x-b) \ldots (x-l) \frac{d^{n+1}}{d\xi^{n+1}} u_\xi \right] \Big/ (n+1)!.$$

When the intervals are all unity, this becomes

$$R_{n+1}(x) = x_{(n+1)} \frac{d^{n+1}}{d\xi^{n+1}} u_\xi,$$

where ξ is some value in the interval including all the arguments involved, i.e. the given arguments $a, b \ldots l$ and also x.

EXAMPLES 3

1. Given terms at unequal intervals, explain how to apply the method of divided differences to find an interpolated value: illustrate your answer by finding u_5 given

$$u_{4\cdot50} = 1345, \quad u_{4\cdot55} = 1470, \quad u_{4\cdot70} = 2010, \quad u_{4\cdot90} = 3815, \quad u_{5\cdot15} = 10965.$$

2. $u_{40} = 43833, \quad u_{42} = 46568, \quad u_{44} = 49431, \quad u_{45} = 50912.$ Use divided differences to find u_{43}.

3. Given the following table, find log 656:

No.	654	658	659	661
Log	2·8156	2·8182	2·8189	2·8202

4. $u_{50} = 1\cdot6990, \quad u_{52} = 1\cdot7160, \quad u_{54} = 1\cdot7324, \quad u_{55} = 1\cdot7404.$ Find u_{53} by divided differences.

5. $u_{35\cdot0} = 1175, \quad u_{35\cdot5} = 1280, \quad u_{39\cdot5} = 2180, \quad u_{40\cdot5} = 2420.$ Obtain a value for u_{40} (i) by advancing differences, (ii) by divided differences.

6. $u_{7\cdot0} = 235, u_{7\cdot1} = 256, u_{7\cdot9} = 436, u_{8\cdot1} = 484.$ Find $u_{8\cdot0}$.

7. Find the first three divided differences of the function $y = x^{-2}$ for the arguments $x = l, m, n, p$.

Find by Lagrange's formula the value of

8. u_{48} given $u_{40} = 15\cdot22, \quad u_{45} = 13\cdot99, \quad u_{50} = 12\cdot62, \quad u_{55} = 11\cdot13.$

9. u_8 given $u_0 = 17\cdot378, u_5 = 15\cdot894, u_{10} = 14\cdot270, u_{15} = 12\cdot412.$

10. u_{22} given $u_{10} = 22\cdot40, \quad u_{15} = 21\cdot66, \quad u_{20} = 20\cdot82, \quad u_{25} = 19\cdot85.$

11. u_1 given $u_0 = \cdot400, u_2 = \cdot128, u_3 = \cdot224, u_4 = \cdot376.$

12. Use Lagrange's formula to find the form of the function $y = f(x)$ given

x	0	2	3	6
$f(x)$	659	705	729	804

13. Values of u_x are given for all integral values of x from 0 to $n-1$. Show that u_x is capable of expression in the form

$$\frac{x!}{(x-n)!\,(n-1)!} \left[\frac{u_{n-1}}{x-n+1} - (n-1)_{(1)} \frac{u_{n-2}}{x-n+2} \right.$$

$$\left. + (n-1)_{(2)} \frac{u_{n-3}}{x-n+3} - \ldots \pm (n-1)_{(n-1)} \frac{u_0}{x} \right].$$

Find u_4 given $u_0 = 4, \; u_1 = 7, \; u_2 = 12, \; u_3 = 20,$ by using the above formula.

14. By means of Lagrange's formula, prove that, approximately,

(1) $u_1 = u_3 - \cdot 3\,(u_5 - u_{-3}) + \cdot 2\,(u_{-3} - u_{-5})$,

(2) $u_0 = \frac{1}{2}\,[u_1 + u_{-1}] - \frac{1}{8}\,[\frac{1}{2}\,(u_3 - u_1) - \frac{1}{2}\,(u_{-1} - u_{-3})]$.

15. Four equidistant values u_{-1}, u_0, u_1, and u_2 being given, a value is interpolated by Lagrange's formula. Show that it may be written in the form

$$u_x = yu_0 + xu_1 + \frac{y\,(y^2 - 1)}{3!}\,\Delta^2 u_{-1} + \frac{x\,(x^2 - 1)}{3!}\,\Delta^2 u_0,$$

where $x + y = 1$.

16. If $f\,(a_1, a_0) = \dfrac{f\,(a_1) - f\,(a_0)}{a_1 - a_0}$, $f\,(a_2, a_1) = \dfrac{f\,(a_2) - f\,(a_1)}{a_2 - a_1}$, etc. be divided differences of the first order; $f\,(a_2, a_1, a_0) = \dfrac{f\,(a_2, a_1) - f\,(a_1, a_0)}{a_2 - a_0}$, etc. divided differences of the second order and so on, find $f\,(2, 4, 9, 10)$, where $f\,(x) = $ (i) $x^3 - 2x$, (ii) $x^4 + x^2 + 1$.

17. Prove that if u_x be a polynomial of the nth degree in x, and if values u_a, u_b, u_c, ... of u_x be given, then the expressions for u_x in terms of its divided differences are identically equal whatever the order of arrangement of the u's.

18. Apply Lagrange's formula to find $f\,(5)$ and $f\,(6)$, given that

$$f\,(1) = 2,\ f\,(2) = 4,\ f\,(3) = 8,\ f\,(4) = 16 \text{ and } f\,(7) = 128;$$

and explain why the results differ from those obtained by completing the series of powers of 2.

19. $u_{-30} = 30$; $u_{-13} = 34$; $u_3 = 38$; $u_{18} = 42$. Find u_0.

20. $u_{70} = 7\cdot69$; $u_{72} = 7\cdot07$; $u_{73} = 6\cdot78$; $u_{75} = 6\cdot18$. Interpolate to find u_{71} by divided differences, using the following orders of the argument:

(i) 70, 73, 75, 72; (ii) 72, 75, 70, 73.

21. By means of divided differences, find the value of u_{19} from the following table:

x	11	17	21	23	31
u_x	14,646	83,526	194,486	279,846	923,526

22. Prove that $\underset{yz}{\Delta^2}\,x^3 = x + y + z$ and that

$$\underset{bc}{\Delta^2}\left(\frac{1}{a}\right) = \frac{1}{abc}.$$

23. If the data are u_0, u_3, u_4, u_7, u_{11}, and the interpolation formula is

$$u_x = u_4 + C_1 \underset{3}{\triangle} u_4 + C_2 \underset{4,7}{\triangle^2} u_3 + C_3 \underset{3,4,7}{\triangle^3} u_0 + C_4 \underset{3,4,7,11}{\triangle^4} u_0,$$

find the values of C_1, C_2, C_3 and C_4.

24. If the data are as in Qu. 23 above, and the formula is

$$u_x = u_3 + (x-3) \triangle u + (x-3)(x-4) \triangle^2 u + (x-3)(x-4) x \triangle^3 u$$
$$+ (x-3)(x-4) x (x-7) \triangle^4 u,$$

find the missing suffixes of the operators and the subscripts of the u's.

CHAPTER IV

CENTRAL DIFFERENCES

1. If a series of values of u_x be given, we can interpolate to find any intermediate value by one of the methods in the preceding chapters. Where the values of the argument x proceed by unit intervals it has been shown that, on certain assumptions, Newton's advancing difference formula can be applied to give satisfactory results. If the value of u_x were required for some value of x between $x = 0$ and $x = 1$, it might be considered that we should obtain a better result if our knowledge of the shape of the curve extended on both sides of the values of x between which we wish to interpolate. That is to say, where we may choose any values of u_x at unit intervals for our data, it might be of advantage if we could use a formula involving values such as u_{-3}, u_{-2}, u_{-1}, u_0, u_1, u_2, u_3, ... rather than u_0, u_1, u_2, u_3, u_4, ... By the advancing difference formula we expand u_x in terms of a given value of u_x and its leading differences and, by giving x a suitable value, such a formula can be made to embrace any values of u that we wish. It is however convenient to use special formulae called *central difference* formulae, based on differences obtained from the values of u_x on either side of the origin; this is found to result in smaller coefficients and a more rapidly converging series of terms.

2. There are various central difference formulae that are of use in actual practice, and the development of the better-known formulae is an exercise in the application of the fundamental principles of finite differences which will be advantageous to the student. These formulae apply whether the values of the function correspond to equidistant values of the argument or to values with unequal intervals. We shall consider first the general case and pass from it to the simpler and more usual case of equal intervals.

3. Gauss's formulae.

Suppose that we are given the values ... u_m, u_l, u_a, u_b, u_c ... and that we wish to deduce a formula for u_x in terms of u_a, the even differences which fall on the line of u_a and the odd differences which fall on the line between u_a and u_b, as shown by the lower of the two series of dotted lines in the following difference table:

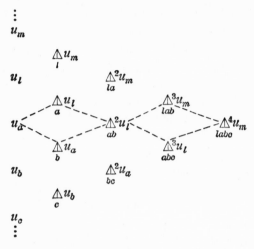

The formula will thus involve in succession

$$u_a, \quad \underset{b}{\triangle} u_a, \quad \underset{ab}{\triangle^2} u_l, \quad \underset{abc}{\triangle^3} u_l, \quad \underset{labc}{\triangle^4} u_m \ ....$$

As we pass from each of these to the next, the new arguments brought in, one at a time, are b, l, c, m, ... Hence, applying rule (iii) of Chap. III, paragraph 7, namely, that each new argument gives the new factor for use in the next term, and adopting the abbreviated notation $x - a = A$, $x - b = B$ etc., we can at once write down the required formula.

The formula will be

$$u_x = u_a + A \underset{b}{\triangle} u_a + AB \underset{ab}{\triangle^2} u_l + ABL \underset{abc}{\triangle^3} u_l + ABCL \underset{labc}{\triangle^4} u_m + ...,$$

where the law of formation is evident.

Now let the intervals between the arguments be all equal to unity and let $a = 0$, so that $b = 1$, $c = 2$, ..., $l = -1$, $m = -2$, ...

Then, as in Chap. III, paragraph 10, we have

$$\underset{b}{\triangle}u_a = \Delta u_0;$$

$$\underset{ab}{\triangle^2}u_l = \Delta^2 u_{-1}/2!;$$

$$\underset{abc}{\triangle^3}u_l = \Delta^3 u_{-1}/3!;$$

$$\underset{labc}{\triangle^4}u_m = \Delta^4 u_{-2}/4!.$$

Further,

$$A = x - a = x,$$

$$B = x - b = x - 1,$$

$$L = x - l = x + 1,$$

. . . .

The formula for equal intervals is thus

$$u_x = u_0 + x\Delta u_0 + \frac{x(x-1)}{2!}\Delta^2 u_{-1} + \frac{(x+1)x(x-1)}{3!}\Delta^3 u_{-1}$$

$$+ \frac{(x+1)x(x-1)(x-2)}{4!}\Delta^4 u_{-2} + \dots$$

or

$$u_0 + x_{(1)}\Delta u_0 + x_{(2)}\Delta^2 u_{-1} + (x+1)_{(3)}\Delta^3 u_{-1} + (x+1)_{(4)}\Delta^4 u_{-2} + \dots.$$

This is known as Gauss's "forward" formula for equal intervals.

4. If we take the even differences as above but the odd differences which fall on the line between u_l and u_a (the upper of the two series of dotted lines in the table in the preceding paragraph) we obtain a formula which involves in succession

$$u_a, \quad \underset{a}{\triangle}u_l, \quad \underset{ab}{\triangle^2}u_l, \quad \underset{lab}{\triangle^3}u_m, \quad \underset{labc}{\triangle^4}u_m \quad \dots.$$

The new arguments brought in are l, b, m, c, ... and, using the rule as before, we evolve the form

$$u_x = u_a + A\underset{a}{\triangle}u_l + AL\underset{ab}{\triangle^2}u_l + ABL\underset{lab}{\triangle^3}u_m + ABLM\underset{labc}{\triangle^4}u_m + \dots.$$

From this we may pass at once to the formula for equal intervals of unity:

$$u_x = u_0 + x_{(1)}\Delta u_{-1} + (x+1)_{(2)}\Delta^2 u_{-1} + (x+1)_{(3)}\Delta^3 u_{-2}$$
$$+ (x+2)_{(4)}\Delta^4 u_{-2} + \dots.$$

This is Gauss's "backward" formula.

Note. It is useful to remember that, after u_0, as we advance from each term to the next, in the forward form we alternately *deduct* unity from the subscript of u and *add* unity to the number whose factorial is the coefficient; while in the backward form we alternately *add* unity to the number whose factorial is the coefficient and *deduct* unity from the subscript of u.

5. Stirling's formula.

Taking the mean of the two Gauss formulae we arrive at the following expansion:

$$u_x = u_0 + x \cdot \tfrac{1}{2}\left(\Delta u_0 + \Delta u_{-1}\right) + \frac{x^2}{2!}\Delta^2 u_{-1}$$
$$+ \frac{x\left(x^2 - 1^2\right)}{3!}\tfrac{1}{2}\left(\Delta^3 u_{-1} + \Delta^3 u_{-2}\right) + \frac{x^2\left(x^2 - 1^2\right)}{4!}\Delta^4 u_{-2} + \dots,$$

in which we have alternately mean *coefficients* and mean *differences*, falling on the line through u_0 in the difference table.

This is known as Stirling's formula. In using it x should lie in the range $-\tfrac{1}{2}$ to $+\tfrac{1}{2}$, i.e. $\tfrac{1}{2}$ on each side of the line of u_0.

6. Bessel's formula.

Transferring the origin in the Gauss backward formula from o to 1, we have

$$u_x = u_1 + (x-1)\Delta u_0 + \frac{x(x-1)}{2!}\Delta^2 u_0 + \frac{x(x-1)(x-2)}{3!}\Delta^3 u_{-1}$$
$$+ \frac{(x+1)x(x-1)(x-2)}{4!}\Delta^4 u_{-1} + \dots.$$

The mean of this and the forward formula is

$$u_x = \tfrac{1}{2}(u_0 + u_1) + (x - \tfrac{1}{2})\Delta u_0$$
$$+ \frac{x(x-1)}{2!}\tfrac{1}{2}\left(\Delta^2 u_{-1} + \Delta^2 u_0\right) + \frac{(x-\tfrac{1}{2})x(x-1)}{3!}\Delta^3 u_{-1}$$
$$+ \frac{(x+1)x(x-1)(x-2)}{4!}\tfrac{1}{2}\left(\Delta^4 u_{-1} + \Delta^4 u_{-2}\right) + \dots,$$

which is Bessel's formula. In using the formula x should lie in the range 0 to 1, i.e. $\frac{1}{2}$ on each side of the central line.

In this formula we have alternately mean u's or differences, falling on the central line between u_0 and u_1, and mean coefficients.

If we write $y + \frac{1}{2}$ for x in Bessel's formula, we obtain the simpler and more symmetric form:

$$u_x = u_{y+\frac{1}{2}} = \frac{1}{2}(u_0 + u_1) + y\Delta u_0 + \frac{y^2 - \frac{1}{4}}{2!}\, \frac{1}{2}(\Delta^2 u_{-1} + \Delta^2 u_0)$$

$$+ \frac{y(y^2 - \frac{1}{4})}{3!}\Delta^3 u_{-1} + \frac{(y^2 - \frac{1}{4})(y^2 - \frac{9}{4})}{4!}\, \frac{1}{2}(\Delta^4 u_{-2} + \Delta^4 u_{-1}) + \dots,$$

the most convenient shape of the formula for practical purposes.

7. An alternative method of obtaining Gauss's forward formula for equal intervals is as follows:

The ordinary advancing difference expansion is

$$u_x = u_0 + x_{(1)}\Delta u_0 + x_{(2)}\Delta^2 u_0 + x_{(3)}\Delta^3 u_0 + x_{(4)}\Delta^4 u_0 + \dots.$$

Now $\quad \Delta^2 u_0 = \Delta^2 u_{-1} + \Delta^3 u_{-1};$

$$\Delta^3 u_0 = \Delta^3 u_{-1} + \Delta^4 u_{-1}; \quad \Delta^4 u_{-1} = \Delta^4 u_{-2} + \Delta^5 u_{-2};$$

$$\dots\dots\dots\dots\dots \qquad \dots\dots\dots\dots\dots$$

Therefore we may write

$$u_x = u_0 + x_{(1)}\Delta u_0 + x_{(2)}(\Delta^2 u_{-1} + \Delta^3 u_{-1})$$
$$+ x_{(3)}(\Delta^3 u_{-1} + \Delta^4 u_{-1}) + x_{(4)}(\Delta^4 u_{-1} + \Delta^5 u_{-1}) + \dots$$

$$= u_0 + x_{(1)}\Delta u_0 + x_{(2)}\Delta^2 u_{-1} + (x_{(2)} + x_{(3)})\,\Delta^3 u_{-1}$$
$$+ (x_{(3)} + x_{(4)})\,\Delta^4 u_{-1} + \dots$$

$$= u_0 + x_{(1)}\Delta u_0 + x_{(2)}\Delta^2 u_{-1} + (x+1)_{(3)}\,\Delta^3 u_{-1}$$
$$+ (x+1)_{(4)}(\Delta^4 u_{-2} + \Delta^5 u_{-2}) + \dots,$$

since $\qquad\qquad x_{(r)} + x_{(r+1)} = (x+1)_{(r+1)},$

and so on.

A proof similar to the above, in which the general term is evolved, and which depends upon the method of separation of symbols, will be found in *J.I.A.* vol. L, pp. 31, 32.

The backward form may be obtained similarly by grouping the terms in a slightly different way and using the relations

$$\Delta u_0 = \Delta u_{-1} + \Delta^2 u_{-1},$$
$$\Delta^2 u_0 = \Delta^2 u_{-1} + \Delta^3 u_{-1},$$
$$\Delta^3 u_{-1} = \Delta^3 u_{-2} + \Delta^4 u_{-2},$$
$$\text{etc.}$$

8. Everett's formula.

The Gauss forward formula with interval x and initial term v_1 may be written

$$v_{x+1} = v_1 + x_{(1)}\Delta v_1 + x_{(2)}\Delta^2 v_0 + (x+1)_{(3)}\Delta^3 v_0 + (x+1)_{(4)}\Delta^4 v_{-1}$$
$$+ (x+2)_{(5)}\Delta^5 v_{-1} + \dots$$

The backward formula with interval $(x-1)$ and initial term v_1 gives

$$v_x = v_1 + (x-1)_{(1)}\Delta v_0 + x_{(2)}\Delta^2 v_0 + x_{(3)}\Delta^3 v_{-1} + (x+1)_{(4)}\Delta^4 v_{-1}$$
$$+ (x+1)_{(5)}\Delta^5 v_{-2} + \dots$$

Subtract the second series from the first: then, since

$$v_{x+1} - v_x = \Delta v_x,$$

we have

$$\Delta v_x = x_{(1)}\Delta v_1 + (x+1)_{(3)}\Delta^3 v_0 + (x+2)_{(5)}\Delta^5 v_{-1} + \dots$$
$$- (x-1)_{(1)}\Delta v_0 - x_{(3)}\Delta^3 v_{-1} - (x+1)_{(5)}\Delta^5 v_{-2} - \dots.$$

Put u_x, Δu_x, $\Delta^2 u_x$, ... for Δv_x, $\Delta^2 v_x$, $\Delta^3 v_x$, ...
Then

$$u_x = x_{(1)}u_1 + (x+1)_{(3)}\Delta^2 u_0 + (x+2)_{(5)}\Delta^4 u_{-1} + \dots$$
$$- (x-1)_{(1)}u_0 - x_{(3)}\Delta^2 u_{-1} - (x+1)_{(5)}\Delta^4 u_{-2} - \dots. \qquad \dots\dots(\text{i})$$

When x is less than unity a convenient form of this formula for interpolation between u_0 and u_1 is obtained by putting $\xi = 1 - x$; thus

$$u_x = xu_1 + \frac{x(x^2-1)}{3!}\Delta^2 u_0 + \frac{x(x^2-1)(x^2-4)}{5!}\Delta^4 u_{-1} + \dots$$
$$+ \xi u_0 + \frac{\xi(\xi^2-1)}{3!}\Delta^2 u_{-1} + \frac{\xi(\xi^2-1)(\xi^2-4)}{5!}\Delta^4 u_{-2} + \dots,$$

the most common form of Everett's formula.

The above elegant proof is due to G. J. Lidstone (*J.I.A.* vol. LX, pp. 349–52). In his note on this formula Mr Lidstone shows how to obtain another formula similar to the above for interpolation between $u_{-\frac{1}{2}}$ and $u_{\frac{1}{2}}$.

If we difference formula (i) bearing in mind that

$$\Delta (x+r)_{(t)}=(x+r)_{(t-1)},$$

we have
$$\Delta u_x = u_1 + (x+1)_{(2)} \Delta^2 u_0 + (x+2)_{(4)} \Delta^4 u_{-1} + \dots$$
$$-u_0 - x_{(2)} \Delta^2 u_{-1} - (x+1)_{(4)} \Delta^4 u_{-2} - \dots,$$

or, writing u_x for Δu_x, Δu_x for $\Delta^2 u_x$ and so on,

$$u_x = u_0 + (x+1)_{(2)} \Delta u_0 + (x+2)_{(4)} \Delta^3 u_{-1} + \dots$$
$$-x_{(2)} \Delta u_{-1} - (x+1)_{(4)} \Delta^3 u_{-2} - \dots.$$

The formula then becomes

$$u_{p-\frac{1}{2}} = u_0 + \frac{p^2-\frac{1}{4}}{2!} \Delta u_0 + \frac{(p^2-\frac{1}{4})(p^2-\frac{9}{4})}{4!} \Delta^3 u_{-1} + \dots$$
$$- \frac{q^2-\frac{1}{4}}{2!} \Delta u_{-1} - \frac{(q^2-\frac{1}{4})(q^2-\frac{9}{4})}{4!} \Delta^3 u_{-2} - \dots,$$

where $p=\frac{1}{2}+x$ and $q=\frac{1}{2}-x$.

This form is generally known as Everett's "second" formula. Both formulae, perhaps more particularly the first, are specially adapted for use in statistical work. They can be applied in the case of unequal intervals: see Todhunter, *J.I.A.* vol. L, p. 137, and Lidstone, *Proc. Edin. Math. Soc.* Series 1, vol. XL, pp. 25–6.

9. Everett's formulae can also be obtained from Gauss's formulae by a simple transformation depending upon the properties of the binomial coefficients.

Any pair of terms of the form

$$y_{(r)} \Delta^r u_t + (y+1)_{(r+1)} \Delta^{r+1} u_t$$
$$= (y+1)_{(r+1)} (\Delta^r u_t + \Delta^{r+1} u_t) - \{(y+1)_{(r+1)} - y_{(r)}\} \Delta^r u_t$$
$$= (y+1)_{(r+1)} \Delta^r u_{t+1} - y_{(r+1)} \Delta^r u_t,$$

since
$$(y+1)_{(r+1)} - y_{(r)} = y_{(r+1)}.$$

Taking the pairs

1–2; 3–4; 5–6 … in Gauss's forward formula,

and 2–3; 4–5; 6–7 … in Gauss's backward formula,

the two forms of Everett's formula are at once obtained.

*10. It is of interest to show in a simple manner the relations between Everett's and Bessel's formulae. The formulae are closely related, and the following demonstration indicates clearly the connection between corresponding coefficients in the two expansions.

In Bessel's formula let b_{2n} denote the coefficient of the "mean" difference

$$\tfrac{1}{2}\left(\Delta^{2n}u_{-n}+\Delta^{2n}u_{-n+1}\right)$$

and b_{2n+1} the coefficient of the difference $\Delta^{2n+1}u_{-n}.$

Then, since

$$\Delta^{2n}u_{-n+1}=\Delta^{2n}u_{-n}+\Delta^{2n+1}u_{-n},$$

the sum of the terms

$$b_{2n}\cdot\tfrac{1}{2}\left(\Delta^{2n}u_{-n}+\Delta^{2n}u_{-n+1}\right)+b_{2n+1}\Delta^{2n+1}u_{-n}$$

may be written as

$$b_{2n}\Delta^{2n}u_{-n}+\left(\tfrac{1}{2}b_{2n}+b_{2n+1}\right)\Delta^{2n+1}u_{-n}. \qquad \ldots\ldots(a)$$

Consider the expression

$$e_{2n}\Delta^{2n}u_{-n}+\epsilon_{2n}\Delta^{2n}u_{-n+1}.$$

This is the same as

$$\left(e_{2n}+\epsilon_{2n}\right)\Delta^{2n}u_{-n}+\epsilon_{2n}\Delta^{2n+1}u_{-n}. \qquad \ldots\ldots(b)$$

Again, by reference to Bessel's formula, it will be seen that

$$b_{2n+1}=\frac{x-\tfrac{1}{2}}{2n+1}\,b_{2n}. \qquad \ldots\ldots(c)$$

Equating (a) and (b), and introducing the relation (c), we have

$$e_{2n}+\epsilon_{2n}=b_{2n},$$

and

$$\epsilon_{2n}=\tfrac{1}{2}b_{2n}+b_{2n+1}$$
$$=b_{2n}\left\{\tfrac{1}{2}+(x-\tfrac{1}{2})/(2n+1)\right\}$$
$$=\frac{x+n}{2n+1}\,b_{2n};$$

whence

$$e_{2n}=\tfrac{1}{2}b_{2n}-b_{2n+1}$$
$$=b_{2n}\left\{\tfrac{1}{2}-(x-\tfrac{1}{2})/(2n+1)\right\}$$
$$=-\frac{x-n-1}{2n+1}\,b_{2n};$$

from which the coefficients already given in Everett's formula can at once be deduced.

The same analysis applies to each pair of terms.

It should be noted that

(i) ϵ_r and e_r are the same functions of x and $1-x$ respectively;

[In fact, $\qquad \epsilon_{2n} = (x+n)_{(2n+1)},$

$$e_{2n} = -(x+n-1)_{(2n+1)}$$
$$= (1-x+n)_{(2n+1)}]$$

(ii) the pair of terms in Everett's formula is exactly equivalent to the corresponding pair in Bessel's formula. In Everett's formula, therefore, precise allowance is made for the next odd difference, although this difference does not appear explicitly.

Similarly, by taking the pair of terms

$$s_{2n+1} \cdot \tfrac{1}{2}\left(\Delta^{2n+1}u_{-n} + \Delta^{2n+1}u_{-n-1}\right)$$

and $\qquad\qquad s_{2n+2}\Delta^{2n+2}u_{-n}$

in Stirling's formula, Everett's second formula may be obtained.

11. It will be instructive to compare the results brought out by applying first, Gauss's forward formula, and, secondly, the ordinary advancing difference formula, to the same set of data.

Example 1.

Interpolate by means of Gauss's forward formula to find the present value of an annuity of 1 p.a. for 27 years at 5 per cent. compound interest, given the following table:

No. of years	15	20	25	30	35	40
Annuity-value	10·3797	12·4622	14·0939	15·3725	16·3742	17·1591

If we take 25 years as the origin and 5 years as the unit, the value required will be $u_{.4}$.

x	u_x	Δu_x	$\Delta^2 u_x$	$\Delta^3 u_x$	$\Delta^4 u_x$	$\Delta^5 u_x$
-2	10·3797					
		2·0825				
-1	12·4622		$-·4508$			
		1·6317		·0977		
0	14·0939		$-·3531$		$-·0215$	
		1·2786		·0762		·0054
1	15·3725		$-·2769$		$-·0161$	
		1·0017		·0601		
2	16·3742		$-·2168$			
		·7849				
3	17·1591					

The Gauss forward formula is

$$u_x = u_0 + x_{(1)}\Delta u_0 + x_{(2)}\Delta^2 u_{-1} + (x+1)_{(3)}\Delta^3 u_{-1} + (x+1)_{(4)}\Delta^4 u_{-2}$$
$$+ (x+2)_{(5)}\Delta^5 u_{-2}.$$

When $x = \cdot 4$ the successive coefficients are

$$\cdot 4; \quad -\cdot 12; \quad -\cdot 056; \quad \cdot 0224; \quad \cdot 010752$$

and to four decimal places the value of $u_{\cdot 4}$ is $14\cdot 6430$, which agrees with the tabulated value.

To apply the advancing difference formula we take 15 years as the origin and are required to find u_x when $x = 2\cdot 4$.

In the formula

$$u_x = u_0 + x_{(1)}\Delta u_0 + x_{(2)}\Delta^2 u_0 + x_{(3)}\Delta^3 u_0 + x_{(4)}\Delta^4 u_0 + x_{(5)}\Delta^5 u_0$$

the coefficients are

$$2\cdot 4; \quad 1\cdot 68; \quad \cdot 224; \quad -\cdot 0336; \quad -\cdot 010752.$$

On evaluating the expansion we obtain for $u_{2\cdot 4}$ the value $14\cdot 6430$ as above.

It will be seen that the two results are in agreement (as indeed they must be, since the same values of u are used), and it may be asked therefore wherein lies the advantage of using the central difference formula. This question will be discussed in the next paragraph.

12. Consider an approximation to a particular value of u_x based on, say, r values out of n available. The error in the approximation, as measured approximately by the first neglected term, is least when the coefficient of that term is least. It can be shown that this happens when the values of u_x upon which the interpolation is based range round the space in which x falls, so that x is as nearly as possible central. The central difference formulae give a systematic method for building up the table subject to these conditions.

Again, the central difference coefficients are as a general rule smaller and more rapidly convergent than those required for the calculations in the advancing difference formula (as will be seen in the Example) and, by a suitable choice of origin, the arithmetical work may be reduced to a minimum.

It should be noted that, in the phrase "as measured approximately by the first neglected term", this measure is not theoretically complete;

it is however generally sufficient in practice if the first neglected order of differences is constant or is changing but slowly. When this is not so it will not necessarily be true that a central difference formula beginning with u_0 is more accurate than the advancing difference formula beginning with the same term. [See p. 337 of Sheppard's paper, cited on p. 72.]

We may even make the result worse by introducing differences of a higher order (cf. Chap. V, paragraph 15). In general, however, these anomalous cases arise only rarely.

13. It should be noted that the greater accuracy of central difference formulae as compared with the advancing difference form is not due to the formulae but to placing x in the central interval of the range of the given values. Provided that this is done—which is very important—it is immaterial whether we use a central difference formula or the advancing difference formula with the same u's. A disadvantage of the latter form is that the coefficients are larger and are not tabulated as, in practice, are those of the principal central difference formulae.

14. Relative accuracy of the formulae.

The relative accuracy of the various central difference formulae can be investigated in an elementary manner on the following lines.

The Gauss forward formula is

$$u_x = u_0 + x_{(1)}\Delta u_0 + x_{(2)}\Delta^2 u_{-1} + (x+1)_{(3)}\Delta^3 u_{-1} + (x+1)_{(4)}\Delta^4 u_{-2} + \dots.$$

If we expand u_x by Stirling's formula as far as a certain order of even differences we shall obtain by a simple transformation the above formula to even differences, for the same u's are involved in both. Similarly, Bessel's formula and Gauss's formula are identical to odd differences. Now the Gauss formula involves only ordinary differences while the other two series involve mean differences of the form $\frac{1}{2}(\Delta^n u_r + \Delta^n u_{r+1})$. If instead of proceeding to constant differences the series stop short at, say, rth differences—which are not constant—the use of any of the formulae will involve an error. It remains to examine which of these formulae gives the best result in different circumstances.

The following demonstration is based on that given in greater detail by Mr D. C. Fraser in *J.I.A.* vol. L, p. 25:

Suppose that x is not greater than ·5. Then, by calculating the coefficients in Gauss's formula, it will be found that for positive values of x none of the coefficients (except that multiplying Δu_0) differs greatly from $\pm$ ·5 times the preceding coefficient. (See Table, *J.I.A.* vol. L, p. 25.) Thus the terms after that involving the third difference are approximately equal to

$$(x+1)_{(4)}\,(\Delta^4+\tfrac{1}{2}\Delta^5)\,u_{-2},$$

i.e. to $\qquad\qquad (x+1)_{(4)}\,\tfrac{1}{2}\,(\Delta^4 u_{-2}+\Delta^4 u_{-1}).$

If therefore we substitute $\tfrac{1}{2}\,(\Delta^4 u_{-2}+\Delta^4 u_{-1})$, the mean difference in line with $u_{\frac{1}{2}}$, for $\Delta^4 u_{-2}$ in Gauss's formula, we make the formula very nearly correct to fifth differences, without having to calculate the actual coefficient of the fifth difference. The substitution therefore greatly improves the accuracy of the formula.

When, however, the substitution is made, it will be found to reproduce Bessel's formula to the fourth mean difference. Therefore Bessel's formula to fourth mean differences is usually more accurate than Stirling's to the fourth difference.

It may be shown similarly that Stirling's formula to odd mean differences is usually more accurate than Bessel's to the same order of differences.

The above demonstration is only approximate: a strict investigation into the relative accuracy of central and advancing difference formulae requires rather more elaborate mathematical discussion. (See Whittaker and Robinson, *Calculus of Observations*, p. 49; Lidstone, *T.F.A.* vol. IX, pp. 246–57; Fraser, *J.I.A.* vol. L, pp. 25–7; Sheppard, *Proceedings of the London Mathematical Society*, Series 2, vol. IV, pp. 320–41 and vol. X, pp. 139–72.)

Mr D. C. Fraser has given the following criteria summarizing the properties of interpolation formulae:

(i) Formulae which proceed to constant differences are exact and are true for all values of n whether integral or fractional.

(ii) Formulae which stop short of constant differences are approximations.

(iii) Formulae which terminate with the same difference are identically equal, for they involve the same u's.

It should be noted that these rules are quite general; they apply to all formulae based on finite differences, not ending with mean differences.

15. Apart from the general superiority of central difference formulae certain of the formulae possess distinct advantages in special circumstances. For example, for the bisection of an interval Bessel's form is convenient, since the alternate terms are zero. We have, at once,

$$u_{\frac{1}{2}} = \tfrac{1}{2}\,(u_0 + u_1) - \tfrac{1}{8}\left[\tfrac{1}{2}\,(\Delta^2 u_{-1} + \Delta^2 u_0)\right] + \tfrac{3}{128}\left[\tfrac{1}{2}\,(\Delta^4 u_{-2} + \Delta^4 u_{-1})\right] - \dots$$

Again, in using Everett's formula for the subdivision of intervals the terms are such that they may be used twice: they occur both in an "x" expansion and in reverse order in the next "ξ" expansion. An example will make this clear.

Example 2.

Given	x	30	35	40	45	50	55	60
	u_x	771	862	1001	1224	1572	2123	2983

obtain values for u_x for all integral values of x between $x = 40$ and $x = 50$.

The difference table is

x	u_x	Δu_x	$\Delta^2 u_x$	$\Delta^3 u_x$	$\Delta^4 u_x$
30	771				
		91			
35	862		48		
		139		36	
40	1001		84		5
		223		41	
45	1224		125		37
		348		78	
50	1572		203		28
		551		106	
55	2123		309		
		860			
60	2983				

Everett's formula gives

$$u_x = x_{(1)} u_1 + (x+1)_{(3)} \Delta^2 u_0 + (x+2)_{(5)} \Delta^4 u_{-1} + \ldots$$
$$+ \xi_{(1)} u_0 + (\xi+1)_{(3)} \Delta^2 u_{-1} + (\xi+2)_{(5)} \Delta^4 u_{-2} + \ldots,$$

also　　$$u_{1+\xi} = \xi_{(1)} u_2 + (\xi+1)_{(3)} \Delta^2 u_1 + (\xi+2)_{(5)} \Delta^4 u_0 + \ldots$$
$$+ x_{(1)} u_1 + (x+1)_{(3)} \Delta^2 u_0 + (x+2)_{(5)} \Delta^4 u_{-1} + \ldots,$$

and the second line in $u_{1+\xi}$ is the same as the first line in u_x.

Since the data are given at quinquennial points and we require values at individual points, we may write $x = \cdot2$, $\cdot4$, $\cdot6$, ... and $\xi = \cdot8$, $\cdot6$, $\cdot4$, ... The first line of $u._2$ will be the same as the second line for $u_{1\cdot8}$, but in the reverse order, and so on.

The coefficients of the terms in the first line of the formula for u_x are, to fourth differences,

·2	− ·032	·006336
·4	− ·056	·010752
·6	− ·064	·011648
·8	− ·048	·008064

The work is best arranged in tabular form, thus:

x	xu_1	$\dfrac{x(x^2-1)}{3!} \Delta^2 u_0$	$\dfrac{x(x^2-1)(x^2-4)}{5!} \Delta^4 u_{-1}$	Sum of first three terms (ii)+(iii)+(iv)	Sum of second three terms	Inter-polated result (v)+(vi)
(i)	(ii)	(iii)	(iv)	(v)	(vi)	(vii)
·2	200·2	− 2·7	0·0	197·5		
·4	400·4	− 4·7	0·1	395·8		
·6	600·6	− 5·4	0·1	595·3		
·8	800·8	− 4·0	0·0	796·8		
·2	244·8	− 4·0	0·2	241·0	796·8	1037·8
·4	489·6	− 7·0	0·4	483·0	595·3	1078·3
·6	734·4	− 8·0	0·4	726·8	395·8	1122·6
·8	979·2	− 6·0	0·3	973·5	197·5	1171·0
·2	314·4	− 6·5	0·2	308·1	973·5	1281·6
·4	628·8	−11·4	0·3	617·7	726·8	1344·5
·6	943·2	−13·0	0·3	930·5	483·0	1413·5
·8	1257·6	− 9·7	0·2	1248·1	241·0	1489·1

The only column which needs explanation is column (vi). This column represents the second set of three terms of the formula, correct to fourth central differences, and is obtained by writing down *in the reverse order* the values of the previous column applicable to the sum of the first three terms.

It should be mentioned that the values in column (vii) of the table do not quite agree with the tabular values: the tabular values are 1038, 1081, 1122, 1172, 1281, 1345, 1415, 1490. The reason for this is that the function upon which the original values depend is not a rational integral function of the independent variable and that therefore a formula based on finite differences is only an approximate representation of the function. The example is based on the rates of mortality according to the H^M Table, the data being 10^5 times the probability of dying in the year of age x.

16. The following example is instructive:

Example 3.

Use an appropriate formula to obtain successive approximations to $u_{28\cdot3}$ given $u_{26} = \cdot038462$, $u_{27} = \cdot037037$, $u_{28} = \cdot035714$, $u_{29} = \cdot034483$, $u_{30} = \cdot033333$.

It should be noted that, where the data are extensive and it is required to obtain successive approximations to a result by the use of some or all of the data, it is more advantageous to use a central difference formula than advancing differences.

From the data, we obtain

x	$10^6 u_x$	$10^6\Delta u_x$	$10^6\Delta^2 u_x$	$10^6\Delta^3 u_x$	$10^6\Delta^4 u_x$
26	38462				
		-1425			
27	37037		102		
		-1323		-10	
28	35714		92		-1
		-1231		-11	
29	34483		81		
		-1150			
30	33333				

In its simple form, Stirling's formula is

$$u_x = u_0 + x \cdot \tfrac{1}{2}(\Delta u_0 + \Delta u_{-1}) + \frac{x^2}{2!}\Delta^2 u_{-1}$$

$$+ \frac{x(x^2-1^2)}{3!}\tfrac{1}{2}(\Delta^3 u_{-1} + \Delta^3 u_{-2}) + \frac{x^2(x^2-1^2)}{4!}\Delta^4 u_{-2}.$$

Taking the origin at 28 and letting $x = \cdot3$ we have, as a first approximation,

$$u_{\cdot3} = 35714 + \cdot3\left[\tfrac{1}{2}(-1323 - 1231)\right] = 35331.$$

For the next approximation all that we need do is to add

$$\frac{\cdot 09}{2} 92 = 4 \cdot 14.$$

$$\therefore \quad u_{\cdot 3} = 35335 \cdot 14 \text{ (say } 35335).$$

Similarly, the next term is $\dfrac{\cdot 3 \, (-\cdot 91)}{6} \cdot \frac{1}{2} \cdot (-21)$

$$= \cdot 478 \ldots$$

so that $\qquad u_{\cdot 3} = 35335 \cdot 62 \ldots \text{ (say } 35336).$

The addition of the next term will not affect the last figure. The required successive approximations are therefore

$$\cdot 035331, \quad \cdot 035335, \quad \cdot 035336, \quad \cdot 035336.$$

*17. Sheppard's central difference notation.

Just as $\Delta \equiv E - 1$, or $\Delta u_x = u_{x+1} - u_x$, similar symbolic identities may be deduced from the relations existing between u_x, $u_{x+\frac{1}{2}}$ and $u_{x-\frac{1}{2}}$. Dr Sheppard has introduced the following notation, which is widely used by mathematicians:

$$\delta u_x = u_{x+\frac{1}{2}} - u_{x-\frac{1}{2}},$$

and $\qquad \mu u_x = \frac{1}{2} \left(u_{x+\frac{1}{2}} + u_{x-\frac{1}{2}} \right).$

In this notation the difference table takes the following form:

x	u_x				
$\vdots$	$\vdots$				
-2	u_{-2}				
		$\delta u_{-\frac{3}{2}}$			
-1	u_{-1}		$\delta^2 u_{-1}$		
		$\delta u_{-\frac{1}{2}}$		$\delta^3 u_{-\frac{1}{2}}$	
0	u_0		$\delta^2 u_0$		$\delta^4 u_0$
		$\delta u_{\frac{1}{2}}$		$\delta^3 u_{\frac{1}{2}}$	
1	u_1		$\delta^2 u_1$		
		$\delta u_{\frac{3}{2}}$			
2	u_2				

It is specially to be noted that the subscript corresponds to the argument which falls on the same line as the difference.

The relationships between E, δ and μ are quite easy to establish.

$$\delta \equiv E^{\frac{1}{2}} - E^{-\frac{1}{2}} \equiv E^{-\frac{1}{2}}\left[E-1\right] \equiv E^{-\frac{1}{2}}\Delta.$$

$$\therefore \quad \delta^{2n} \equiv E^{-n}\Delta^{2n}.$$

Also $\quad \mu \equiv \frac{1}{2}\left(E^{\frac{1}{2}} + E^{-\frac{1}{2}}\right),$

and $\quad \mu\delta \equiv \frac{1}{2}\left(E - E^{-1}\right) \equiv \frac{1}{2}\left(\Delta E^{-1} + \Delta\right),$

$$\mu\delta^{2n+1} \equiv \frac{1}{2}\left[E^{-(n-1)} - E^{-(n+1)}\right]\Delta^{2n}$$

$$\equiv \frac{1}{2}\left(\Delta E^{-1} + \Delta\right)\Delta^{2n}E^{-n} \equiv \frac{1}{2}\Delta^{2n+1}\left(E^{-1}+1\right)E^{-n}.$$

Again $\quad 2\mu \equiv 2E^{\frac{1}{2}} - \delta,$

or $\quad E^{\frac{1}{2}} \equiv \mu + \frac{1}{2}\delta.$

By means of these symbols the central difference formulae can be written down in very convenient form.

For example, Gauss's forward formula is

$$u_x = u_0 + x_{(1)}\delta u_{\frac{1}{2}} + x_{(2)}\delta^2 u_0 + (x+1)_{(3)}\delta^3 u_{\frac{1}{2}} + (x+1)_{(4)}\delta^4 u_0 + \ldots,$$

and Stirling's becomes

$$u_x = u_0 + x\mu\delta u_0 + \frac{1}{2}x^2\delta^2 u_0 + (x+1)_{(3)}\mu\delta^3 u_0 + \ldots.$$

EXAMPLES 4

1. Apply a central difference formula to obtain u_{25}, given $u_{20} = 14$, $u_{24} = 32$, $u_{28} = 35$, $u_{32} = 40$.

2. Given $u_2 = 10$, $u_1 = 8$, $u_0 = 5$, $u_{-1} = 10$, find $u_{\frac{1}{2}}$ by Gauss's forward formula.

3. Use Stirling's formula to find u_{28}, given $u_{20} = 49225$, $u_{25} = 48316$, $u_{30} = 47236$, $u_{35} = 45926$, $u_{40} = 44306$.

4. Given $u_{20} = 2854$, $u_{24} = 3162$, $u_{28} = 3544$, $u_{32} = 3992$; find u_{25} by Bessel's formula.

5. $a_{21} = 18\cdot4708$; $\quad a_{25} = 17\cdot8144$; $\quad a_{29} = 17\cdot1070$; $\quad a_{33} = 16\cdot3432$; $a_{37} = 15\cdot5154$. Find a_{30} by Gauss's forward formula.

6. What are the practical advantages arising from the use of central differences in interpolation?

Employ Stirling's formula to obtain successive approximations to $(1 \cdot 02125)^{50}$, given

$$(1 \cdot 01)^{50} = 1 \cdot 64463; \quad (1 \cdot 02)^{50} = 2 \cdot 69159; \quad (1 \cdot 03)^{50} = 4 \cdot 38391;$$

$$(1 \cdot 015)^{50} = 2 \cdot 10524; \quad (1 \cdot 025)^{50} = 3 \cdot 43711.$$

7. Find formulae true to third differences for the bisection of an interval

    (i) in terms of the two nearest values of the function and of differences of the functions;

    (ii) in terms of values of the function only.

Apply either formula to find P_{35}, given the values of P_x at 20, 30, 40, 50 to be 1313, 1727, 2392, 3493 respectively.

8. Given the table

x	310	320	330	340	350	360
$\log x$	2·4914	2·5052	2·5185	2·5315	2·5441	2·5563

find the value of $\log 3375$ by a central difference formula.

9. Prove that if third differences are assumed to be constant

$$u_x = x u_1 + \frac{x(x^2 - 1)}{6} \Delta^2 u_0 + y u_0 + \frac{y(y^2 - 1)}{6} \Delta^2 u_{-1},$$

where $y = 1 - x$.

Apply this formula to find the values of u_{11} to u_{14} and u_{16} to u_{19}, given that $u_0 = 3010$, $u_5 = 2710$, $u_{10} = 2285$, $u_{15} = 1860$, $u_{20} = 1560$, $u_{25} = 1510$ and $u_{30} = 1835$.

10. From the table of annual net premiums given below find the annual net premium at age 25 by means of Bessel's formula:

Age	Annual net premiums
20	·01427
24	·01581
28	·01772
32	·01996

11. Apply a central difference formula to find $f(32)$, given

$$f(25) = \cdot 2707, \quad f(30) = \cdot 3027, \quad f(35) = \cdot 3386, \quad f(40) = \cdot 3794.$$

12. Use Gauss's interpolation formula to obtain the value of $f(41)$, given $f(30) = 3678 \cdot 2$, $f(35) = 2995 \cdot 1$, $f(40) = 2400 \cdot 1$, $f(45) = 1876 \cdot 2$, $f(50) = 1416 \cdot 3$.

Verify your result by using Lagrange's formula over the same figures.

13. Prove the following formulae for the general case of unequal intervals:

(i) $u_x = u_a + A\,\tfrac{1}{2}\,(\triangle u_l + \triangle u_a) + \tfrac{1}{2}A\,(B+L)\,\triangle^2 u_l$
$\qquad + ABL\,\tfrac{1}{2}\,(\triangle^3 u_m + \triangle^3 u_l) + \dots$ (Stirling)

(ii) $u_x = \tfrac{1}{2}\,(u_a + u_b) + \tfrac{1}{2}\,(A+B)\,\triangle u_a + AB\,\tfrac{1}{2}\,(\triangle^2 u_l + \triangle^2 u_a)$
$\qquad + \tfrac{1}{2}\,(ABC + ABL)\,\triangle^3 u_l + \dots$ (Bessel)

and show how to obtain a general Everett form.

14. Show that any central difference formula can be developed from Lagrange. Apply a central difference formula obtained thus to find $f(3\tfrac{1}{2})$, given that $f(2) = 2\cdot626$; $f(3) = 3\cdot454$; $f(4) = 4\cdot784$ and $f(5) = 6\cdot986$.

15. Given $u_0, u_1, u_2, u_3, u_4, u_5$ (fifth differences constant), prove that

$$u_{2\frac{1}{2}} = \tfrac{1}{2}c + \frac{25\,(c-b) + 3\,(a-c)}{256},$$

where $\qquad a = u_0 + u_5; \quad b = u_1 + u_4; \quad c = u_2 + u_3.$

16. A series is formed by the division of the terms of the two series

u_x	1	2	6	24 ... $n!$
v_x	4	20	120	840 ... $\tfrac{1}{6}\,(n+3)!$

Obtain an interpolated value for $u_{2\frac{1}{2}}/v_{2\frac{1}{2}}$ of the new series by a central difference formula and compare the result with the quotient of $u_{2\frac{1}{2}}$ by $v_{2\frac{1}{2}}$ in the component series.

17. The following is a difference table written down in Woolhouse's notation:

u_{-2}
$\qquad\qquad a_{-2}$
$u_{-1} \qquad\qquad\qquad\qquad b_{-1}$
$\qquad\qquad a_{-1} \qquad\qquad\qquad\qquad c_{-1}$
$u_0 \qquad\qquad\qquad\qquad b_0 \qquad\qquad\qquad\qquad d_0$
$\qquad\qquad a_1 \qquad\qquad\qquad\qquad c_1$
$u_1 \qquad\qquad\qquad\qquad b_1$
$\qquad\qquad a_2$
u_2

If $a_0 = \tfrac{1}{2}\,(a_{-1} + a_1)$ and $c_0 = \tfrac{1}{2}\,(c_{-1} + c_1)$, show that Stirling's formula (to fourth differences) can be expressed as

$$u_x = u_0 + Ax + Bx^2 + Cx^3 + Dx^4,$$

where A, B, C, D are functions of a_0, b_0, c_0, d_0 only.

18. Prove that in Woolhouse's notation

$$u_x = u_0 + x_{(1)} a_1 + x_{(2)} b_0 + (x+1)_{(3)} c_1 + (x+1)_{(4)} d_0$$

correct to fourth differences.

19. Show that the sum of the terms of the series u_{-2}, u_{-1}, u_0, u_1, u_2 can be expressed in the following form

$$A u_0 + B \delta^2 u_0 + C \delta^4 u_0,$$

where $\delta^2 u_0$ and $\delta^4 u_0$ denote the second and fourth central differences of u_0; and find A, B and C.

20. By splitting up the fraction of the form

$$\frac{u_x}{(x^2 - a^2)(x^2 - b^2)(x^2 - c^2)}$$

into partial fractions, show how to arrive at u_x in terms of known values of the function of which x occupies the central position.

21. If $u_x = A u_0 + B \Delta u_0 + C \Delta^2 u_{-1} + \dots$, i.e. a general expression for u_x in terms of central differences, prove by expressing all differences in terms of advancing differences of u_0 that

$$u_x = u_0 + x_{(1)} \Delta u_0 + x_{(2)} \Delta^2 u_{-1} + (x+1)_{(3)} \Delta^3 u_{-1} + \dots,$$

obtaining the general term in the expansion.

22. Show that in the general divided difference interpolation formula any two successive terms can be reduced to a pair in Everett form.

CHAPTER V

INVERSE INTERPOLATION

1. When performing direct interpolation, values of y corresponding to various values of the argument x are given and we are required to find a value of the entry y corresponding to a value of x intermediate between the given values. If it is required to obtain an interpolated value of the *argument* corresponding to an intermediate value of the *entry*, the process adopted is called "inverse interpolation". In other words, for direct interpolation we assume a curve $y = u_x$ passing through the points (x, y) and estimate the value of y corresponding to some intermediate value x': for inverse interpolation we have a similar curve but are required to find a value of x corresponding to a value y'.

For certain functions we may obtain the result easily. If $y = \sin x$, then $x = \sin^{-1} y$; if $y = x^3$, then $x = y^{\frac{1}{3}}$; if $y = a^x$, then $x = \log y / \log a$. The required values of x can be calculated immediately in these examples.

On the other hand, if the data are simply corresponding numerical values of x and y, all that we can write down is a formula such as Newton's or Stirling's: we must then endeavour to obtain a value for x by solving an equation. For example

$$y = u_x = (1 + \Delta)^x u_0 = u_0 + x_{(1)} \Delta u_0 + x_{(2)} \Delta^2 u_0 + x_{(3)} \Delta^3 u_0 + \dots.$$

If second differences may be assumed constant we have a quadratic equation which can be solved at once. Should this assumption be inadmissible, then we are faced with an equation of higher degree than the second and the solution of such an equation may be very laborious. In these circumstances we resort to approximate methods of solution of the equation.

2. Consider the problem of reversion of series. If

$$y = bx + cx^2 + dx^3 + \dots$$

and we wish to obtain an approximate value for x in terms of y, we may write $x = By + Cy^2 + Dy^3 + ... + Ky^n + ...$ The coefficients $B, C, D ... K ...$ may then be found by equating the coefficients of the various powers of x in the identity

$$x = B (bx + cx^2 + ...) + C (bx + cx^2 + ...)^2 + ...$$

If y is numerically less than unity and we use only n terms in the expansion for x in terms of y—i.e. we let

$$x = By + Cy^2 + ... + Ky^n$$

—we are neglecting only y^{n+1} and higher powers. Since y is less than unity, the neglected terms will usually be small.

If however $y = u_x = u_0 + x_{(1)}\Delta u_0 + x_{(2)}\Delta^2 u_0 + ... + x_{(n)}\Delta^n u_0 + ...$ and we wish to find x from this equation, we cannot with equal safety neglect the terms $x_{(n+1)}\Delta^{n+1} u_0 + ...$, for these all contain $x, x^2, x^3 ....$

It is thus seen that the problem of inverse interpolation, although analogous to that of reversion of series, involves considerable difficulties. The best method of approach is from a practical point of view.

Given a problem in direct interpolation, the results obtained by the use of an interpolation formula are justified only on certain assumptions. Similarly, in interpolation by differences for an inverse function the results must be judged practically by the progression of the differences. It may be stated however that if interpolation to nth differences is accurate enough for $f(x)$ it does not follow that the same number of differences will suffice or will be required for the inverse function.

3. The problem of inverse interpolation may be viewed in two ways. We may, by graphic or other indication, observe that the value of x which we require corresponding to some given value of u_x lies in a certain narrow interval. Thus, if we are given the following table:

Rate of interest

per cent.	$2\frac{1}{2}$	3	$3\frac{1}{2}$	4	$4\frac{1}{2}$	5
Annuity-value	8·7521	8·5302	8·3166	8·1109	7·9127	7·7217

and we are asked to find the rate of interest for which the annuity-value is 8·000, we may take the interval 4–4½ as the interval (0, 1) or $(-\frac{1}{2}, +\frac{1}{2})$ and write down an interpolation formula, using only a quadratic or cubic function. As the interval and the values of the variable are small and the differences are rapidly decreasing, the solution of such an equation will, in general, give sufficiently satisfactory results. If the equation is a quadratic the solution will present no difficulty; for a cubic various methods are available, some of which are discussed later.

4. Alternatively, we may exchange the dependent and independent variables. That is, given a table of $y = u_x$ we may use the inverse function $x = v_y$.

This method of interchanged variables is subject to very severe restrictions on the function u_x over the range of values used. In the first place, u_x must be strictly monotonic—i.e. uniformly increasing or decreasing—over the range of values given and the unknown value of x, the value of x in all practical cases lying not outside, but within the given range and near the middle of it. If u_x is not strictly monotonic, the inverse function becomes two-valued at least—possibly many-valued—and hence cannot be represented by a polynomial. In these circumstances the ordinary methods of finite difference interpolation are unsafe.

In consequence, before this method of inverse interpolation can be attempted we must have some extraneous knowledge, graphical or otherwise, of the nature of the function u_x. We must usually, in fact, be able to see roughly the position of x. These conditions being premised and being generally satisfied, the necessity for a sufficient number of values of u_x and a small enough interval is naturally seen.

5. The point here made is clearly brought out by a consideration of the following example.

Example 1.

Obtain a value for x when $u_x = 19$, given the following values:

x	0	1	2
u_x	0	1	20

There would seem to be two possible methods at our disposal:

(i) We might write down at once (if we think it safe to assume that second differences are constant)

$$y = u_x = (1 + \Delta)^x u_0 = u_0 + x_{(1)} \Delta u_0 + x_{(2)} \Delta^2 u_0;$$

i.e.
$$19 = x + 9\,(x^2 - x),$$

so that
$$9x^2 - 8x - 19 = 0,$$

from which
$$x = 1{\cdot}964 \ldots \quad \text{or} \quad -1{\cdot}075 \ldots.$$

(ii) Since we have to find an interpolated value of x corresponding to a value of y we might treat y as the argument and x as the entry. Let us write the data in the form

y	0	1	20
$x = v_y$	0	1	2

and apply the Lagrange formula to calculate v_{19} as if for direct interpolation.

We shall have

$$\frac{v_{19}}{19 \cdot 18 \cdot (-1)} = \frac{1}{18 \cdot 1 \cdot (-19)} + \frac{2}{(-1) \cdot 20 \cdot 19}$$

or
$$v_{19} = 2{\cdot}8.$$

It will be seen therefore that we have obtained two distinct sets of results. By adopting the first method x has the values $1{\cdot}964\ldots$ or $-1{\cdot}075\ldots$ and by adopting the second method x has the unique value $2{\cdot}8$. It remains to examine the reasons for the difference and to ascertain which result, if any, is more likely to approximate to the true interpolated value or values.

In the first method it will be apparent that we have taken a curve of parabolic form, $y = a + bx + cx^2$, and have obtained values of x corresponding to $y = 19$. This gives two values of x, one on each side of the vertex of the parabola. In applying the Lagrange formula inversely we have assumed that x is a quadratic function of y and have given y a particular value (19) in the equation $x = \alpha + \beta y + \gamma y^2$. If we substitute the value of y corresponding to each value of x from the data, it is easily seen that $\alpha = 0$, $\beta = 398/380$ and $\gamma = -18/380$. The Lagrange equation is therefore $190x = 199y - 9y^2$.

Now if the two curves

$$y = 9x^2 - 8x$$

and $$x = \frac{199}{190}y - \frac{9}{190}y^2$$

be plotted on the same graph, it will be seen that they take different shapes, thus:

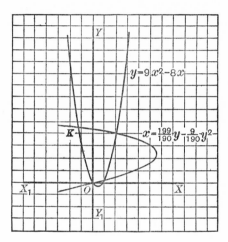

Fig. 1.

On the curve $y = 9x^2 - 8x$ the abscissae of the points whose ordinates are 19 are 1·96... and $-1·07...$, whereas on the other curve there is only one point for which the ordinate is 19, namely the point (2·8, 19). Unless therefore the two curves obtained from the data, (i) by treating x as the argument and (ii) by treating y as the argument, intersect at the required interpolated value, as for example at K in the above figure, the two methods are bound to give different results.

6. Although there would seem to be three different and possible answers to the question above, we must be very careful before we draw any conclusions from the results.

In the first place, we are not told, and have no right to assume, that $\Delta^2 u_x$ is constant, and that consequently second difference

7

interpolation for y is sufficient. On the data as given the only conclusion would be that they are inadequate either for direct or inverse interpolation.

Secondly, even if we may assume that $\Delta^2 u_x$ is constant, we see that

(a) a portion of the curve over the given range, namely from $x=0$ to $x=1$, is non-monotonic and one of the essential conditions set out in paragraph 4 is thereby infringed;

(b) notwithstanding the assumption that second differences may be used for direct interpolation, we are not justified in assuming that this order of differences is sufficient for inverse interpolation: we cannot therefore safely use Lagrange's formula.

If we make the assumption that second differences are constant, we cannot properly use the point (o, o) for inverse interpolation, as the given values do not indicate the form of the curve between $x=0$ and $x=1$. By omitting the value (o, o) and using the values for y when $x=1, 2, 3$ and 4, a more satisfactory interpolated value can be found. The student should attempt this by one of the methods described below.

7. The formulae of direct interpolation are based on the properties of rational integral functions of the variable, and any formula which proceeds to nth differences gives exact results when applied to a rational integral function of the nth degree. By stopping short of nth differences the formula can, of course, be used to obtain approximate results, and the success of the interpolation depends on the magnitude of the terms omitted. Thus, if we use rth differences for a polynomial of the nth degree in x, the result is the exact value of terms up to and including the term in x^r. The terms beyond x^r are disregarded, and this can only be done legitimately if they are relatively unimportant.

In questions of direct interpolation there is only one value of y, i.e. of u_x, for a given value of x. There may be, however, more than one value of x for a given value of y. In fact, if y is a polynomial in x, x is a polynomial in y only when both functions are of the first degree. In other cases the inverse function may be an infinite series or an irrational function. For example, in the H^M Table of Mortality there is only one value of d_x for a given value of l_x (where l_x represents the number of persons attaining exact age x in any year of time, and d_x is the number of these who die before reaching age $x+1$). In the neighbourhood of the peak of the death curve, however, there will be two values of l_x within a short range of interpolation for a given value in d_x.

For these reasons the subject of inverse interpolation is more troublesome than that of direct interpolation, although it should always be remembered that the conditions attaching to the differences of u_x for direct interpolation are the same as those attaching to the differences of v_y for inverse interpolation. One principal condition is that within the range of interpolation there should be only one value of x corresponding to a given value of y.

Let us consider the equation in Example 1, namely

$$y = -8x + 9x^2,$$

where the range of interpolation is from 0 to 2. The first point to note is that the function is not a good subject for direct interpolation except when the formula is applied to its fullest extent—the second degree. The reason is that the last term is the predominating term throughout the greater part of the range.

In most instances, by altering the interval and reducing the range of interpolation, a function can be reduced to a good form for direct interpolation. Such a question as the following might be put:

Given the function $y = u_x = -8x + 9x^2$, for what intervals of x should u_x be tabulated so that in any interval an interpolated value of y can be obtained by first difference interpolation with an error less than, say, ·001?

Put
$$x = z/a;$$

then
$$u_x = v_z = -\frac{8z}{a} + \frac{9z^2}{a^2},$$

i.e.
$$a^2 v_z = -8az + 9z^2,$$

$$a^2 \Delta v_z = -8a + 18z + 9,$$

7-2

and $$a^2\Delta^2 v_z = 18,$$

so that $$\Delta^2 v_z = 18/a^2.$$

Suppose v_z to be tabulated for values of z at unit intervals. Then, for an interpolated value v_{z+t} between v_z and v_{z+1},

$$v_{z+t} = v_z + t\Delta v_z + \tfrac{1}{2}t\,(t-1)\,\Delta^2 v_z.$$

If we take $v_z + t\Delta v_z$ as the interpolated value, there is an error $\tfrac{1}{2}t\,(t-1)\,\Delta^2 v_z$ and the maximum numerical value of $\tfrac{1}{2}t\,(t-1)$ is $\tfrac{1}{8}$, being the value when t is $\tfrac{1}{2}$.

Therefore, by the conditions,

$$\tfrac{1}{2}t\,(t-1)\,\Delta^2 v_z < \cdot 001,$$

$$\tfrac{1}{8}\Delta^2 v_z < \cdot 001.$$

But $\Delta^2 v_z = 18/a^2$, $\therefore$ $18/8a^2 < \cdot 001$;

i.e. $$a^2 > 18000/8,$$

i.e. $$> 2250,$$

or $$a > \sqrt{2250},$$

and the most convenient value for a is 50.

We must therefore tabulate u_x at intervals of $\tfrac{1}{50}$ of unity, i.e. at intervals of $\cdot 02$.

For example, $$y = u_x = -8x + 9x^2.$$

x	z	$u_x = v_z$	Δv_z
1·10	55	2·0900	
			·2396
1·12	56	2·3296	
			·2468
1·14	57	2·5764	
			·2540
1·16	58	2·8304	
			·2612
1·18	59	3·0916	
			·2684
1·20	60	3·3600	

Both for direct and inverse interpolation this table is better than one proceeding by larger intervals. It must not be assumed, however, that a table which is good for direct interpolation is necessarily good for inverse interpolation: in particular, inverse interpolation always presents difficulties if $\Delta u_x/\Delta x$ is small.

8. Practical methods of inverse interpolation.

It is evident that the problem of inverse interpolation is the same as that of direct interpolation for unequal intervals. The methods of Lagrange or of divided differences can therefore be employed to obtain any intermediate value of x corresponding to a value of y, given a table of $y = u_x$, by the use of the inverse relation $x = v_y$. Alternatively, we may treat the problem as one involving the approximate solution of an algebraic equation. Two of the methods often adopted in practice are given below. They are simple to apply and generally lead to satisfactory results. There are, however, certain objections to the methods—for example, it is difficult to ascertain the degree of accuracy which has been reached in the approximate answers—and for many purposes the most convenient and practical plans are probably Aitken's methods of cross-means, to which reference is made in Chapter VIII.

9. Successive approximation.

In the first place we obtain either by inspection or by a rough graph two values of x lying on either side of the required interpolated value. (For example, a value for x when y is zero in the function $y = x^2 - 4x + 2$, i.e. a solution of the equation $x^2 - 4x + 2 = 0$, lies between the values $x = 0$ and $x = 1$.) We then choose a suitable origin and unit of differencing so that if x be the interpolated value and lies between two successive values of the argument, the interval will be small and x will be as near to the origin as possible.

Suppose that the required value lies between 0 and 1.

The method proceeds as follows:

$$u_x = u_0 + x\Delta u_0 + \tfrac{1}{2}x\,(x-1)\,\Delta^2 u_0 + \tfrac{1}{6}x\,(x-1)\,(x-2)\,\Delta^3 u_0 + \dots.$$

Since x is small, a first approximation (α_1) will be obtained by neglecting terms involving second and higher differences of u_0.

$$\therefore \quad u_x = u_0 + \alpha_1 \Delta u_0 \text{ approximately,}$$

i.e. $\qquad\qquad \alpha_1 = (u_x - u_0)/\Delta u_0, \qquad$ first approximation.

Again, neglecting third and higher differences, we may write

$$u_x = u_0 + \alpha_2 \Delta u_0 + \tfrac{1}{2}\alpha_2 (\alpha_1 - 1) \Delta^2 u_0,$$

where α_2 is a second approximation and is therefore not very different from α_1. This gives

$$\alpha_2 = \frac{u_x - u_0}{\Delta u_0 + \tfrac{1}{2}(\alpha_1 - 1)\Delta^2 u_0}, \text{ second approximation.}$$

Similarly

$$\alpha_3 = \frac{u_x - u_0}{\Delta u_0 + \tfrac{1}{2}(\alpha_2 - 1)\Delta^2 u_0 + \tfrac{1}{6}(\alpha_2 - 1)(\alpha_2 - 2)\Delta^3 u_0},$$

and so on. $\qquad\qquad\qquad\qquad\qquad$ third approximation,

10. Elimination of third differences.

We have, as far as third differences, by expressing u_x in terms of u_0, Δu_0, ...,

$$u_x = u_0 + x\Delta u_0 + \tfrac{1}{2}x (x-1) \Delta^2 u_0 + \tfrac{1}{6}x (x-1)(x-2)\Delta^3 u_0.$$

Also, in terms of u_1, Δu_1, ...,

$$u_x = u_1 + (x-1)\Delta u_1 + \tfrac{1}{2}(x-1)(x-2)\Delta^2 u_1$$
$$+ \tfrac{1}{6}(x-1)(x-2)(x-3)\Delta^3 u_1.$$

If now we ignore the terms containing third differences and multiply both sides of the first equation by $3 - \alpha$ and both sides of the second equation by α (where α is an approximation to the required value, found by inspection or otherwise) and add, a new quadratic equation in x will be formed. The error involved in ignoring the third differences will be small, since

$$\tfrac{1}{6}x (x-1)(x-2)(3-\alpha)\Delta^3 u_0 + \tfrac{1}{6}\alpha (x-1)(x-2)(x-3)\Delta^3 u_1$$

will be small provided that $\Delta^3 u_0$ and $\Delta^3 u_1$ are not very different.

11. The following question is solved by both these methods:

Example 2.

Find the value of x for which y is 18,600, given

x	52	53	54	55	56
y	19,231	18,868	18,519	18,182	17,855

Changing the origin, the difference table is

x	y	Δy	$\Delta^2 y$	$\Delta^3 y$
0	19,231			
		-363		
1	18,868		14	
		-349		-2
2	18,519		12	
		-337		-2
3	18,182		10	
		-327		
4	17,855			

By the ordinary advancing difference formula

$$18,600 = 19,231 - 363x + \frac{14x\,(x-1)}{2!} - \frac{2x\,(x-1)\,(x-2)}{3!},$$

where the value of x is required corresponding to the value 18,600 of y.

(i) Successive approximation.

Since x is small, a first approximation will be

$$\alpha_1 = \frac{19,231 - 18,600}{363} \quad \text{or} \quad 1\cdot 7383\dots.$$

Including the next term,

$$\alpha_2 = \frac{631}{363 - 7\,(\alpha_1 - 1)} \quad \text{or} \quad 1\cdot 7634\dots.$$

Similarly,

$$\alpha_3 = \frac{631}{363 - 7\,(\alpha_2 - 1) + \tfrac{1}{3}\,(\alpha_2 - 1)\,(\alpha_2 - 2)} \quad \text{or} \quad 1\cdot 7646\dots.$$

The required result is therefore $52 + 1\cdot 7646\dots = 53\cdot 7646\dots$, where, it should be noted, the last digit is uncertain.

(ii) Elimination of third differences.

We have

$$18,600 = u_x = (1 + \Delta)^x\, u_0 = 19,231 - 363x + 7x\,(x-1) - \tfrac{1}{3}x\,(x-1)\,(x-2)$$

and

$$18,600 = u_x = (1 + \Delta)^{x-1}\, u_1 = 18,868 - 349\,(x-1) + 6\,(x-1)\,(x-2)$$
$$- \tfrac{1}{3}\,(x-1)\,(x-2)\,(x-3).$$

By inspection a rough value of the interpolated value is 1·75, allowing for the change of origin.

If, therefore, we multiply the two equations by $(3-1·75)$ and $1·75$ respectively, and add, we may neglect the fourth term. The factors being $1·25$ and $1·75$ we can use 5 and 7: we thus obtain

$$12 \times 18,600 = 5\left[19,231 - 363x + 7x\,(x-1)\right]$$
$$+ 7\left[18,868 - 349\,(x-1) + 6\,(x-1)\,(x-2)\right]$$

or
$$223,200 = 230,758 - 4419x + 77x^2,$$

i.e.
$$77x^2 - 4419x + 7558 = 0.$$

Solving the quadratic, the value required is $x = 1·7646\ldots$, which agrees with the value of α_3 in method (i) to four decimal places.

12. In Example 2 the advancing difference formula has been used; in practice, however, it is more usual for many reasons to employ a central difference formula as the basic equation. Central difference formulae are more convenient because the coefficients are smaller and converge more quickly; this in itself is a decided advantage. Having placed x in the middle interval the first approximation is generally much more accurate (thus, in Example 2, the use of Stirling's formula gives

$$\alpha_1 = 1 + 268/356$$
$$= 1·753).$$

Also, x is smaller, and the maximum number of significant digits which the data will yield may mean an additional place.

Consider the following example.

Example 3.

Find the root of the equation $x^3 - 9x - 14 = 0$ which lies between 3 and 4.

Let $y = x^3 - 9x - 14$. Then we have, by actual calculation,

x	3·0	3·2	3·4	3·6	3·8	4·0
y	$-14·000$	$-10·032$	$-5·296$	·256	6·672	14·000

The difference table is

x	y	Δy	$\Delta^2 y$	$\Delta^3 y$
3·0	− 14·000			
		3·968		
3·2	− 10·032		·768	
		4·736		·048
3·4	− 5·296		·816	
		5·552		·048
3·6	·256		·864	
		6·416		·048
3·8	6·672		·912	
		7·328		
4·0	14·000			

Taking the origin at 3·6 and using Stirling's formula:

$$u_x = u_0 + x\,\frac{\Delta u_0 + \Delta u_{-1}}{2} + \frac{x^2}{2}\,\Delta^2 u_{-1} + \frac{x\,(x^2-1)}{6}\,\frac{\Delta^3 u_{-1} + \Delta^3 u_{-2}}{2},$$

the interval of differencing being 0·2;

i.e. $\qquad 0 = ·256 + 5·984x + ·432x^2 + ·008x\,(x^2 - 1).$

The cubic equation can be solved by successive approximation, or we can repeat Stirling's formula for the next value of u_x and adopt the alternative method outlined above.

If the first of these methods be adopted, it will be found that successive approximations to the value of x are − ·04278, − ·042913, − ·042971. From the last we obtain as the required solution

$$3·6 - (·042971 \times ·2) \quad \text{or} \quad 3·5914058,$$

which is correct to six decimal places, the seventh being nearer to 7.

If we choose our origin at the point (x, y) and the value of the interpolated value is $x + \alpha$, then, when α lies between $-\frac{1}{4}$ and $\frac{1}{4}$, it is advantageous to use Stirling's formula. If α lies between $\frac{1}{4}$ and $\frac{3}{4}$ Bessel's formula should be applied. (Whittaker and Robinson, *Interpolation*, p. 60.)

13. In general, if Δu_x has n significant digits we cannot rely on more than n significant digits in x. Even then the last digit is doubtful and may in fact be misleading. In Example 3 above we have been able to obtain the fifth significant digit in ·042971 from a four-figure value of Δy only because y and Δy happen quite unusually to be exact and not rounded off.

14. The method of successive approximation is a convenient method for ordinary use. If we want a result that can be obtained to the required degree of accuracy by taking out differences as far as $\Delta^3 u$, or if the curve is a cubic, the elimination method will give a satisfactory answer. The disadvantage of this process is that we cannot approach our interpolated value by steps as is done in the method of successive approximation. Moreover when fourth and higher differences are not negligible the elimination method breaks down.

15. The general investigation of the accuracy of finite difference methods of approximation is a problem in direct interpolation, and has been dealt with previously. In dealing with the subject of successive approximation, however, it is of interest to include in the present chapter an elementary illustration of the fact that in certain circumstances a better interpolation can be obtained by neglecting higher differences than by retaining them.

For example, if we have a third difference curve, then

$$u_x = u_0 + x_{(1)}\Delta u_0 + x_{(2)}\Delta^2 u_0 + x_{(3)}\Delta^3 u_0 \text{ exactly.}$$

The error (α) in taking two terms is $x_{(2)}\Delta^2 u_0 + x_{(3)}\Delta^3 u_0$,

and (β) in taking three terms is $x_{(3)}\Delta^3 u_0$.

(α) may be expressed as

$$\frac{x(x-1)(x-2)}{6}\left[\frac{3}{x-2}\frac{\Delta^2 u_0}{\Delta^3 u_0} + 1\right]\Delta^3 u_0,$$

and (β) as

$$\frac{x(x-1)(x-2)}{6}\Delta^3 u_0.$$

Then, ignoring the sign of $\dfrac{x(x-1)(x-2)}{6}\Delta^3 u_0$, which will be the same for both (α) and (β), (α) will be less than (β) if

$$\frac{3}{x-2}\frac{\Delta^2 u_0}{\Delta^3 u_0}$$

is negative and numerically less than 2.

In these circumstances the error made by retaining first differences only is less than that made in continuing to second differences.

As an illustration consider the function $x^3 + 5x + 50$.

It is easily seen that $u_0 = 50$; $\Delta u_0 = 6$; $\Delta^2 u_0 = 6$; $\Delta^3 u_0 = 6$. If x is $\frac{1}{4}$, for example, $\dfrac{3}{x-2}\dfrac{\Delta^2 u_0}{\Delta^3 u_0} = -3/1\frac{3}{4}$, which is negative and less than 2.

(α) is therefore less than (β).

This can be otherwise shown by finding the values of the errors.

$$u_{\frac{1}{4}} = 51\tfrac{17}{64} \text{ exactly.}$$

Also
$$u_{\frac{1}{4}} = (1+\Delta)^{\frac{1}{4}} u_0$$
$$= u_0 + \tfrac{1}{4}\Delta u_0 - \tfrac{3}{32}\Delta^2 u_0 + \ldots,$$

$$u_0 + \tfrac{1}{4}\Delta u_0 = 51\tfrac{1}{2} = 51\tfrac{32}{64},$$

$$u_0 + \tfrac{1}{4}\Delta u_0 - \tfrac{3}{32}\Delta^2 u_0 = 50\tfrac{15}{16} = 50\tfrac{60}{64},$$

$$51\tfrac{32}{64} - 51\tfrac{17}{64} = \tfrac{15}{64}, \qquad \ldots\ldots(\alpha)$$

and
$$51\tfrac{17}{64} - 50\tfrac{60}{64} = \tfrac{21}{64}. \qquad \ldots\ldots(\beta)$$

(α) is less than (β), so that the approximation to first differences is better than that to second differences.

16. In conclusion it should be emphasized that the accuracy of the result depends greatly on the fineness of the interval of tabulation. In cases of doubt it may be desirable to halve the interval before applying the process of inverse interpolation. This will reduce first differences by about one-half, second differences in the ratio of about 1:4, third differences in the ratio of about 1:8, and so on. The comparative effect of higher differences is therefore much reduced.

EXAMPLES 5

1. Given $u_1 = 0$, $u_2 = 112$, $u_3 = 287$, $u_5 = 612$, find u_4. Using u_1, u_2, u_3 and u_4, find a value for x when $u_x = 270$.

2. The following values of u_x are given: $u_{10} = 544$, $u_{15} = 1227$, $u_{20} = 1775$. Find, correct to one decimal place, the value of x for which $u_x = 1000$.

3. Having given $\log 1 = 0$, $\log 2 = \cdot 30103$, $\log 3 = \cdot 47712$ and $\log 4 = \cdot 60206$, find the number whose logarithm is $\cdot 30500$:

(i) by expressing $\log x$ in terms of $\log 1$ and its differences and solving for x;

(ii) by using Lagrange's formula applied inversely.

Explain the nature of the assumptions in each case.

4. Apply Lagrange's formula inversely to find to one decimal place the age for which the annuity-value is $13 \cdot 6$, given the following table:

Age x	30	35	40	45	50
Annuity-value at $4\frac{1}{2}$ per cent. a_x	15·9	14·9	14·1	13·3	12·5

5. $f(0) = 16 \cdot 35$, $f(5) = 14 \cdot 88$, $f(10) = 13 \cdot 59$, $f(15) = 12 \cdot 46$. Find x when $f(x) = 14 \cdot 00$.

6. Given the following table of $f(x)$:

$$f(0) = 217, \quad f(1) = 140, \quad f(2) = 23, \quad f(3) = -6,$$

find approximately the value of x for which the function is zero.

7. The following values of $f(x)$ are given:

$$f(10) = 1754, \quad f(15) = 2648, \quad f(20) = 3564.$$

Find, correct to one decimal place, the value of x for which $f(x) = 3000$.

8. Given four values of a function u_0, u_1, u_2, u_3, show how to calculate an approximate value for x from the equation

$$u_x = u_0 + x\Delta u_0 + \frac{x(x-1)}{2!}\Delta^2 u_0 + \frac{x(x-1)(x-2)}{3!}\Delta^3 u_0$$

by obtaining a quadratic equation in place of a cubic.

Use the method to find x when $u_x = 1 \cdot 05$, given $u_{1 \cdot 0} = 1 \cdot 0000$, $u_{1 \cdot 1} = 1 \cdot 0323$, $u_{1 \cdot 2} = 1 \cdot 0627$, $u_{1 \cdot 3} = 1 \cdot 0914$.

9. Given that $(1 \cdot 20)^3 = 1 \cdot 728$, $(1 \cdot 21)^3 = 1 \cdot 772$, $(1 \cdot 22)^3 = 1 \cdot 816$, $(1 \cdot 23)^3 = 1 \cdot 861$, $(1 \cdot 24)^3 = 1 \cdot 907$, explain carefully how to find the real root of the equation $x^3 + x - 3 = 0$ by a method of inverse interpolation. What method would you adopt in practice? Obtain a value for the root to four decimal places.

10. The following table is available:

Age x	44	45	46	47
a_x at $4\frac{1}{2}$ per cent.	13·40	13·16	12·93	12·68

Find, to two decimal places, the age corresponding to an annuity of $13 \cdot 00$.

11. Find, to two decimal places, the real root of the equation

$$x^3 + x - 5 = 0$$

by means of divided differences applied inversely, using the values of the expression when $x = 0, 1, 2$ and 3.

What is the reason for the poor result obtained in this case?

(The true solution is $x = 1 \cdot 516$ approximately.)

12. The equation $x^3 - 6x - 11 = 0$ has a root between 3 and 4. Obtain it by inverse interpolation correct to three places of decimals.

13. The formula for the value of an annuity-certain for n years at rate per cent. i is given by

$$a_{\overline{n}|} = \frac{1 - v^n}{i}, \text{ where } v = (1 + i)^{-1}.$$

Given the following table, obtain to three decimal places the rate per cent. for which $a_{\overline{20}|}$ is 14:

Rate per cent.	3	$3\frac{1}{2}$	4	$4\frac{1}{2}$
$a_{\overline{20}|}$	14·8775	14·2124	13·5903	13·0079

14. Solve the equation $x = 10 \log_{10} x$, given the following data:

Argument x	1·35	1·36	1·37	1·38
$\log x$ ...	·1303	·1335	·1367	·1399

15. Apply Lagrange's formula (inversely) to find a root of the equation $u_x = 0$, when $u_{30} = -30$, $u_{34} = -13$, $u_{38} = 3$, $u_{42} = 18$.

CHAPTER VI

SUMMATION

1. Certain series whose law is given or of which there are sufficient terms to enable the law to be assumed may be summed by the methods of finite differences.

By definition we have

$$f(a+h)-f(a)=\Delta f(a)=\phi(a), \text{ say,}$$
$$f(a+2h)-f(a+h)=\Delta f(a+h)=\phi(a+h),$$

....

$$f(a+nh)-f(a+\overline{n-1}h)=\Delta f(a+\overline{n-1}h)=\phi(a+\overline{n-1}h);$$

$$\therefore \quad f(a+nh)-f(a)=\phi(a)+\phi(a+h)+\ldots+\phi(a+\overline{n-1}h).$$

If therefore $f(x)$ is the function whose first difference is $\phi(x)$ we can find the sum of any number of terms of the series whose general term is $\phi(x)$ in terms of values of $f(x)$, for any given interval of differencing.

By a suitable change of origin and scale we can make the interval of differencing unity and the first term of the algebraic series under consideration $\phi(1)$. On putting a and h each $=1$, the required relation then becomes

$$\sum_{1}^{n} \phi(x)=f(n+1)-f(1).$$

The expression $f(n+1)-f(1)$ is sometimes written in the form

$$\left[f(x)\right]_{1}^{n+1}.$$

This represents the process of substituting $n+1$ and 1 for x successively in $f(x)$ and deducting the second result from the first.

Note. It should be remembered that $\sum_{a}^{b} \phi(x)$ leads to $\left[f(x)\right]_{a}^{b+1}$ and not to $\left[f(x)\right]_{a}^{b}$.

2. Although any function of x can be differenced, there is only a limited number of functions which are the first differences of other explicit functions. The principal forms of such functions are given below.

(i) It can be easily seen that, since $\Delta a^x = (a-1) a^x$,

$$\Delta \left\{\frac{a^x}{a-1}\right\} = a^x.$$

$\therefore \dfrac{a^x}{a-1}$ is the function whose difference is a^x.

We can therefore find $\overset{n}{\underset{1}{\Sigma}} u_x$ by the method above if u_x is of the form $k a^x$.

(ii) The relations $\Delta x^{(m)} = m x^{(m-1)}$ and $\Delta x_{(m)} = x_{(m-1)}$ enable the sum of any series whose nth term can be expressed in the factorial notation to be summed immediately.

Example 1.

Sum to n terms the series whose xth term is $x (x-1) (x-2)$.

Now $\qquad\qquad x (x-1) (x-2) = x^{(3)}$,

and since $\qquad\qquad \Delta x^{(4)} = 4 x^{(3)}$,

$$\overset{n}{\underset{1}{\Sigma}} x^{(3)} = \left[\tfrac{1}{4} x^{(4)}\right]_1^{n+1}$$

$$= \tfrac{1}{4} \left[(n+1)^{(4)} - 1^{(4)}\right]$$

$$= \tfrac{1}{4} (n+1) n (n-1) (n-2),$$

since the product of four successive terms of which 1 is the first includes 0 and is therefore obviously zero.

If the interval of differencing does not happen to be unity the identity $\Delta x^{(m)} = mh x^{(m-1)}$ may be applied, but care must be taken in doing so. Here $x^{(m-1)}$ is the difference of the function $x^{(m)}/mh$, so that in summing a series whose xth term is, for example, $2x (2x-2) (2x-4)$, we must divide $2x (2x-2) (2x-4) (2x-6)$ by $h=2$ as well as by $m=4$ before taking the limits $n+1$ and 1.

(iii) Any polynomial $P_n (x)$ of the nth degree can be expressed by an interpolation formula ending with $\Delta^n u_x$ in which each coefficient is of the form $x_{(m)}$ or $\tfrac{1}{2} \left[x_{(m)} + (x+1)_{(m)}\right]$.

Since $\qquad x_{(r)}=(x+\mathrm{I})_{(r+1)}-x_{(r+1)}$

$$=\Delta x_{(r+1)},$$

it follows that $\qquad \Sigma x_{(r)}=x_{(r+1)}.$

Each term of the formula can therefore be summed at sight. Thus, the advancing difference formula

$$u_{a+x}=u_a+x_{(1)}\Delta u_a+x_{(2)}\Delta^2 u_a+x_{(3)}\Delta^3 u_a+\ldots$$

yields $\quad \Sigma u_{a+x}=x_{(1)}u_a+x_{(2)}\Delta u_a+x_{(3)}\Delta^2 u_a+x_{(4)}\Delta^3 u_a+\ldots.$

The Gauss forward formula in its simple form is

$$u_x=u_0+x_{(1)}\Delta u_0+x_{(2)}\Delta^2 u_{-1}+(x+\mathrm{I})_{(3)}\Delta^3 u_{-1}+\ldots$$

and therefore

$$\Sigma u_x=x_{(1)}u_0+x_{(2)}\Delta u_0+x_{(3)}\Delta^2 u_{-1}+(x+\mathrm{I})_{(4)}\Delta^3 u_{-1}+\ldots.$$

Stirling's formula may be written in Sheppard's notation as

$$u_x=u_0+x_{(1)}\mu\delta u_0+\tfrac{1}{2}\left[(x+\mathrm{I})_{(2)}+x_{(2)}\right]\delta^2 u_0+(x+\mathrm{I})_{(3)}\mu\delta^3 u_0+\ldots;$$

whence

$$\Sigma u_x=x_{(1)}u_0+x_{(2)}\mu\delta u_0+\tfrac{1}{2}\left[(x+\mathrm{I})_{(3)}+x_{(3)}\right]\delta^2 u_0+(x+\mathrm{I})_{(4)}\mu\delta^3 u_0+\ldots.$$

Example 2.

Find the sum of n terms of the series 0, 10, 33, 77, 150, ..., given that third differences are constant.

By taking out the differences it is seen that $\Delta u=10$, $\Delta^2 u=13$ and $\Delta^3 u=8$.

The advancing difference formula gives

$$u_x=0+10x_{(1)}+13x_{(2)}+8x_{(3)}.$$

If the series is u_0, u_1, u_2 ... u_x ... u_{n-1}, then we require $\displaystyle\sum_0^{n-1} u_x$.

$$\sum_0^{n-1} u_x=\sum_0^{n-1}\left[10x_{(1)}+13x_{(2)}+8x_{(3)}\right]$$

$$=\left[10x_{(2)}+13x_{(3)}+8x_{(4)}\right]_0^n$$

$$=10n_{(2)}+13n_{(3)}+8n_{(4)}$$

$$=\tfrac{1}{6}n\,(n-\mathrm{I})\,(2n^2+3n+16) \text{ on reduction.}$$

Alternatively, we may continue the table backwards to obtain the differences required for the central difference formulae.

Stirling's formula then gives

$$\Sigma u_x = 7{\cdot}5 x_{(2)} + 5{\cdot}\tfrac{1}{2}\left[(x+1)_{(3)} + x_{(3)}\right] + 8\,(x+1)_{(4)}$$

and
$$\sum_0^{n-1} u_x = 7{\cdot}5 n_{(2)} + 2{\cdot}5\left[(n+1)_{(3)} + n_{(3)}\right] + 8\,(n+1)_{(4)}$$
$$= \tfrac{1}{6}n\,(n-1)\,(2n^2 + 3n + 16)\ \text{as before.}$$

Should the series be given in the form $u_1, u_2, u_3 \ldots u_x \ldots u_n$, then

$$u_x = u_1 + (x-1)_{(1)}\Delta u_1 + (x-1)_{(2)}\Delta^2 u_1 + (x-1)_{(3)}\Delta^3 u_1.$$

$$\therefore\ \Sigma u_x = (x-1)_{(1)}u_1 + (x-1)_{(2)}\Delta u_1 + (x-1)_{(3)}\Delta^2 u_1 + (x-1)_{(4)}\Delta^3 u_1$$

and

$$\sum_1^n u_x = \left[(x-1)_{(1)}u_1 + (x-1)_{(2)}\Delta u_1 + (x-1)_{(3)}\Delta^2 u_1 + (x-1)_{(4)}\Delta^3 u_1\right]_1^{n+1}$$

$$= n_{(1)}u_1 + n_{(2)}\Delta u_1 + n_{(3)}\Delta^2 u_1 + n_{(4)}\Delta^3 u_1,$$

which, on substituting for Δu_1, $\Delta^2 u_1$ and $\Delta^3 u_1$, gives the result obtained above.

3. Since $\Delta x^{(-m)} = -m x^{(-m-1)}$, the series whose xth term is of the form $[(x+1)\,(x+2)\,\ldots\,(x+k)]^{-1}$ can be summed immediately.

Example 3.

Sum to n terms the series whose xth term is $\dfrac{1}{(x+1)\,(x+2)\,(x+3)}$.

$$\Delta\left[\frac{1}{(x+1)\,(x+2)}\right] = -2\,\frac{1}{(x+1)\,(x+2)\,(x+3)}.$$

$$\therefore\ \sum_1^n \frac{1}{(x+1)\,(x+2)\,(x+3)} = -\frac{1}{2}\left[\frac{1}{(x+1)\,(x+2)}\right]_1^{n+1}$$

$$= -\frac{1}{2}\left[\frac{1}{(n+2)\,(n+3)} - \frac{1}{2{\cdot}3}\right].$$

4. It is worthy of remark that the rules for the summation of series of the types given in paragraphs 2 (ii) and 3, as given in the textbooks on algebra, are precisely the same as those stated above, and

8

are based on the same principle. For example, for a series whose nth term is

$$(a+nb)\,(a+\overline{n+1b})\,(a+\overline{n+2b})\,\ldots\,(a+\overline{n+r-1b}),$$

the finite difference method is simply to write this in factorial form, with interval of differencing b, and then to proceed on the lines laid down, thus:

$$\sum_{1}^{n} u_n = \sum_{1}^{n} (a+\overline{n+r-1b})^{(r)} = \left[\frac{(a+\overline{n+r-1b})^{(r+1)}}{b\,(r+1)}\right]_{1}^{n+1}$$

$$=\frac{(a+\overline{n+rb})^{(r+1)}-(a+rb)^{(r+1)}}{b\,(r+1)}$$

$$=\frac{(a+\overline{n+rb})\,u_n}{b\,(r+1)}+\text{a constant.}$$

This, of course, produces the same result as is given by the algebraic rule: "Write down the nth term, affix the next factor at the end, divide by the number of factors thus increased and by the common difference, and add a constant".

For the series whose nth term is the reciprocal of the one above the inverse factorial is used, and a similar result is obtained.

5. It sometimes happens that on taking out successive differences of a series a stage is reached where a particular set of differences forms a geometrical progression. In that event the series can be considered as consisting of two separate series, (i) a series whose general term is $a+bx+cx^2+\ldots+kx^{n-1}$ (a rational integral function of x), and (ii) a geometrical progression.

Suppose, for example, that second differences are in geometrical progression with common ratio r. Then

$$u_x = a+bx+cr^x.$$

For $\qquad\qquad\qquad \Delta u_x = b+c\,(r-1)\,r^x,$

and $\qquad\qquad\qquad \Delta^2 u_x = c\,(r-1)^2\,r^x = kr^x,$

where $\qquad\qquad\qquad k = c\,(r-1)^2.$

It follows that for nth differences

$$\Delta^n u_x = c\,(r-1)^n\,r^x.$$

Example 4.

Sum to n terms the series 1, 6, 11, 18, 31, 58, 115, ...

The difference table is

u_x	Δu_x	$\Delta^2 u_x$	$\Delta^3 u_x$
1			
	5		
6		0	
	5		2
11		2	
	7		4
18		6	
	13		8
31		14	
	27		16
58		30	
	57		
115			

Third differences are in G.P. with common ratio 2.

Assume therefore that

$$u_x = a + bx^{(1)} + cx^{(2)} + d2^x,$$
$$\Delta u_x = b + 2cx^{(1)} + d2^x (2 - 1)$$
$$= b + 2cx^{(1)} + d2^x,$$
$$\Delta^2 u_x = 2c + d2^x,$$
$$\Delta^3 u_x = d2^x.$$

Inserting the differences for the value $x = 1$, we have

$$2 = \Delta^3 u_1 = 2d; \quad 0 = \Delta^2 u_1 = 2c + 2d;$$
$$5 = \Delta u_1 = b + 2c + 2d.$$

From these equations we find easily that

$$d = 1; \quad c = -1; \quad b = 5.$$

Putting $x = 1$ in $u_x = a + bx^{(1)} + cx^{(2)} + d2^x$, we have

$$1 = u_1 = a + b + 2d,$$

whence

$$a = 1 - b - 2d = -6;$$

$$\therefore \quad u_x = -6 + 5x^{(1)} - x^{(2)} + 2^x;$$

$$\therefore \quad \sum_1^n u_x = \left[-6x^{(1)} + \frac{5x^{(2)}}{2} - \frac{x^{(3)}}{3} + \frac{2^x}{2-1} \right]_1^{n+1}$$

$$= -6(n+1)^{(1)} + 6 + \frac{5(n+1)^{(2)}}{2} - \frac{(n+1)^{(3)}}{3} + 2^{n+1} - 2,$$

since all the factorials except the first vanish for the lower limit.

This simplifies to

$$2^{n+1} - 2 - \frac{n}{6}(2n^2 - 15n + 19).$$

Alternatively, we may proceed thus:

$$\Delta^3 u_x = d2^x.$$

Deduct $d2^x$ from u_x and difference the function $u_x - d2^x$ in the usual way.

By giving x the values 1, 2, 3, 4 in succession it is easily seen that $u_x - d2^x$ takes the values -1, 2, 3, 2 respectively. On forming a difference table we find that the leading differences are

$$\Delta (u_x - d2^x) = 3, \quad \Delta^2 (u_x - d2^x) = -2.$$

Then $\qquad u_x = 2^x - 1 + 3 (x-1)_{(1)} - 2 (x-1)_{(2)},$

so that

$$\sum_{1}^{n} u_x = \left[2^x - (x-1)_{(1)} + 3 (x-1)_{(2)} - 2 (x-1)_{(3)} \right]_{1}^{n+1}$$

$$= 2^{n+1} - 2 - n_{(1)} + 3n_{(2)} - 2n_{(3)},$$

which, on simplification, gives the same result as that above.

Note. In the methods above we have called the terms $u_1, u_2, u_3 \ldots$ and have used the property $\Delta x^{(t)} = tx^{(t-1)}$. We may shorten the work slightly by beginning with $x = 0$ (so that all the factorials vanish at the lower limit) and using $x_{(t)}$ instead of $x^{(t)}$. Further, the two methods give the same result without transformation. It will be instructive for the student to rework the problem on these lines.

6. The form $u_x v_x$. Summation by parts.

When the general term of the series is the product of two functions of x and the value of each of the summations $\sum\limits_{1}^{n} u_x$ and $\sum\limits_{1}^{n} v_x$ is known, a method known as "summation by parts" can be adopted.

We have $\quad \Delta (U_x V_x) = U_{x+1} V_{x+1} - U_x V_x$

$$= U_{x+1} (V_{x+1} - V_x) + V_x (U_{x+1} - U_x)$$

$$= U_{x+1} \Delta V_x + V_x \Delta U_x;$$

$$\therefore \quad V_x \Delta U_x = \Delta (U_x V_x) - U_{x+1} \Delta V_x;$$

$$\therefore \quad \sum_{1}^{n} [V_x \Delta U_x] = \left[U_x V_x \right]_{1}^{n+1} - \sum_{1}^{n} [U_{x+1} \Delta V_x].$$

It follows that when the function $u_x v_x$ can be put in the form $V_x \Delta U_x$ the summation can be performed at once if $\sum\limits_{1}^{n} [U_{x+1} \Delta V_x]$ can be evaluated (but not otherwise).

Note. For extensions of the formulae for summation by parts see Chapter VII.

Example 5.

Find the sum of the series $a + 2a^2 + 3a^3 + 4a^4 + \ldots$ to n terms. The terms are successive values of the function $y = xa^x$, and since

$$\Delta \left(\frac{a^x}{a-1} \right) = a^x,$$

we may write x for V_x and $\dfrac{a^x}{a-1}$ for U_x in the relation above.

$$\therefore \quad \sum_1^n [xa^x] = \sum_1^n \left[x\Delta \left(\frac{a^x}{a-1} \right) \right]$$

$$= \left[\frac{a^x}{a-1} x \right]_1^{n+1} - \sum_1^n \left[\frac{a^{x+1}}{a-1} \Delta x \right]$$

$$= \left[\frac{a^x}{a-1} x \right]_1^{n+1} - \sum_1^n \left[\frac{a^{x+1}}{a-1} \right], \quad \text{since } \Delta x = 1,$$

$$= \left[\frac{a^x}{a-1} x \right]_1^{n+1} - \left[\frac{a^{x+1}}{(a-1)^2} \right]_1^{n+1}$$

$$= (n+1) \frac{a^{n+1}}{a-1} - \frac{a}{a-1} - \frac{a^{n+2}}{(a-1)^2} + \frac{a^2}{(a-1)^2}.$$

7. The result in paragraph 1, namely, that $\sum\limits_1^n \phi(x) = f(n+1) - f(1)$, where $\Delta f(x) = \phi(x)$, can be obtained by the use of the operator E.

We have
$$\sum_1^n \phi(x) = \phi(1) + \phi(2) + \ldots + \phi(n)$$

$$= (1 + E + E^2 + \ldots + E^{n-1}) \phi(1)$$

$$= \frac{E^n - 1}{E - 1} \phi(1)$$

$$= \frac{E^n - 1}{E - 1} (E - 1) f(1),$$

since
$$\phi(1) = \Delta f(1) = (E-1) f(1).$$

$$\therefore \quad \sum_1^n \phi(x) = (E^n - 1) f(1)$$

$$= f(n+1) - f(1).$$

Thus the operator $\overset{n}{\underset{1}{\Sigma}}$ is equivalent to the operator $\dfrac{E^n - 1}{E - 1}$, and we may safely substitute $\dfrac{E^n - 1}{E - 1}$ for $\overset{n}{\underset{1}{\Sigma}}$ in any series of operations.

Again, since $E^n u_x = u_{x+n}$, the identity $\overset{n}{\underset{1}{\Sigma}} u_x = \dfrac{E^n - 1}{E - 1} u_1$ can be expressed as

$$\overset{n}{\underset{1}{\Sigma}} u_x = \frac{1}{E - 1} (u_{n+1} - u_1)$$

$$= \frac{1}{\Delta} (u_{n+1} - u_1)$$

$$= \Delta^{-1} (u_{n+1} - u_1).$$

8. The relation between the operators Σ and Δ.

It has been seen that if

$$\Delta f(x) = \phi(x)$$

then $\qquad\qquad f(x) = \Sigma \phi(x),$

where the summation is performed between certain limits.

If therefore we omit the limits we may say that with certain reservations summation is the inverse process to differencing.

Consequently $\qquad \phi(x) = \Delta f(x) = \Delta \Sigma \phi(x),$

so that $\qquad\qquad\qquad \Delta \Sigma \equiv 1,$

i.e. $\qquad\qquad\qquad \Sigma \equiv \dfrac{1}{\Delta} \equiv \Delta^{-1}.$

Now although $\Delta \Sigma \equiv 1$ it does not follow that $\Sigma \Delta \equiv 1$, for we shall obtain the same result by differencing $f(x) + c$, where c is a constant, as by differencing $f(x)$ alone.

Thus $\qquad\qquad \Delta[f(x) + c] = \phi(x);$

$$\therefore\ f(x) + c = \Delta^{-1} \phi(x) = \Sigma \phi(x) = \Sigma \Delta f(x),$$

so that $\qquad\qquad\qquad \Sigma \Delta \not\equiv 1.$

The symbol Σ may be and often is used in place of the inverse symbol Δ^{-1} provided that it be remembered that Σ (or Δ^{-1}) and

Δ are not commutative, and that in the indefinite finite integral we must include, or imagine, an arbitrary constant which disappears in the definite integral.

Thus, the process of summation in finite differences is similar to the corresponding process in the integral calculus and the relations between the symbols are analogous to those existing between the symbols of differentiation and integration. As a result, finite difference summation is often referred to as finite integration. Σu_x is said to be the indefinite finite integral of u_x; $\sum_{1}^{n} u_x$ the definite finite integral; and a function that can be integrated, such as a^x, to be "immediately integrable".

9. Other uses of the symbol Σ.

One of the commonest functions in the theory of life contingencies is the expression obtained by multiplying l_x (the number attaining age x) by the interest factor v^x. This product is denoted by D_x, and the connection between certain functions dependent on D_x is indicated thus:

$$N_x = \Sigma D_x; \quad S_x = \Sigma N_x.$$

Here Σ denotes summation from age x to the end of the mortality table, it being understood that values beyond the end of the table are zero.

In point of fact, the correct way of showing the relation between the functions D and N, etc., is

$$N_x = \sum_{t=0}^{t=\infty} D_{x+t},$$

where x is fixed and t is the variable.

In modern mathematical works it is now usual to use the notations $\sum_{t=0}^{\infty}$, $\sum_{t=a}^{n}$ etc., where the variable t is specified for the lower limit only. The still shorter form $\sum_{a}^{b}$ is often used where there is no doubt about the variable.

(i) When Σ is used in the special sense

$$\Sigma u_x = u_x + u_{x+1} + u_{x+2} + \dots \text{ to the end of the table;}$$

$$\Delta\Sigma u_x = (u_{x+1} + u_{x+2} + u_{x+3} + \dots) - (u_x + u_{x+1} + u_{x+2} + \dots)$$

$$= -u_x,$$

so that here $\qquad \Delta\Sigma \equiv -1.$

(ii) If, however, Σ is specially defined so that Σu_x indicates a summation beginning with u_1 and ending with the last term preceding u_x, then

$$\Sigma u_x = u_1 + u_2 + u_3 + \dots + u_{x-1};$$

$$\therefore \quad \Delta\Sigma u_x = (u_1 + u_2 + u_3 + \dots + u_x) - (u_1 + u_2 + u_3 + \dots + u_{x-1})$$

$$= u_x.$$

In these circumstances therefore $\Delta\Sigma \equiv 1.$

(iii) Again, in algebraic series, Σ is often used loosely to indicate the sum of the first x terms of a series, thus:

$$\Sigma u_x = u_1 + u_2 + \dots + u_x;$$

$$\therefore \quad \Delta\Sigma u_x = (u_1 + u_2 + \dots + u_{x+1}) - (u_1 + u_2 + \dots + u_x)$$

$$= u_{x+1}$$

$$= Eu_x,$$

whence $\qquad \Delta\Sigma \equiv E.$

These illustrations serve to show that great care must be exercised in introducing Σ into any formula. The sense in which it is to be used should be clearly defined in every instance: the safest course is always to state the limits where possible.

10. Application of the relation between Σ and Δ.

By treating the operator Σ as equivalent to Δ^{-1}, the method of separation of symbols can be employed for the solution of problems. For example, a convenient formula for the evaluation of $\Sigma a^x u_x$ can be evolved by which the necessity for the continued application of summation by parts can be obviated.

Example 6.

Prove that

$$\Sigma a^x u_x = \frac{a^x}{a-1}\left\{1 - \frac{a\Delta}{a-1} + \frac{a^2\Delta^2}{(a-1)^2} - \frac{a^3\Delta^3}{(a-1)^3} + \dots\right\} u_x.$$

Now $\qquad E^p a^x u_x = a^{x+p} u_{x+p} = a^x (aE)^p u_x$

and $\qquad \Sigma a^x u_x = \Delta^{-1} a^x u_x$, omitting the arbitrary constant

$$= (E-1)^{-1} a^x u_x.$$

Let $\qquad \phi(E) \equiv A_0 + A_1 E + A_2 E^2 + \dots + A_r E^r + \dots.$

Then the $(r+1)$th term in $\phi(E) a^x u_x$ is $A_r E^r a^x u_x.$

I.e. $\qquad A_r a^{x+r} u_{x+r} = a^x A_r a^r u_{x+r}$

$$= a^x A_r a^r E^r u_x$$

$$= a^x A_r (aE)^r u_x;$$

$$\therefore \quad \phi(E) a^x u_x = a^x \phi(aE) u_x,$$

so that if $\phi(E)$ is the operation $(E-1)^{-1}$

$$(E-1)^{-1} a^x u_x = a^x (aE-1)^{-1} u_x;$$

$$\therefore \quad \Sigma a^x u_x = a^x (aE-1)^{-1} u_x$$

$$= a^x (a + a\Delta - 1)^{-1} u_x$$

$$= a^x (a-1)^{-1} \left[1 + \frac{a\Delta}{a-1} \right]^{-1} u_x$$

$$= \frac{a^x}{a-1} \left[1 - \frac{a\Delta}{a-1} + \frac{a^2\Delta^2}{(a-1)^2} - \dots \right] u_x,$$

omitting the arbitrary constant.

Note. An alternative (and simpler) proof of this formula can be obtained by the use of the expansion of $\Sigma u_x v_x$ in a series. See Chap. VII, paragraph 12.

Example 7.

Apply the above formula to evaluate $\Sigma 3^x (x^3 + x^2 + x + 1)$.

$$\Delta u_x = \Delta (x^3 + x^2 + x + 1) = 3x^2 + 5x + 3,$$

$$\Delta^2 u_x = \Delta^2 (x^3 + x^2 + x + 1) = 6x + 8,$$

and $\qquad \Delta^3 u_x = \Delta^3 (x^3 + x^2 + x + 1) = 6;$

$$\therefore \quad \Sigma 3^x (x^3 + x^2 + x + 1)$$

$$= \frac{3^x}{3-1} \left\{ u_x - \frac{3}{(3-1)} \Delta u_x + \frac{3^2}{(3-1)^2} \Delta^2 u_x - \frac{3^3}{(3-1)^3} \Delta^3 u_x \right\} + c$$

$$= \frac{3^x}{2} \left[x^3 + x^2 + x + 1 - \tfrac{3}{2}(3x^2 + 5x + 3) + \tfrac{9}{4}(6x+8) - \tfrac{27}{8}.6 \right] + c$$

$$= \frac{3^x}{8} (4x^3 - 14x^2 + 28x - 23) + c.$$

It is often of advantage to set out the rational integral function in factorial or binomial notation; the successive differences can then be obtained with little difficulty.

Thus, by the method given in Chap. I, paragraph 22,

$$x^3 + x^2 + x + 1 = x^{(3)} + 4x^{(2)} + 3x^{(1)} + 1,$$

so that
$$\Delta u_x = 3x^{(2)} + 8x^{(1)} + 3,$$

$$\Delta^2 u_x = 6x^{(1)} + 8,$$

$$\Delta^3 u_x = 6,$$

and, by adopting the formula for $\Sigma a^x u_x$, we have easily that

$$\Sigma 3^x \left(x^3 + x^2 + x + 1\right) = \frac{3^x}{8}\left(4x^{(3)} - 2x^{(2)} + 18x^{(1)} - 23\right) + c.$$

To express $4x^{(3)} - 2x^{(2)} + 18x^{(1)} - 23$ in the form

$$ax^3 + bx^2 + cx + d,$$

we use the method of detached coefficients applied inversely:

2	4	-2	18	-23
	0	8	-10	
1	4	-10	28	
	0	4		
0	4	-14		
	0			
	4			

Hence
$$\Sigma 3^x \left(x^3 + x^2 + x + 1\right) = \frac{3^x}{8}\left(4x^3 - 14x^2 + 28x - 23\right) + c,$$

as before.

11. The following examples are instructive.

Example 8.

Evaluate
$$\sum_1^n \frac{2x+3}{x(x+1)} 3^{-x}.$$

$$u_x = \frac{2x+3}{x(x+1)} \frac{1}{3^x} = \left\{\frac{3}{x} - \frac{1}{x+1}\right\} \frac{1}{3^x}$$

$$= \frac{3}{x} \frac{1}{3^x} - \frac{3}{x+1} \frac{1}{3^{x+1}}$$

$$= -3\Delta \left[\frac{1}{x} \frac{1}{3^x}\right];$$

$$\therefore \sum_1^n u_x = 3 \left[-\frac{1}{x} \frac{1}{3^x}\right]_1^{n+1}$$

$$= 1 - \frac{1}{n+1} \frac{1}{3^n}.$$

Example 9.

Show that the general term of the recurring series

$$u_0 + u_1 x + u_2 x^2 + \ldots + u_r x^r + \ldots,$$

for which the scale of relation is $1 - px - qx^2$, is $Aa^n + Bb^n$, where a, b are functions of p, q and A, B are constants.

Since $1 - px - qx^2$ is the scale of relation,

$$u_n - pu_{n-1} - qu_{n-2} = 0;$$

i.e. $$u_n - pE^{-1}u_n - qE^{-2}u_n = 0,$$

or $$(1 - pE^{-1} - qE^{-2})\, u_n = 0.$$

Therefore $$(1 - aE^{-1})(1 - bE^{-1})\, u_n = 0$$

if $$a + b = p \quad \text{and} \quad ab = -q.$$

This will be true if either

$$(1 - aE^{-1})\, u_n \quad \text{or} \quad (1 - bE^{-1})\, u_n = 0,$$

i.e. if $$u_n - au_{n-1} \quad \text{or} \quad u_n - bu_{n-1} = 0.$$

Now if $$u_n - au_{n-1} = 0,$$

then $$u_n = au_{n-1},$$

and the series is a geometrical progression with common ratio a. The general term of the "a" series is therefore Aa^n.

Similarly the general term of the "b" series is Bb^n, where A and B are constants. But if a new series be formed by the addition of these two progressions the relationship will hold good for this new series. In other words the most general solution is

$$u_n = Aa^n + Bb^n,$$

where we may give A and B any values, but a and b must satisfy the equations

$$a + b = p \quad \text{and} \quad ab = -q.$$

Example 10.

If fourth and higher differences are ignored, prove that the sum of n successive terms of a function, of which u_0 is the central term, is

$$nu_0 + \tfrac{1}{24}\left(n^3 - n\right)\Delta^2 u_{-1},$$

where n is odd.

Since u_0 is the central term, it will be convenient to use a central difference formula.

Gauss's forward formula gives

$$u_x = u_0 + x\Delta u_0 + \tfrac{1}{2}x\left(x-1\right)\Delta^2 u_{-1} + \tfrac{1}{6}\left(x+1\right)x\left(x-1\right)\Delta^3 u_{-1}$$

$$= u_0 + x^{(1)}\Delta u_0 + \tfrac{1}{2}x^{(2)}\Delta^2 u_{-1} + \tfrac{1}{6}\left(x+1\right)^{(3)}\Delta^3 u_{-1};$$

$$\therefore \ \ \Sigma u_x = C + xu_0 + \tfrac{1}{2}x^{(2)}\Delta u_0 + \tfrac{1}{6}x^{(3)}\Delta^2 u_{-1} + \tfrac{1}{24}\left(x+1\right)^{(4)}\Delta^3 u_{-1}.$$

On summation between the limits $-\tfrac{1}{2}\left(n-1\right)$ and $\tfrac{1}{2}\left(n-1\right)$ the co-efficients of Δu_0 and $\Delta^3 u_{-1}$ will cancel, and we shall have

$$\sum_{-\frac{1}{2}(n-1)}^{\frac{1}{2}(n-1)} u_x = \left[C + xu_0 + \tfrac{1}{2}x^{(2)}\Delta u_0 + \tfrac{1}{6}x^{(3)}\Delta^2 u_{-1} + \tfrac{1}{24}\left(x+1\right)^{(4)}\Delta^3 u_{-1} \right]_{-\frac{1}{2}(n-1)}^{\frac{1}{2}(n+1)}$$

$$= \left[\frac{n+1}{2} - \left(-\frac{n-1}{2}\right) \right] u_0$$

$$+ \frac{1}{6}\left[\frac{n+1}{2}\cdot\frac{n-1}{2}\cdot\frac{n-3}{2} - \left(-\frac{n-1}{2}\cdot\frac{n+1}{2}\cdot\frac{n+3}{2}\right) \right]\Delta^2 u_{-1}$$

$$= nu_0 + \tfrac{1}{24}\left(n^3 - n\right)\Delta^2 u_{-1}.$$

12. The use of symbols of operation in the summation of algebraic series.

Many forms of algebraic series which at first sight do not seem to lend themselves to summation by the method of separation of symbols can in fact be summed very simply by that method.

For example, if c_r be the coefficient of x^r in the expansion of $(1+x)^n$, where n is a positive integer, the sum of the series whose rth term is $(-1)^{r-1}c_{r-1}\left[a-(r-1)\right]$ may be written down almost at sight. The series is

$$c_0 a - c_1\left(a-1\right) + c_2\left(a-2\right) - \ldots$$

i.e. $\qquad c_0 a - c_1 E^{-1}a + c_2 E^{-2}a - \ldots = (1 - E^{-1})^n\, a$

$$= \Delta^n E^{-n} a$$

$$= \Delta^n\left(a-n\right)$$

$$= 0, \text{ for all values of } a.$$

Again, consider the well-known series

$$\frac{c_0}{x} - \frac{c_1}{x+1} + \frac{c_2}{x+2} - \dots$$

This may be written as

$$\left(c_0 - c_1 E + c_2 E^2 - \dots\right) x^{-1}$$
$$= (1 - E)^n x^{-1}$$
$$= (-1)^n \Delta^n x^{-1}$$
$$= \frac{n!}{x(x+1)(x+2)\dots(x+n)}.$$

The following examples are illustrative of the method.

Example 11.

Evaluate

$$\frac{1}{x+1} - \frac{n}{(x+1)(x+2)} + \frac{n(n-1)}{(x+1)(x+2)(x+3)} - \dots + \frac{(-1)^n n!}{(x+1)\dots(x+n+1)}.$$

This series is $x^{(-1)} - n x^{(-2)} + n(n-1) x^{(-3)} \dots + (-1)^n n! x^{(-n-1)}$

$$= x^{(-1)} + \frac{n}{1!}\Delta x^{(-1)} + \frac{n(n-1)}{2!}\Delta^2 x^{(-1)} + \dots + \frac{n!}{n!}\Delta^n x^{(-1)}$$
$$= (1+\Delta)^n x^{(-1)}$$
$$= E^n x^{(-1)}$$
$$= (x+n)^{(-1)}$$
$$= \frac{1}{(x+n+1)}.$$

Example 12.

Find the value of

$$a^{n+1} - n(a+b)^{n+1} + \frac{n(n-1)}{2!}(a+2b)^{n+1}$$
$$- \frac{n(n-1)(n-2)}{3!}(a+3b)^{n+1} - \dots.$$

Taking the interval of differencing to be b, the series may be written as

$$(1 - n_{(1)} E + n_{(2)} E^2 - \dots) a^{n+1}$$
$$= (1 - E)^n a^{n+1}$$
$$= (-1)^n \Delta^n a^{n+1}.$$

Now
$$a^{n+1} = a^{(n+1)} + \tfrac{1}{2}n(n+1)a^{(n)}b + \text{terms in } a^{(r)}b^{n+1-r} \quad (r < n).$$

$$\therefore \quad \Delta^n a^{n+1} = (n+1)!\,b^n a^{(1)} + \tfrac{1}{2}n(n+1)b^{n+1}n!$$

$$= \tfrac{1}{2}b^n(n+1)!\,(2a+nb),$$

and the sum of the series

$$= \tfrac{1}{2}(-b)^n(n+1)!\,(2a+nb).$$

Example 13.

Sum the series

$$x^3 + (x+1)^3 + (x+2)^3 + \ldots + (x+n-1)^3.$$

The series may be written in the form

$$S = (1 + E + E^2 + \ldots + E^{n-1})\,x^3$$

$$= \frac{E^n - 1}{E - 1}\,x^3$$

$$= (E^n - 1)\,\Delta^{-1}x^3$$

$$= \Delta^{-1}(x+n)^3 - \Delta^{-1}x^3$$

$$= \Delta^{-1}\left[(x+n)_{(1)} + 6(x+n)_{(2)} + 6(x+n)_{(3)}\right]$$

$$\qquad - \Delta^{-1}\left[x_{(1)} + 6x_{(2)} + 6x_{(3)}\right]$$

$$= \tfrac{1}{4}\left[(x+n)^2(x+n-1)^2 - x^2(x-1)^2\right], \text{ on reduction.}$$

Note. It is unnecessary to introduce any constant of integration: for if we put

$$\Delta^{-1}x^3 = u_x + c,$$

the constant disappears on operation by $E^n - 1$.

13. "Summation n", or $[n]$.

An interesting example of the development of a series of operations by the method of separation of symbols occurs in the theory of graduation. One of the objects of graduation is to obtain a smooth series of numbers instead of the rough series given by the actual data. A step to the solution of the problem consists in replacing each term of the series by the arithmetic mean of the n successive terms of which the given term is the central term. The operation of summing these successive terms is generally denoted by $[n]$ ("summation n"). For the present we will assume that n is odd.

For example $[5]\,u_0 = u_{-2} + u_{-1} + u_0 + u_1 + u_2,$

$[n]\,u_0 = u_{-\frac{n-1}{2}} + u_{-\frac{n-3}{2}} + \ldots + u_{\frac{n-3}{2}} + u_{\frac{n-1}{2}}.$

Consider a simple summation: $[3]\,u_0$

By definition $[3]\,u_0 = u_{-1} + u_0 + u_1,$

and if we write v_0 for $[3]\,u_0$ we may operate again on v_0 to obtain $[3]\,v_0$.

In that event we shall have

$$[3]\,v_0 = [3]\,u_{-1} + [3]\,u_0 + [3]\,u_1$$
$$= u_{-2} + 2u_{-1} + 3u_0 + 2u_1 + u_2$$
$$= u_0 + (u_{-1} + u_0 + u_1) + (u_{-2} + u_{-1} + u_0 + u_1 + u_2)$$
$$= [1]\,u_0 + [3]\,u_0 + [5]\,u_0.$$

If therefore we denote the double operation $[3]\,[3]\,u_0$ by $[3]^2\,u_0$, we have the symbolic identity

$$[3]^2 \equiv [1] + [3] + [5].$$

Similarly $[5]^2 \equiv [1] + [3] + [5] + [7] + [9],$

and $[n]^2 \equiv [1] + [3] + [5] + [7] + \ldots + [2n-1],$

where n is odd.

The identity between $[3]^2$ and $[1] + [3] + [5]$ can be seen at once by writing down the terms in diagrammatic form:

$[3]^2\,u_0 = [3]\,u_{-1} + [3]\,u_0 + [3]\,u_1$

$= [5]\,u_0 + [3]\,u_0 + [1]\,u_0.$ (Fraser.)

These results are general. The sum of n consecutive odd operations is $[n]$ $[r]$, where $[r]$ is the middle operator. E.g.

$$[5] + [7] + [9] + [11] + [13] \equiv [5]\,[9] \equiv [9]\,[5].$$

14. We can express $[n]$ in terms of the ordinary finite difference symbols thus:

For a simple value of n, say 3,

$$[3]\,u_0 = u_{-1} + u_0 + u_1 = 3u_0 + u_{-1} - 2u_0 + u_1$$
$$= 3u_0 + \Delta^2 u_{-1}$$
$$= (3 + \delta^2)\,u_0,$$

where δ^2 is the symbol denoting the second central difference.

Generally $[n] \equiv n + \dfrac{n^3 - n}{24}\,\delta^2 +$ terms in δ^4 and higher differences if these exist. (Cf. Ex. 10.)

The relations above are on the assumption that n is odd. If n be even we must find a meaning for the summation symbol.

By analogy $[2]\,u_0$ is the sum of two values of u whose suffixes are such that their sum is zero and their difference unity.

I.e. $\qquad\qquad [2]\,u_0 = u_{-\frac{1}{2}} + u_{\frac{1}{2}}.$

Hence $\qquad\qquad [2]^2\,u_0 = \{[1] + [3]\}\,u_0$

$$= (4 + \delta^2)\,u_0,$$

so that $\qquad\qquad [2] \equiv 2\,(1 + \tfrac{1}{4}\delta^2)^{\frac{1}{2}}$

$$\equiv 2\,(1 + \tfrac{1}{8}\delta^2 - \tfrac{1}{128}\delta^4 + \dots),$$

which is otherwise obtained by expressing $u_{-\frac{1}{2}} + u_{\frac{1}{2}}$ in terms of central differences. This agrees with

$$[n] \equiv n + \frac{n^3 - n}{24}\,\delta^2$$

as far as third differences.

The meaning of $[n]$ when n is even is now evident, and we need no longer restrict the values of n to odd integers. Thus the formula

$$[n]\,u_0 = u_{-\frac{n-1}{2}} + u_{-\frac{n-3}{2}} + \dots + u_{\frac{n-3}{2}} + u_{\frac{n-1}{2}}$$

applies for any integral value of n whether odd or even.

15. The following alternative form for exhibiting relations between the operators, whether odd or even, is due to Mr G. J. Lidstone:

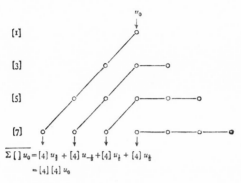

$$\overline{\Sigma\,[\,]}\,u_0 = [4]\,u_{\frac{3}{4}} + [4]\,u_{-\frac{1}{4}} + [4]\,u_{\frac{1}{4}} + [4]\,u_{\frac{3}{4}}$$
$$= [4]\,[4]\,u_0$$

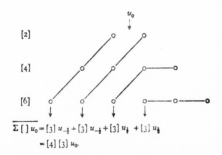

$$\overline{\Sigma\,[\,]}\,u_0 = [3]\,u_{-\frac{1}{3}} + [3]\,u_{-\frac{1}{3}} + [3]\,u_{\frac{1}{3}} + [3]\,u_{\frac{1}{3}}$$
$$= [4]\,[3]\,u_0.$$

The tracks marked —— show the re-grouping. The diagram is of virtually the same form if we begin later:

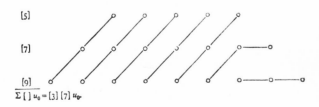

$$\overline{\Sigma\,[\,]}\,u_0 = [3]\,[7]\,u_0.$$

16. By means of the relations already proved we may develop an unlimited number of formulae involving $[n]$, $[m]$, etc.

F M A S

Example 14.

Prove that $10 [1] - 3 [3] \equiv 2 [3] - [5]$ as far as third differences.

$$\{10 [1] - 3 [3]\} u_0 = 10u_0 - 3 (3u_0 + \tfrac{24}{24}\delta^2 u_0)$$

$$= u_0 - 3\delta^2 u_0.$$

Also $\qquad \{2 [3] - [5]\} u_0 = 2 (3u_0 + \tfrac{24}{24}\delta^2 u_0) - (5u_0 + \tfrac{120}{24}\delta^2 u_0)$

$$= u_0 - 3\delta^2 u_0.$$

Example 15.

Given $[5] u_{-5}$, $[5] u_0$, $[5] u_5$, find u_0, fourth and higher differences being neglected.

By Stirling's formula,

$$u_x = u_0 + x \frac{\Delta u_{-1} + \Delta u_0}{2} + \frac{x^2}{2} \Delta^2 u_{-1} + \frac{x (x^2 - 1)}{6} \frac{\Delta^3 u_{-1} + \Delta^3 u_{-2}}{2} + \dots,$$

$$u_{-x} = u_0 - x \frac{\Delta u_{-1} + \Delta u_0}{2} + \frac{x^2}{2} \Delta^2 u_{-1} - \frac{x (x^2 - 1)}{6} \frac{\Delta^3 u_{-1} + \Delta^3 u_{-2}}{2} + \dots.$$

$$\therefore \quad u_x + u_{-x} = 2u_0 + x^2 \Delta^2 u_{-1}.$$

$$\therefore \quad [5] u_0 = u_{-2} + u_{-1} + u_0 + u_1 + u_2 = (u_2 + u_{-2}) + (u_1 + u_{-1}) + u_0$$

$$= 5u_0 + 5\Delta^2 u_{-1}.$$

Similarly $\qquad [5] u_{-5} + [5] u_5 = 10u_0 + 135\Delta^2 u_{-1}.$

Eliminating $\Delta^2 u_{-1}$, we have

$$125u_0 = 27 [5] u_0 - [5] u_{-5} - [5] u_5.$$

An interesting note by Mr D. C. Fraser on the properties of the operator $[n]$ occurs in the *Actuarial Students' Magazine*, No. 3 (Edinburgh, 1930). Here the general form for $[n] u_0$ is given by Mr Fraser as

$$\frac{E^{\frac{n}{2}} - E^{-\frac{n}{2}}}{E^{\frac{1}{2}} - E^{-\frac{1}{2}}} u_0,$$

which defines the operation whether n is odd or even; and the proof of the identity $[3]^2 \equiv [1] + [3] + [5]$ is made to depend on the development of the operator E. Thus:

$$[3]^2 u_0 = \frac{E^{\frac{3}{2}} - E^{-\frac{3}{2}}}{E^{\frac{1}{2}} - E^{-\frac{1}{2}}} [3] u_0$$

$$= \frac{E^{\frac{3}{2}} - E^{-\frac{3}{2}}}{E^{\frac{1}{2}} - E^{-\frac{1}{2}}} (u_{-1} + u_0 + u_1)$$

$$= \frac{(E^{\frac{3}{2}} - E^{-\frac{3}{2}})(E^{-1} + E^0 + E^1)}{E^{\frac{1}{2}} - E^{-\frac{1}{2}}} u_0$$

$$= \frac{(E^{\frac{1}{2}} - E^{-\frac{1}{2}}) + (E^{\frac{3}{2}} - E^{-\frac{3}{2}}) + (E^{\frac{5}{2}} - E^{-\frac{5}{2}})}{E^{\frac{1}{2}} - E^{-\frac{1}{2}}} u_0$$

$$= [1] u_0 + [3] u_0 + [5] u_0.$$

The general formula for $[n]^2 u$ can be proved in the same manner.

Many further examples of the use of $[n]$ will be found in various papers in the *Journal of the Institute of Actuaries*. For simple extensions of the method see particularly Hardy, *J.I.A.* vol. XXXII, p. 371, and Todhunter, *J.I.A.* vol. XXXII, p. 378, and for generalizations, Lidstone, *J.I.A.* vol. LV, p. 177, and Aitken, *J.I.A.* vol. LX, p. 339.

EXAMPLES 6

Sum the following series:

1. 7, 14, 19, 22, 23, 22, ... to n terms.
2. 2, 12, 36, 80, 150, 252, ... to n terms.
3. 10, 9, 7, 4, 0, -5, ... to 30 terms.
4. 5, 10, 17, 28, 47, 82, ... to 20 terms.
5. 10, 23, 60, 169, 494, ... to n terms.
6. 1, 2, 4, 8, 17, 40, 104, ... to n terms.
7. 1, 0, -1, 0, 7, 28, 79, ... to $2k$ terms.
8. 10, 14, 10, 6, ... to n terms.
9. 125, 343, 729, 1331, 2197, ... to n terms.
10. 1, 0, 1, 8, 29, 80, 193, ... to 17 terms.

Use the methods of finite differences to sum to n terms the series whose xth terms are

11. $(x+3)(x+4)(x+5)$. 12. $x(x+2)(x+4)$.
13. $(3x-2)(3x+1)(3x+4)$. 14. $x(x+1)(x+3)$.

15. $x(x+1)(x+3)(x+4)$.   16. $(2x+3)(2x+5)(2x+7)(2x+9)$.

17. $\dfrac{1}{(x+3)(x+4)}$.   18. $\dfrac{1}{(x+1)(x+3)}$.

19. $\dfrac{x}{(x+2)(x+3)(x+4)}$.   20. $\dfrac{1}{(3x-2)(3x+1)(3x+4)}$.

21. $\dfrac{x+3}{x(x+1)(x+2)}$.

22. Sum to n terms $2.4.8.14 + 4.6.10.16 + 6.8.12.18 + \dots$

23. Obtain the general term of the series

$$\frac{3}{1.4.10} + \frac{5}{4.7.13} + \frac{7}{7.10.16} + \dots$$

and find the sum to n terms and to infinity.

24. Find $\overset{n}{\underset{1}{\Sigma}} u_x$, where $u_x = x(x+2)(x+5)$.

25. The two series $6, 24, 60, 120, \dots$ and $0, 0, 0, 6, 24, 60, 120, \dots$ are given. Find the sum of n terms of each of the two series. Compare the results and explain the difference.

26. Sum the series $1, 5, 17, 53, 161, \dots$ to n terms.

27. Evaluate $\Delta^{-1}(x^2 a^x)$.

28. Show that $\Delta(x!) = x(x!)$ and hence sum to n terms the series

$$1 + 3.2! + 7.3! + 13.4! + 21.5! + \dots$$

29. Find $\overset{n}{\underset{1}{\Sigma}} u_x$, where $u_x = (3x-1)(3x+2)(3x+5)(3x+8)$.

30. Sum to n terms $1.3^2 + 3.5^2 + 5.7^2 + 7.9^2 + \dots$

31. Obtain the formula

$$\overset{a+n-1}{\underset{a}{\Sigma}} u_x = n_{(1)}u_a + n_{(2)}\Delta u_a + n_{(3)}\Delta^2 u_a + \dots$$

and use the formula to find the sum of n terms of the series

$$-8, -5, 0, 14, 44, \dots$$

32. Prove that $\overset{n}{\underset{1}{\Sigma}}(x^2+1).x! = n.(n+1)!$.

33. Sum to n terms the series whose xth terms are (i) $x^2(3x+2)$, (ii) $2^x(x^3+x)$ by finite integration.

34. Evaluate $\sum\limits_{1}^{n}\left\{\dfrac{x^2 4^x}{(x+1)(x+2)}\right\}$.

35. Sum to infinity $\dfrac{1}{2.6.10}+\dfrac{1}{4.8.12}+\dfrac{1}{6.10.14}+\dots$

36. Find the sum of n terms of the series

$$1^2+\frac{3^2}{2}+\frac{5^2}{2^2}+\frac{7^2}{2^3}+\dots$$

37. Obtain the indefinite integral of $(2x-1)3^x$.

38. Show that the series 10, 24, 61, 163, 452, 1290, 3759, ... can be split up into two other series. Find the two series and hence sum the original series to n terms.

39. Prove that $\Delta^{-1}[u_x v_x]=u_x\Delta^{-1}v_x-\Delta^{-1}[\Delta u_x\Delta^{-1}v_{x+1}]$ and apply this formula to find the sum of the first n terms of the series whose rth term is $(r+1)x^{r-1}$.

40. Evaluate $\Delta^{-1}\left\{\dfrac{(x+1)^2}{x(x+2)(x+3)(x+4)}\right\}$.

41. Find the sum of the squares of the first n natural numbers by the method of finite integration.

42. Sum to n terms $\dfrac{3}{2.5.8}+\dfrac{5}{5.8.11}+\dfrac{7}{8.11.14}+\dots$

43. Find the sum of the infinite series $\dfrac{1.3}{2}+\dfrac{3.5}{2^2}+\dfrac{5.7}{2^3}+\dots$

44. Find the sum of n terms of the series

$$2.2+7.4+14.8+23.16+34.32+\dots$$

45. Prove that $\sum\limits_{0}^{n-1}u_r x^r=\dfrac{u_0-x^n u_n}{1-x}+\dfrac{x}{(1-x)^2}(\Delta u_0-x^n\Delta u_n)$

$$+\frac{x^2}{(1-x)^3}(\Delta^2 u_0-x^n\Delta^2 u_n)+\dots$$

Apply this formula to find the sum of the first n terms of the series whose rth term is $r(r+1)x^{r-1}$.

46. Evaluate $\Delta^{-1}\left[2^x.x.\dfrac{x!}{(2x+1)!}\right]$.

47. Use the method of finite integration to obtain the sum of n terms of the series $1 . 3^3 + 3 . 5^3 + 5 . 7^3 + \dots$.

48. Find the function whose first difference is $ax^3 + bx^2 + cx + d$.

49. Prove that $1^r + 2^r x + 3^r x^2 + \dots$ is a recurring series, and find its scale of relation.

50. If u_n is the nth term of the series $1, 2, 3, 5, 8, 13, \dots$ in which each term after the second is the sum of the two preceding terms, prove by the process of mathematical induction or otherwise that

$$u_n{}^2 - u_{n-1} u_{n+1} = (-1)^n.$$

51. Show how the methods of finite differences can be employed to find the sum of a series of the form

$$(a+k)^r + (a+2k)^r + \dots + (a+xk)^r + \dots.$$

52. Sum the series

$$\frac{1!}{a+1} + \frac{2!}{(a+1)(a+2)} + \dots + \frac{n!}{(a+1)(a+2)\dots(a+n)}.$$

53. Find the value of $\sum\limits_{r=1}^{r=n} n_{(r)} r^4$.

54. Prove that $\quad \{2\,[3] - [5]\}\, u_0 = u_0 - 3\Delta^2 u_{-1}$ approximately.

55. Obtain the approximate formula

$$125 u_0 = [5]^3 \{u_0 + \Delta u_{-2} - \Delta u_1\}. \qquad \text{(Woolhouse.)}$$

56. Prove that $\quad [n]^2 - [m]^2 \equiv \{[n] - [m]\}\,\{[n] + [m]\}$.

57. One of Hardy's graduation formulae is

$$\frac{[4]\,[5]\,[6]}{120} \{u_0 + \Delta u_{-2} - \Delta u_1\} = u_0.$$

Prove that this is approximately true.

58. Express $\{[3] + [5] - [7]\}\, u_0$ in terms of u_{-3}, u_{-1}, u_0, u_1, u_3, and hence prove that

$$\frac{[5]\,[13]}{65} \{[3] + [5] - [7]\}\, u_0 \text{ reproduces } u_0 \text{ to third differences.}$$

59. If $w_n = [5]\, u_n$, prove King's formula:

$$u_0 = \cdot 2 w_0 - \cdot 008 \Delta^2 w_{-5},$$

fourth and higher differences being neglected.

CHAPTER VII

MISCELLANEOUS THEOREMS

1. In this chapter it is proposed to treat of certain propositions and applications of finite difference methods which are not essential to a first reading of the subject and which may conveniently be dealt with at a later stage. Some of the theorems are developments of familiar processes: others are alternative methods of approach for the solution of problems involving the principles of finite differences.

DIFFERENCES OF ZERO

2. If in the identical relation

$$\Delta^n x^m = (E-1)^n x^m$$
$$= (x+n)^m - n_{(1)} (x+n-1)^m + n_{(2)} (x+n-2)^m - \ldots$$

we put $x = 0$, we obtain

$$[\Delta^n x^m]_{x=0} = n^m - n_{(1)} (n-1)^m + n_{(2)} (n-2)^m - \ldots.$$

By continued application of this formula we can obtain values of $\Delta^n x^m$ when $x = 0$ for all integral values of n and m.

For example, if $m = 3$,

$$[\Delta x^3]_{x=0} = 1^3 = 1,$$
$$[\Delta^2 x^3]_{x=0} = 2^3 - 2 \cdot 1^3 = 6,$$
$$[\Delta^3 x^3]_{x=0} = 3^3 - 3 \cdot 2^3 + 3 \cdot 1^3 = 6.$$

The values of $[\Delta^n x^m]_{x=0}$ are known as "differences of zero", and in accordance with this definition the expression is often written as $\Delta^n 0^m$.

It is evident that a table of values of differences of zero can be constructed if we can obtain a relation between corresponding values of $\Delta^n 0^m$.

We have from the above

$$\Delta^n o^m = n^m - n_{(1)} (n-1)^m + n_{(2)} (n-2)^m - \dots$$
$$= n \left[n^{m-1} - (n-1)_{(1)} (n-1)^{m-1} + (n-1)_{(2)} (n-2)^{m-1} - \dots \right]$$
$$= n \left[(1+n-1)^{m-1} - (n-1)_{(1)} (1+n-2)^{m-1} \right.$$
$$\left. + (n-1)_{(2)} (1+n-3)^{m-1} - \dots \right]$$
$$= n \left[(E-1)^{n-1} x^{m-1} \right]_{x=1}$$
$$= n \Delta^{n-1} 1^{m-1}$$
$$= n \Delta^{n-1} E o^{m-1}$$
$$= n \Delta^{n-1} (1+\Delta) o^{m-1}$$
$$= n (\Delta^{n-1} o^{m-1} + \Delta^n o^{m-1}).$$

Alternatively,

$$\Delta^n o^m = n^m - n_{(1)} (n-1)^m + n_{(2)} (n-2)^m - \dots . \qquad (a)$$

But, since

$$\Delta^n x^m = (x+n)^m - n_{(1)} (x+n-1)^m + n_{(2)} (x+n-2)^m - \dots$$

we may put $n-1$ for n, $m-1$ for m and 1 for x, and obtain

$$\Delta^{n-1} 1^{m-1} = n^{m-1} - (n-1)_{(1)} (n-1)^{m-1} + (n-1)_{(2)} (n-2)^{m-1} - \dots$$
$$= \frac{1}{n} (a)$$
$$= \frac{1}{n} \Delta^n o^m;$$

$$\therefore \quad \Delta^n o^m = n \Delta^{n-1} 1^{m-1} = n (\Delta^{n-1} o^{m-1} + \Delta^n o^{m-1}).$$

This proof is given by de Morgan.

Another method for obtaining this relation, depending upon the formula for the nth difference of the compound function $u_x v_x$, is given below (paragraph 11).

3. Since $\Delta^n x^n = n!$ for interval of differencing unity

$$\Delta^n o^n = n!.$$

Similarly, since

$$\Delta^{n+r} x^n = 0, \quad \Delta^{n+r} o^n = 0.$$

i.e. $\Delta^n o^m = 0, \quad$ when $n > m$.

We can now build up a table of differences of zero by continued application of the relation given in paragraph 1 above.

The table is

m	$\Delta 0^m$	$\Delta^2 0^m$	$\Delta^3 0^m$	$\Delta^4 0^m$	$\Delta^5 0^m$	$\Delta^6 0^m$
1	1	0				
2	1	2	0			
3	1	6	6	0		
4	1	14	36	24	0	
5	1	30	150	240	120	0
6	1	62	540	1560	1800	720

and so on.

4. An interesting application of the use of the differences of zero for the calculation of the coefficients in an expansion is as follows.

The fundamental formula

$$u_x = u_0 + x_{(1)}\Delta u_0 + x_{(2)}\Delta^2 u_0 + x_{(3)}\Delta^3 u_0 + \ldots$$

can be written as

$$u_x = u_0 + x^{(1)}\Delta u_0 + \frac{x^{(2)}}{2!}\Delta^2 u_0 + \frac{x^{(3)}}{3!}\Delta^3 u_0 + \ldots .$$

$$\therefore \quad x^m = 0^m + x^{(1)}\Delta 0^m + \frac{x^{(2)}}{2!}\Delta^2 0^m + \frac{x^{(3)}}{3!}\Delta^3 0^m + \ldots .$$

By use of the relation

$$\Delta^n 0^m = n\left(\Delta^n 0^{m-1} + \Delta^{n-1} 0^{m-1}\right), \quad \text{i.e.} \quad \frac{\Delta^n 0^m}{n!} = \frac{n\Delta^n 0^{m-1}}{n!} + \frac{\Delta^{n-1} 0^{m-1}}{(n-1)!},$$

a table of the coefficients in the expansion of x^m in terms of successive values of the factorial $x^{(k)}$ can be written down in a similar manner to that given above.

5. The differences of zero have many special properties, and they are used in higher work in the theory of series. A simple example involving their use is given below.

Example 1.

If $(1+x)^n = c_0 + c_1 x + \ldots + c_n x^n$, n being a positive integer, find the value of

$$(n-1)^2 c_1 + (n-3)^2 c_3 + (n-5)^2 c_5 + \ldots .$$

Now $\quad (x-1)^2\,c_1 + (x-3)^2\,c_3 + (x-5)^2\,c_5 + \ldots$

$$= (E^{-1}c_1 + E^{-3}c_3 + E^{-5}c_5 + \ldots)\,x^2$$

$$= \tfrac{1}{2}\left[(1+E^{-1})^n - (1 - E^{-1})^n\right]x^2$$

$$= \tfrac{1}{2}\left[(\Delta+2)^n - \Delta^n\right]E^{-n}x^2$$

$$= \tfrac{1}{2}\left[(\Delta+2)^n - \Delta^n\right](x-n)^2$$

$$= \tfrac{1}{2}\left[(\Delta+2)^n - \Delta^n\right]\mathrm{o}^2 \quad \text{when } x=n$$

$$= \tfrac{1}{2}\left[2^n\mathrm{o}^2 + n2^{n-1}\Delta\mathrm{o}^2 + \tfrac{1}{2}n\,(n-1)\,2^{n-2}\,\Delta^2\mathrm{o}^2 + \ldots\right]$$

$$= \tfrac{1}{2}\left[n2^{n-1} + n\,(n-1)\,2^{n-2}\right]$$

$$= 2^{n-3}\,n\,(n+1) \quad \text{on simplification.}$$

RELATIONS BETWEEN THE OPERATORS D AND Δ

6. The series

$$f(x) + hf'(x) + \frac{h^2}{2!}f''(x) + \ldots + \frac{h^{n-1}}{(n-1)!}f^{(n-1)}(x) + \ldots$$

converges to the limit $f(x+h)$, provided that $\underset{n\to\infty}{\mathrm{Lt}}\;R_n(x)$ is zero, where

$$R_n(x) \equiv \frac{h^n}{n!}f^{(n)}(x+\theta h).$$

This is Taylor's theorem for a convergent series, and we may write it in the following form:

$$u_{x+rh} = u_x + rhDu_x + \frac{(rh)^2}{2!}D^2u_x + \frac{(rh)^3}{3!}D^3u_x + \ldots$$

$$= \left\{1 + rhD + \frac{(rh)^2}{2!}D^2 + \frac{(rh)^3}{3!}D^3 + \ldots\right\}u_x$$

$$= e^{rhD}u_x.$$

But, for interval of differencing h,

$$u_{x+rh} = E^r u_x.$$

$$\therefore \quad E^r \equiv e^{rhD},$$

so that $\qquad hD \equiv \log E \equiv \log (1 + \Delta)$

$$\equiv \Delta - \frac{\Delta^2}{2} + \frac{\Delta^3}{3} - \frac{\Delta^4}{4} + \dots$$

and $\qquad Du_x = \frac{1}{h}\left[\Delta u_x - \frac{\Delta^2}{2} u_x + \frac{\Delta^3}{3} u_x - \frac{\Delta^4}{4} u_x + \dots\right].$

If $h = 1$, then $\qquad (1 + \Delta)^r \equiv e^{rD}$

and we have a result analogous to the important relation in the theory of Compound Interest, namely $(1 + i)^n = e^{n\delta}$, where δ is the force of interest corresponding to a rate of interest i.

7. Since $\qquad D \equiv \frac{1}{h}\left[\Delta - \frac{\Delta^2}{2} + \frac{\Delta^3}{3} - \frac{\Delta^4}{4} + \dots\right],$

$$D^2 \equiv \frac{1}{h^2}\left[\Delta - \frac{\Delta^2}{2} + \frac{\Delta^3}{3} - \frac{\Delta^4}{4} + \dots\right]^2$$

$$\equiv \frac{1}{h^2}[\Delta^2 - \Delta^3 + \tfrac{11}{12}\Delta^4 - \tfrac{5}{6}\Delta^5 + \dots].$$

Similarly, $\qquad D^3 \equiv \frac{1}{h^3}[\Delta^3 - \tfrac{3}{2}\Delta^4 + \tfrac{7}{4}\Delta^5 - \dots].$

We have therefore a convenient method for expressing the differential coefficients of a function of x in terms of the differences of the function.

Example 2.

μ_x (the force of mortality) $= -\dfrac{1}{l_x}\dfrac{dl_x}{dx}$, where l_x is the number of persons at exact age x in any year of time. Given the following table, find a value for μ_{50}.

Age x ...	50	51	52	53
l_x	73,499	72,724	71,753	70,599

The difference table is

x	l_x	Δl_x	$\Delta^2 l_x$	$\Delta^3 l_x$
50	73,499			
		-775		
51	72,724		-196	
		-971		13
52	71,753		-183	
		-1154		
53	70,599			

$$\therefore \quad \frac{dl_x}{dx} = \left(\Delta - \frac{\Delta^2}{2} + \frac{\Delta^3}{3} \right) l_x,$$

since the interval of differencing is unity

$$= -775 + 98 + 4 \cdot 333 \dots, \quad \text{when } x = 50,$$
$$= -672 \cdot 667.$$

$$\therefore \quad \mu_{50} = \left[-\frac{1}{l_x} \frac{dl_x}{dx} \right]_{x=50} = \frac{672 \cdot 667}{73,499} = \cdot 00915 \dots.$$

Note. If $h \neq 1$, care must be taken to divide by the appropriate power of h in applying the formula. Thus, if u_x is given for quinquennial intervals of x, $\dfrac{d^3 u_x}{dx}$ will be $\dfrac{1}{5^3} (\Delta^3 u_x - \frac{3}{2} \Delta^4 u_x + \dots)$ and not simply

$$\Delta^3 u_x - \tfrac{3}{2} \Delta^4 u_x + \dots.$$

8. The result

$$\frac{du_x}{dx} = \frac{1}{h} \left[\Delta u_x - \frac{\Delta^2}{2} u_x + \frac{\Delta^3}{3} u_x - \dots \right]$$

can easily be obtained by the differentiation of the advancing difference formula for u_x.

Taking the simple case when $h = 1$,

$$u_x = u_0 + x \Delta u_0 + \frac{x(x-1)}{2} \Delta^2 u_0 + \frac{x(x-1)(x-2)}{6} \Delta^3 u_0 + \dots$$

$$\therefore \quad \frac{du_x}{dx} = \Delta u_0 + \frac{2x-1}{2} \Delta^2 u_0 + \frac{3x^2 - 6x + 2}{6} \Delta^3 u_0 + \dots$$

or $\qquad \left(\dfrac{du_x}{dx} \right)_{x=0} = \Delta u_0 - \dfrac{\Delta^2 u_0}{2} + \dfrac{\Delta^3 u_0}{3} - \dots$

which becomes, on changing the origin to x,

$$\frac{du_x}{dx} = \Delta u_x - \frac{\Delta^2 u_x}{2} + \frac{\Delta^3 u_x}{3} - \dots.$$

Similarly, we can express $\dfrac{du_x}{dx}$ in terms of central differences. For example, Stirling's formula is

$$u_x = u_0 + x \frac{\Delta u_0 + \Delta u_{-1}}{2} + \frac{x^2}{2!} \Delta^2 u_{-1} + \frac{x(x^2 - 1)}{3!} \frac{\Delta^3 u_{-1} + \Delta^3 u_{-2}}{2} + \dots.$$

Differentiating with respect to x:

$$\frac{du_x}{dx}=\frac{\Delta u_0+\Delta u_{-1}}{2}+x\Delta^2 u_{-1}+\frac{3x^2-1}{6}\,\frac{\Delta^3 u_{-1}+\Delta^3 u_{-2}}{2}+\dots.$$

$$\therefore\quad\left(\frac{du_x}{dx}\right)_{x=0}=\frac{\Delta u_0+\Delta u_{-1}}{2}-\frac{1}{12}\,[\Delta^3 u_{-1}+\Delta^3 u_{-2}]$$

as far as third differences

$$=\frac{u_1-u_{-1}}{2}-\frac{1}{12}\,[u_2-3u_1+3u_0-u_{-1}+u_1-3u_0+3u_{-1}-u_{-2}]$$

$$=\frac{2}{3}\,(u_1-u_{-1})-\frac{1}{12}\,(u_2-u_{-2})\quad\text{on simplifying.}$$

Changing the origin, we have

$$\frac{du_x}{dx}=\frac{2}{3}\,(u_{x+1}-u_{x-1})-\frac{1}{12}\,(u_{x+2}-u_{x-2}).$$

A first approximation will evidently be

$$\frac{du_x}{dx}=\frac{u_{x+1}-u_{x-1}}{2}.$$

or, if the unit of differencing be h,

$$=\frac{u_{x+h}-u_{x-h}}{2h}.$$

This simple approximation can be seen quite easily from a consideration of the geometry of the figure.

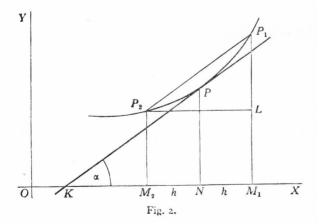

Fig. 2.

Let P be the point whose coordinates are (x, u_x) and let P_1, P_2 be the two points whose coordinates are $(x+h, u_{x+h})$ and $(x-h, u_{x-h})$ respectively.

Then if PK be the tangent at P

$$\frac{du_x}{dx} = \tan \alpha$$

$$= \frac{P_1 L}{P_2 L} \text{ nearly}$$

$$= \frac{P_1 M_1 - L M_1}{M_2 M_1}$$

$$= \frac{u_{x+h} - u_{x-h}}{2h}.$$

9. Another formula, giving the differential coefficient in terms of central differences, can be obtained from Bessel's formula.

$$u_x = \frac{u_0 + u_1}{2} + (x - \tfrac{1}{2})\,\Delta u_0 + \frac{x(x-1)}{2!}\frac{\Delta^2 u_{-1} + \Delta^2 u_0}{2}$$

$$+ \frac{(x - \tfrac{1}{2})\,x\,(x-1)}{3!}\,\Delta^3 u_{-1} + \dots.$$

Changing x to $x + \tfrac{1}{2}$,

$$u_{x+\frac{1}{2}} = \frac{u_0 + u_1}{2} + x\Delta u_0 + \frac{(x + \tfrac{1}{2})(x - \tfrac{1}{2})}{2!}\frac{\Delta^2 u_{-1} + \Delta^2 u_0}{2}$$

$$+ \frac{x(x + \tfrac{1}{2})(x - \tfrac{1}{2})}{3!}\,\Delta^3 u_{-1} + \dots.$$

Differentiating:

$$\frac{d}{dx}u_{x+\frac{1}{2}} = \Delta u_0 + x\,\frac{\Delta^2 u_{-1} + \Delta^2 u_0}{2} + \left(\frac{x^2}{2} - \frac{1}{24}\right)\Delta^3 u_{-1} + \dots.$$

If $x = 0$,
$$\frac{d}{dx}u_{\frac{1}{2}} = \Delta u_0 - \frac{\Delta^3 u_{-1}}{24} + \dots.$$

Changing the origin to $x - \tfrac{1}{2}$ we have the approximation

$$\frac{d}{dx}u_x = \Delta u_{x-\frac{1}{2}} - \frac{\Delta^3 u_{x-\frac{3}{2}}}{24} + \dots.$$

An interesting discussion on the calculation of the values of differential coefficients of a function by means of selected values of the variable will be found in *T.F.A.* vol. IX, pp. 238 *et seq.* (G. J. Lidstone). By means of tables of coefficients prepared for convenience of practical working Mr Lidstone evolves formulae for the values of the successive differential coefficients, both for advancing differences and central differences. In addition, alternative processes are given for the values of the derivatives when the intervals are unequal.

*10. It should be borne in mind that, in choosing a formula for the expression of the differential coefficient of a function in terms of its differences, central difference formulae are to be preferred to advancing differences. These formulae possess smaller coefficients and have the additional advantage that alternate coefficients vanish. Further, a greater degree of accuracy may be obtained by the use of a suitable central difference formula.

Mr G. J. Lidstone has pointed out that if for any reason it is decided to use the relation

$$D \equiv \Delta - \tfrac{1}{2}\Delta^2 + \tfrac{1}{3}\Delta^3 - \ldots$$

considerable increase of accuracy can be secured by the simple and easily remembered device of ending with $\dfrac{1}{n}\Delta^n u_{x-1}$ instead of $\dfrac{1}{n}\Delta^n u_x$. We bring in u_{-1} for the purpose of obtaining $\Delta^n u_{x-1}$, omit u_{x+n+1} and otherwise use the formula as before, beginning with Δu_x. This reverses the sign of the error and reduces it numerically in the ratio $1:(n+1)$. Thus, $\dfrac{1}{n}\Delta^n - \dfrac{1}{n+1}\Delta^{n+1}$ is replaced by

$$\frac{1}{n}\Delta^n - \frac{1}{n}\Delta^{n+1}.$$

It is assumed that $\Delta^{n+1}u$, though not negligible, is not varying greatly. The proportionate improvement increases with n, and if n is at all considerable, we attain approximately the accuracy of a further order of differences with no additional work.

The same process may be employed for the second and third differential coefficients, after which the improvement, though present, is not proportionately so marked.

THE COMPOUND FUNCTION $u_x v_x$

11. We can adapt the principle of separation of symbols to the evaluation of such expressions as $\Delta^n u_x v_x$ by a simple extension of the process of differencing.

Let $\Delta_1, E_1, \Sigma_1, \ldots$ denote operations on u_x alone and $\Delta_2, E_2, \Sigma_2, \ldots$ operations on v_x alone.

Then
$$\Delta u_x v_x = u_{x+1} v_{x+1} - u_x v_x$$
$$= E_1 u_x . E_2 v_x - u_x v_x$$
$$= (E_1 E_2 - 1) u_x v_x.$$
$$\therefore \quad \Delta^n u_x v_x = (E_1 E_2 - 1)^n u_x v_x.$$

By expressing $E_1 E_2$ in terms of Δ_1 and Δ_2 we are enabled to obtain expressions for the expansion of $\Delta^n u_x v_x$.

First, if $n = 1$, we have
$$\Delta u_x v_x = [(1 + \Delta_1)(1 + \Delta_2) - 1] u_x v_x$$
$$= (\Delta_1 + \Delta_2 + \Delta_1 \Delta_2) u_x v_x$$
$$= (\Delta_1 + \Delta_2 E_1) u_x v_x$$
$$= \Delta_1 u_x v_x + \Delta_2 E_1 u_x v_x$$
$$= v_x \Delta_1 u_x + E_1 u_x . \Delta_2 v_x$$
$$= v_x \Delta_1 u_x + u_{x+1} \Delta_2 v_x,$$

or, dropping the suffixes,
$$= v_x \Delta u_x + u_{x+1} \Delta v_x,$$

which is otherwise evident.

Again,
$$\Delta^n u_x v_x = (\Delta_1 + E_1 \Delta_2)^n u_x v_x$$
$$= (\Delta_1^n + n_{(1)} \Delta_1^{n-1} E_1 \Delta_2 + n_{(2)} \Delta_1^{n-2} E_1^2 \Delta_2^2 + \ldots) u_x v_x,$$

which is easily seen to be
$$v_x \Delta^n u_x + n_{(1)} \Delta v_x \Delta^{n-1} u_{x+1} + n_{(2)} \Delta^2 v_x \Delta^{n-2} u_{x+2} + \ldots + u_{x+n} \Delta^n v_x.$$

If in the above expression we put $u_x = x^{m-1}$ and $v_x = x$, we have
$$\Delta^n (x^{m-1} . x) = x \Delta^n x^{m-1} + n \Delta^{n-1} (x+1)^{m-1}.$$

Let $x = 0$; then

$$\Delta^n o^m = n\Delta^{n-1} \mathbf{1}^{m-1} = n\Delta^{n-1} E o^{m-1} = n\left(\Delta^{n-1} o^{m-1} + \Delta^n o^{m-1}\right),$$

which is the relation proved in paragraph 2.

12. The ordinary formula for finite integration by parts is

$$\Sigma u_x v_x = u_x \Sigma v_x - \Sigma\left[\Delta u_x \Sigma v_{x+1}\right] + \text{an arbitrary constant.}$$

In cases where the formula has to be applied more than once we may use the series found below.

$$
\begin{aligned}
\Sigma \equiv \Delta^{-1} &\equiv \left(\Delta_1 + \Delta_2 + \Delta_1 \Delta_2\right)^{-1} \\
&\equiv \left[\Delta_2 + \Delta_1\left(\mathbf{1} + \Delta_2\right)\right]^{-1} \\
&\equiv \Delta_2^{-1}\left[\mathbf{1} + \Delta_1 \Delta_2^{-1}\left(\mathbf{1} + \Delta_2\right)\right]^{-1} \\
&\equiv \Delta_2^{-1}\left[\mathbf{1} - \Delta_1 \Delta_2^{-1}\left(\mathbf{1} + \Delta_2\right) + \Delta_1^2 \Delta_2^{-2}\left(\mathbf{1} + \Delta_2\right)^2 - \ldots\right] \\
&\equiv \Delta_2^{-1} - \Delta_1 \Delta_2^{-2}\left(\mathbf{1} + \Delta_2\right) + \Delta_1^2 \Delta_2^{-3}\left(\mathbf{1} + \Delta_2\right)^2 - \ldots \\
&\equiv \Delta_2^{-1} - \Delta_1 \Delta_2^{-2} E_2 + \Delta_1^2 \Delta_2^{-3} E_2^2 - \ldots.
\end{aligned}
$$

On dropping the suffixes and inserting the appropriate functions, we have

$$\Sigma u_x v_x = u_x \Sigma v_x - \Delta u_x \Sigma^2 v_{x+1} + \Delta^2 u_x \Sigma^3 v_{x+2} - \ldots. \qquad (a)$$

By an alternative treatment another formula is obtained:

$$\Sigma u_x v_x = u_{x-1} \Sigma v_x - \Delta u_{x-2} \Sigma^2 v_x + \Delta^2 u_{x-3} \Sigma^3 v_x - \ldots. \qquad (b)$$

As an example of the use of a series for $\Sigma u_x v_x$ we may prove the formula for $\Sigma a^x u_x$ given in Chap. VI, paragraph 10.

Example 3.

Prove that

$$\Sigma a^x u_x = \frac{a^x}{a-\mathbf{1}}\left\{\mathbf{1} - \frac{a\Delta}{a-\mathbf{1}} + \frac{a^2\Delta^2}{(a-\mathbf{1})^2} - \frac{a^3\Delta^3}{(a-\mathbf{1})^3} + \ldots\right\} u_x$$

$$\Sigma a^x = \frac{a^x}{a-\mathbf{1}}, \quad \Sigma^2 a^{x+1} = \frac{a^{x+1}}{(a-\mathbf{1})^2}, \quad \Sigma^3 a^{x+2} = \frac{a^{x+2}}{(a-\mathbf{1})^3}, \quad \Sigma^4 a^{x+3} = \frac{a^{x+3}}{(a-\mathbf{1})^4},$$

and so on.

Let $a^x = v_x$ in series (a).

Then

$$\Sigma u_x a^x = u_x \Sigma a^x - \Delta u_x \Sigma^2 a^{x+1} + \Delta^2 u_x \Sigma^3 a^{x+2} - \Delta^3 u_x \Sigma^4 a^{x+3} + \ldots$$

$$= u_x \frac{a^x}{a-1} - \Delta u_x \frac{a^{x+1}}{(a-1)^2} + \Delta^2 u_x \frac{a^{x+2}}{(a-1)^3} - \Delta^3 u_x \frac{a^{x+3}}{(a-1)^4} + \ldots$$

$$= \frac{a^x}{a-1}\left\{1 - \frac{a\Delta}{a-1} + \frac{a^2\Delta^2}{(a-1)^2} - \frac{a^3\Delta^3}{(a-1)^3} + \ldots\right\} u_x.$$

13. The following is a further illustration of the application of the above method.

Example 4.

Prove that

$$\Sigma^n (u_x v_x) = u_x \Sigma^n v_x - n_{(1)}\Delta u_x \Sigma^{n+1} v_{x+1} + (n+1)_{(2)} \Delta^2 u_x \Sigma^{n+2} v_{x+2}$$
$$- (n+2)_{(3)} \Delta^3 u_x \Sigma^{n+3} v_{x+3} + \ldots.$$

Now $\quad \Delta u_x v_x = [\Delta_2 + \Delta_1 (1 + \Delta_2)] u_x v_x.$

$\therefore \quad \Sigma^n \equiv \Delta^{-n} \equiv [\Delta_2 + \Delta_1 (1 + \Delta_2)]^{-n} \equiv \Delta_2^{-n} (1 + \Delta_1 \Delta_2^{-1} E_2)^{-n}.$

$\therefore \quad \Sigma^n u_x v_x = \Delta_2^{-n} [1 - n_{(1)}\Delta_1\Delta_2^{-1}E_2 + (n+1)_{(2)} \Delta_1^2\Delta_2^{-2}E_2^2$
$$- (n+2)_{(3)} \Delta_1^3\Delta_2^{-3}E_2^3 + \ldots] u_x v_x$$

$$= u_x \Sigma^n v_x - n_{(1)}\Delta u_x \Sigma^{n+1} v_{x+1} + (n+1)_{(2)} \Delta^2 u_x \Sigma^{n+2} v_{x+2}$$
$$- (n+2)_{(3)} \Delta^3 u_x \Sigma^{n+3} v_{x+3} + \ldots.$$

If $n = 1$ we have

$$\Sigma u_x v_x = \Delta_2^{-1} (1 + \Delta_1\Delta_2^{-1}E_2)^{-1} u_x v_x$$

$$= \Delta_2^{-1} \left(1 - \frac{\Delta_1\Delta_2^{-1}E_2}{1 + \Delta_1\Delta_2^{-1}E_2}\right) u_x v_x$$

$$= \left(\Delta_2^{-1} - \frac{\Delta_1\Delta_2^{-1}E_2}{\Delta_2 + \Delta_1 E_2}\right) u_x v_x$$

$$= \left(\Delta_2^{-1} - \frac{\Delta_1\Delta_2^{-1}E_2}{E_1 E_2 - 1}\right) u_x v_x$$

$$= u_x \Sigma v_x - \Delta^{-1} (\Delta u_x \Sigma v_{x+1})$$

$$= u_x \Sigma v_x - \Sigma (\Delta u_x \Sigma v_{x+1}),$$

the ordinary formula for summation by parts.

The subject of finite integration by parts is treated more fully in Chapter VIII.

FUNCTIONS OF TWO VARIABLES

14. When x and y are independent variables, u_{xy}, $f(x, y)$, ... represent functions which assume different values according to the values of x and y. An alternative notation is $u_{x:y}$ or $f(x:y)$. For example, the function

$$x^2 + 2xy + y^2 + x + 3y,$$

in which x and y both vary, may be written shortly as either u_{xy} or $u_{x:y}$. If y is a function of x, we may reduce u_{xy} to the form v_x and thus obtain a function depending on x alone.

Now suppose that x is changed to $x+h$ and that y is changed to $y+k$ while x remains constant. Then the new value of the function is dependent on $x+h$ and $y+k$. It is not necessary for both x and y to vary: x may become $x+h$ while y remains constant or vice versa.

If the values of the function proceed by equidistant intervals, we have the following scheme:

$u_{x:y}$	$u_{x+h:y}$	$u_{x+2h:y}$	$u_{x+3h:y}$	$\cdots$
$u_{x:y+k}$	$u_{x+h:y+k}$	$u_{x+2h.y+k}$	$u_{x+3h:y+k}$	$\cdots$
$u_{x:y+2k}$	$u_{x+h:y+2k}$	$u_{x+2h:y+2k}$	$u_{x+3h:y+2k}$	$\cdots$
$u_{x:y+3k}$	$u_{x+h:y+3k}$	$u_{x+2h:y+3k}$	$u_{x+3h:y+3k}$	$\cdots$
$\vdots$	$\vdots$	$\vdots$	$\vdots$	

or, if our origin be (0, 0) and $h = k = 1$,

$u_{0:0}$	$u_{1:0}$	$u_{2:0}$	$u_{3:0}$	$\cdots$
$u_{0:1}$	$u_{1:1}$	$u_{2:1}$	$u_{3:1}$	$\cdots$
$u_{0:2}$	$u_{1:2}$	$u_{2:2}$	$u_{3:2}$	$\cdots$
$\vdots$	$\vdots$	$\vdots$	$\vdots$	

15. If we are to apply the processes of finite differences as hitherto defined we must distinguish between an increase in the value of x and an increase in the value of y. We therefore write E_x to denote the operation of increasing the value of x by a unit difference while y remains constant, and E_y similarly for y while x remains constant.

That is, $E_x u_{0:0} = u_{1:0}$ and $E_y u_{0:0} = u_{0:1}$,

so that $\Delta_x u_{0:0} = u_{1:0} - u_{0:0}$ and $\Delta_y u_{0:0} = u_{0:1} - u_{0:0}$.

Again, $\Delta_x \Delta_y u_{0:0} = \Delta_x (\Delta_y u_{0:0})$

$$= \Delta_x (u_{0:1} - u_{0:0})$$

$$= \Delta_x u_{0:1} - \Delta_x u_{0:0}$$

$$= u_{1:1} - u_{0:1} - u_{1:0} + u_{0:0},$$

and $\Delta_x^2 \Delta_y u_{0:0} = \Delta_x^2 (u_{0:1} - u_{0:0})$

$$= \Delta_x^2 u_{0:1} - \Delta_x^2 u_{0.0}$$

$$= (u_{2:1} - 2u_{1:1} + u_{0:1}) - (u_{2:0} - 2u_{1:0} + u_{0:0}).$$

The general formula corresponding to the advancing difference formula for one independent variable is

$$u_{m:n} = (1 + \Delta_x)^m (1 + \Delta_y)^n u_{0:0}$$

$$= (1 + m_{(1)}\Delta_x + m_{(2)}\Delta_x^2 + \ldots)(1 + n_{(1)}\Delta_y + n_{(2)}\Delta_y^2 + \ldots) u_{0:0}$$

$$= (1 + m_{(1)}\Delta_x + m_{(2)}\Delta_x^2 + m_{(3)}\Delta_x^3 + \ldots$$

$$+ n_{(1)}\Delta_y + m_{(1)}n_{(1)}\Delta_x\Delta_y + m_{(2)}n_{(1)}\Delta_x^2\Delta_y + \ldots$$

$$+ n_{(2)}\Delta_y^2 + m_{(1)}n_{(2)}\Delta_x\Delta_y^2 + \ldots$$

$$+ n_{(3)}\Delta_y^3 + \ldots) u_{0:0}$$

$$= u_{0:0} + (m_{(1)}\Delta_x + n_{(1)}\Delta_y) u_{0:0}$$

$$+ (m_{(2)}\Delta_x^2 + m_{(1)}n_{(1)}\Delta_x\Delta_y + n_{(2)}\Delta_y^2) u_{0:0}$$

$$+ (m_{(3)}\Delta_x^3 + m_{(2)}n_{(1)}\Delta_x^2\Delta_y + m_{(1)}n_{(2)}\Delta_x\Delta_y^2 + n_{(3)}\Delta_y^3) u_{0:0} + \ldots.$$

It often happens that a certain order of differences, say the rth, is sufficient for interpolation along the x-line, while a higher order is necessary for the y-line. This is especially so when x is a young age and y an older age (see p. 137, Ex. 5). In this case, the formula can be simplified by omitting all terms involving $\Delta_x^{r+1}u$ whether standing alone or combined with values of $\Delta_y u$. For the same reason it may be desirable in tabulating to use smaller intervals for y than for x, according to the nature of the function.

16. Application of the formula.

Example 5.

Given the following table of values of $u_{x:y}$, estimate the value of $u_{23:17}$.

x	$y=15$	$y=20$	$y=25$
20	5·947	4·418	3·547
25	6·046	4·530	
30	6·144		

Here the interval of differencing is 5. Changing the origin to the point (o, o) and the unit to 1, the data are given for the points (o, o), (1, o), (2, o); (o, 1), (o, 2); (1, 1). The value required is $u_{.6:.4}$.

Differencing downwards for values of $\Delta_x u_{0:0}$, etc., we have

$$\Delta_x u_{0:0} = \cdot 099; \quad \Delta_x^2 u_{0:0} = -\cdot 001.$$

Differencing across for values of $\Delta_y u_{0:0}$, etc.,

$$\Delta_y u_{0:0} = -1\cdot 529; \quad \Delta_y^2 u_{0:0} = \cdot 658.$$

Also $\quad \Delta_x \Delta_y u_{0:0} = u_{1:1} - u_{0:1} - u_{1:0} + u_{0:0} = \cdot 013.$

$$\therefore \quad u_{.6:.4} = (1 + \cdot 6\Delta_x - \cdot 12\Delta_x^2 \ldots)(1 + \cdot 4\Delta_y - \cdot 12\Delta_y^2 \ldots) u_{0:0}$$

$$= (1 + \cdot 6\Delta_x + \cdot 4\Delta_y - \cdot 12\Delta_x^2 + \cdot 24\Delta_x\Delta_y - \cdot 12\Delta_y^2) u_{0:0}$$

$$= 5\cdot 319.$$

Note. Here it is not really necessary to use $\Delta_x^2 u_{0:0}$: see end of paragraph 15.

17. While for most purposes the formula given above is convenient, special circumstances may arise in which other methods may be more suitable. Where the intervals are not equidistant we may apply either a method of divided differences or one of various adaptations of Lagrange's formula depending upon the number of points given. If, for example, four values of $u_{x:y}$ are given, namely $u_{\alpha:a}$; $u_{\alpha:b}$; $u_{\beta:b}$, $u_{\beta:a}$; then it is quite easy to show that

$$u_{x:y} = u_{\alpha:a}\frac{(x-\beta)(y-b)}{(\alpha-\beta)(a-b)} + u_{\alpha.b}\frac{(x-\beta)(y-a)}{(\alpha-\beta)(b-a)}$$

$$+ u_{\beta:b}\frac{(x-\alpha)(y-a)}{(\beta-\alpha)(b-a)} + u_{\beta:a}\frac{(x-\alpha)(y-b)}{(\beta-\alpha)(a-b)}.$$

If more than four values are given the formula becomes unwieldy. It is seldom necessary to interpolate except between equidistant values of the function, and in that event a form of advancing or central difference series is generally preferable.

Two-variable functions are of great frequency in actuarial work. Tables of annuity-values $(a_{x:y})$ depending upon joint lives are often available for quinquennial values of x and y, and when values at ages other than those tabulated are required recourse must be had to methods of interpolation. Although the formulae given above are of general application special methods can be found to meet the requirements of the problem to be solved.

For example, if quinquennial values of $a_{x:y}$ are available, and if the two ages concerned are such that their sum is a multiple of 5, we may choose our origin and interval of differencing so that $x+y=1$. We have then, from the general formula for $u_{x:y}$,

$$u_{x:1-x}=u_{0:0}+[x\Delta_x+(1-x)\,\Delta_y+\tfrac{1}{2}x\,(x-1)\,(\Delta_x{}^2-2\Delta_x\Delta_y+\Delta_y{}^2)]\,u_{0:0};$$

i.e.

$$u_{x:1-x}=u_{0:1}+x\,(u_{1:0}-u_{0:1})+\tfrac{1}{2}x\,(x-1)\,(u_{2:0}-2u_{1:1}+u_{0:2}).$$

Again, if $x+y=2$, this formula becomes

$$u_{x:2-x}=\tfrac{1}{2}x\,(x-1)\,u_{2:0}-x\,(x-2)\,u_{1:1}+\tfrac{1}{2}\,(x-1)\,(x-2)\,u_{0:2},$$

or, on changing the origin,

$$u_{x:-x}=\tfrac{1}{2}\,(x-1)\,(x-2)\,u_{0:0}-x\,(x-2)\,u_{1:-1}+\tfrac{1}{2}x\,(x-1)\,u_{2:-2},$$

for which the data required are $u_{0:0}$, $u_{1:-1}$ and $u_{2:-2}$. The problem is thus reduced to a single variable interpolation.

This second formula is very useful in practice. As a rule we can choose our data within wide limits, and it has been found that with certain functions the three-term formula gives as good approximations to the true results as do formulae involving higher orders of differences (see Spencer, *J.I.A.* vol. XL, pp. 293–301).

The general second difference formula of which the above is a particular example is

$$u_{x:rx}=mu_{0:0}+nu_{1:r}+pu_{2:2r},$$

and in the note referred to above, Spencer gives a table showing the application of this formula according as r takes the values 0, 1, −1 or 2.

Another form of the formula for an interpolated value of $u_{x:y}$ when four values are given is $u_{x:y} = \xi\,(\eta u_{0:0} + y u_{0:1}) + x\,(\eta u_{1:0} + y u_{1:1})$, where x and y are both less than unity and $x + \xi = y + \eta = 1$. The second difference formula can be written as

$$u_{x:y} = [1 - (k_1 \delta_x^2 + k_2 \delta_y^2)]\,[\xi\,(\eta u_{0:0} + y u_{0:1}) + x\,(\eta u_{1:0} + y u_{1:1})],$$

where $\delta_x^2 u$ and $\delta_y^2 u$ are second central differences with respect to x and y respectively and k_1 and k_2 are factors depending upon the values of x and y (Buchanan, *T.F.A.* vol. x, pp. 329, 330).

Example 6.

Values of the joint-life annuity $a_{x:y}$ for quinquennial ages being available, find a value for $a_{44:51}$.

(i) Take the origin at $(40:50)$; then if the interval of differencing be 5 years, $(44:51)$ will be represented by $(\cdot8:\cdot2)$ and $x + y = 1$.

$$u_{x:1-x} = u_{0:1} + x\,(u_{1:0} - u_{0:1}) + \tfrac{1}{2}x\,(x - 1)\,(u_{2:0} - 2u_{1:1} + u_{0:2}).$$

The data required are

$$a_{40:55} = 10\cdot135 \qquad a_{40:60} = 8\cdot926 \qquad a_{45:50} = 10\cdot763$$
$$a_{50:50} = 10\cdot202 \qquad a_{45:55} = \ \ 9\cdot854$$

Then $\quad u_{\cdot8:\cdot2} = 10\cdot135 + \cdot8\,(10\cdot763 - 10\cdot135)$
$$+ \tfrac{1}{2}\,\cdot8\,(-\cdot2)\,(10\cdot202 - 19\cdot708 + 8\cdot926)$$
$$= 10\cdot135 + \cdot5024 + \cdot0464$$
$$= 10\cdot684.$$

(ii) Take the origin at $(40:45)$ so that $(44:51)$ will be $(\cdot8:1\cdot2)$ and $x + y = 2$.

$$u_{x:2-x} = \tfrac{1}{2}\,(x - 1)\,(x - 2)\,u_{0:2} - x\,(x - 2)\,u_{1:1} + \tfrac{1}{2}x\,(x - 1)\,u_{2:0}.$$

The three values required are

$$a_{40:55} = 10\cdot135,$$
$$a_{45:50} = 10\cdot763,$$
$$a_{50:45} = 10\cdot763.$$

$u_{\cdot8:1\cdot2} = \tfrac{1}{2}\,(-\cdot2)\,(-1\cdot2)\,10\cdot135 - \cdot8\,(-1\cdot2)\,10\cdot763 + \tfrac{1}{2}\,(\cdot8)\,(-\cdot2)\,10\cdot763$
$$= 10\cdot688.$$

If nine values surrounding the point $(44:51)$ be taken and a Lagrange formula for these nine values be used, the value for $a_{44:51}$ becomes $10\cdot684$.

This nine-point formula is a safe formula for occasional interpolation, and by its use the risk and labour attaching to the calculation of differences may be avoided. The formula is used centrally, the area of interpolation being as shown in the diagram below. The ordinary single-variable Lagrange interpolation formula is used to interpolate for x in each column, and the formula is used again to interpolate for y from the three calculated values.

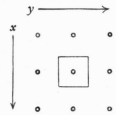

This process is very simple with the aid of a machine, especially for quinquennial intervals, when the coefficients are as follows:

Interval	u_{-1}	u_0	u_1
$-\cdot4$	$-\cdot12$	$+\cdot84$	$+\cdot28$
$-\cdot2$	$-\cdot08$	$+\cdot96$	$+\cdot12$
$+\cdot2$	$+\cdot12$	$+\cdot96$	$-\cdot08$
$+\cdot4$	$+\cdot28$	$+\cdot84$	$-\cdot12$

18. The above example shows that different degrees of accuracy may be obtained by choosing different sets of data on which to work. The general theory follows the same lines as that for single-variable interpolation. It will be remembered that the ordinary advancing difference formula may be applied to the expansion of u_x in terms of the differences of u_x on the assumption that $y = u_x$ is a rational integral function of x. In these circumstances we may represent the function graphically, and the successive values of x and y will be points on the plane curve $y = u_x$. When we are considering a function of two variables x and y we assume similarly that we may represent $z = u_{x:y}$ as a surface. Now in Chapter V (paragraph 15) it was proved that the effect of including higher differences in the expansion for u_x does not necessarily give better results than if they are neglected. In the same way it may be shown that by choosing more points on which to work we may exceptionally produce a result farther from the true value z on the surface $z = u_{x:y}$ than we should obtain by relying on fewer data.

With regular data the formulae with x, y in the central area of the given points are usually preferable. In the space for which x, y are both positive and less than $\frac{1}{2}$, which includes all cases if the origin and direction of the axes are suitably chosen, a simple central difference formula is

$$u_{x:y} = u_{0:0} + \tfrac{1}{2}x\,(u_{1:0} - u_{-1:0}) + \tfrac{1}{2}y\,(u_{0:1} - u_{0:-1}).$$

This is based on five points.

This formula and the six-point formula consisting of the same terms with the addition of

$$\tfrac{1}{2}x^2\,(u_{-1:0} - 2u_{0:0} + u_{1:0}) + \tfrac{1}{2}y^2\,(u_{0:1} - 2u_{0:0} + u_{0:-1})$$
$$+ xy\,(u_{1:1} + u_{0:0} - u_{1:0} - u_{0:1})$$

are probably the most useful interpolation formulae for ordinary actuarial purposes (Todhunter, *J.I.A.* vol. LIII, p. 89). In some cases either the first or the second additional terms may be omitted (see end of paragraph 15).

*19. Taylor's theorem for a function of a single variable,

$$f(x+h) = f(x) + hf'(x) + \frac{h^2}{2!}f''(x) + \dots,$$

may be written symbolically as

$$f(x+h) = e^{hD}f(x) \quad \text{(see paragraph 6 above)}.$$

Denoting as usual partial differentiation by $\dfrac{\partial}{\partial x}$, $\dfrac{\partial}{\partial y}$, we have

$$f(x+h, y+k) = e^{h\frac{\partial}{\partial x}} f(x, y+k)$$
$$= e^{h\frac{\partial}{\partial x}} e^{k\frac{\partial}{\partial y}} f(x, y)$$
$$= e^{h\frac{\partial}{\partial x} + k\frac{\partial}{\partial y}} f(x, y)$$
$$= f(x, y) + \left(h\frac{\partial}{\partial x} + k\frac{\partial}{\partial y}\right) f(x, y) + \frac{1}{2!}\left(h\frac{\partial}{\partial x} + k\frac{\partial}{\partial y}\right)^2 f(x, y) + \dots.$$

This formula is of theoretical interest. For use with tables the partial differential coefficients must be replaced by differences, so that in effect the formula repeats the difference formula already given.

Thus, for quinquennial intervals,

$$(1 + \Delta_x)^{\frac{h}{5}} (1 + \Delta_y)^{\frac{k}{5}} \equiv e^{h\frac{\partial}{\partial x} + k\frac{\partial}{\partial y}}$$

so that
$$\frac{h}{5}\log\left(1+\Delta_x\right)+\frac{k}{5}\log\left(1+\Delta_y\right)\equiv h\frac{\partial}{\partial x}+k\frac{\partial}{\partial y};$$

$$\therefore\quad h\frac{\partial}{\partial x}+k\frac{\partial}{\partial y}\equiv\frac{1}{5}\left[h\left(\Delta_x-\frac{\Delta_x^2}{2}+\ldots\right)+k\left(\Delta_y-\frac{\Delta_y^2}{2}+\ldots\right)\right]$$

and
$$\left(h\frac{\partial}{\partial x}+k\frac{\partial}{\partial y}\right)^2\equiv\frac{1}{25}\left[h^2\Delta_x^2+2hk\Delta_x\Delta_y+k^2\Delta_y^2\right]+\ldots.$$

INTERPOLATION FORMULAE: FRASER'S HEXAGON DIAGRAMS

20. No demonstration of interpolation formulae would be complete without reference to Fraser's graphic method. In this method the ordinary differences of a function of x are combined with the relation $(x+1)_{(r)}=x_{(r)}+x_{(r-1)}$ in diagrammatic form so that by adopting certain conventions any finite difference formula can be written down immediately (Fraser, *J.I.A.* vol. XLIII, pp. 235 *et seq.*).

We have $(x+t+1)_{(r)}=(x+t)_{(r)}+(x+t)_{(r-1)},$

or $(x+t+1)_{(r)}-(x+t)_{(r)}=(x+t)_{(r-1)}.$

A relation similar to the fundamental finite difference identity $u_{x+h}-u_x=\Delta u_x$ exists therefore between these coefficients. If we carry the analogy still further we can construct a table of values of $(x+t)_{(r)}$ corresponding to a difference table.

The tables are set down in reverse order thus:

u_{-2}						$(x+3)_{(3)}$
	Δu_{-2}				$(x+2)_{(2)}$	
u_{-1}		$\Delta^2 u_{-2}$		$(x+1)_{(1)}$		$(x+2)_{(3)}$
	Δu_{-1}		$\Delta^3 u_{-2}$	$x_{(0)}$	$(x+1)_{(2)}$	
u_0		$\Delta^2 u_{-1}$	$\Delta^4 u_{-2}$	$x_{(1)}$		$(x+1)_{(3)}$
	Δu_0		$\Delta^3 u_{-1}$ $(x-1)_{(0)}$	$x_{(2)}$		
u_1		$\Delta^2 u_0$		$(x-1)_{(1)}$		$x_{(3)}$
	Δu_1			$(x-1)_{(2)}$		
u_2						$(x-1)_{(3)}$

If now these two tables be combined, we have the following scheme, where, by convention, $x_{(0)}, (x-1)_{(0)} \ldots = 1$:

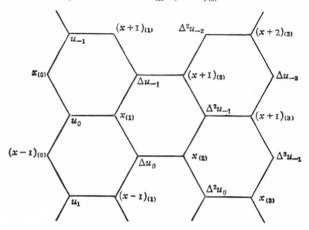

where for any one of the hexagons we may write in general

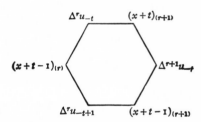

Now

$$(x+t-1)_{(r)} \Delta^r u_{-t} + (x+t)_{(r+1)} \Delta^{r+1} u_{-t} - (x+t-1)_{(r+1)} \Delta^{r+1} u_{-t}$$
$$- (x+t-1)_{(r)} \Delta^r u_{-t+1}$$
$$= (x+t-1)_{(r)} [\Delta^r u_{-t} - \Delta^r u_{-t+1}] + \Delta^{r+1} u_{-t} [(x+t)_{(r+1)}$$
$$- (x+t-1)_{(r+1)}]$$
$$= (x+t-1)_{(r)} [-\Delta^{r+1} u_{-t}] + \Delta^{r+1} u_{-t} (x+t-1)_{(r)}$$
$$= 0.$$

A relation is therefore established between the constituents of the various hexagons. If we make the following assumptions:

(i) the oblique lines denote multiplication and the horizontal lines addition; (ii) a line taken in a right-hand direction gives the product a positive sign, and in the opposite direction a negative sign, we can say that the sum of the operations performed in travelling round any hexagon is zero. It follows easily that the sum of the operations in travelling round any closed circuit is also zero.

It is evident from a consideration of the diagram that if we travel from any value of $(x+t)_{(k)}$ to any difference $\Delta^m u_n$ the result will be the same whatever route be taken. For example, from $(x-1)_{(0)}$ through u_0, $x_{(1)}$, Δu_0, $x_{(2)}$ to $\Delta^2 u_0$ and (by completing the hexagons) back along $(x-1)_{(2)}$, Δu_1, $(x-2)_{(1)}$, u_2, $(x-2)_{(0)}$, u_1 to $(x-1)_{(0)}$ again enables the following identity to be established:

$$(x-1)_{(0)}u_0 + x_{(1)}\Delta u_0 + x_{(2)}\Delta^2 u_0 - (x-1)_{(2)}\Delta^2 u_0 - (x-2)_{(1)}\Delta u_1$$
$$- (x-2)_{(0)}u_2 + (x-2)_{(0)}u_1 - (x-1)_{(0)}u_1 = 0.$$

Re-writing this, we have

$$u_0 + x\Delta u_0 + \tfrac{1}{2}x\,(x-1)\,\Delta^2 u_0 - \tfrac{1}{2}\,(x-1)\,(x-2)\,\Delta^2 u_0$$
$$- (x-2)\,\Delta u_1 - u_2 + u_1 - u_1 = 0,$$

or

$$u_0 + x\Delta u_0 + \tfrac{1}{2}x\,(x-1)\,\Delta^2 u_0 = u_2 + (x-2)\,\Delta u_1 + \tfrac{1}{2}\,(x-2)\,(x-1)\,\Delta^2 u_0.$$

Exactly the same result will be obtained by proceeding along an alternative route

$$(x-1)_{(0)},\, u_0,\, x_{(1)},\, \Delta u_0,\, x_{(2)},\, \Delta^2 u_0$$

and back through

$$(x-1)_{(2)},\, \Delta u_1,\, (x-1)_{(1)},\, u_1,\, (x-1)_{(0)}.$$

The identity will be

$$(x-1)_{(0)}u_0 + x_{(1)}\Delta u_0 + x_{(2)}\Delta^2 u_0 - (x-1)_{(2)}\Delta^2 u_0 - (x-1)_{(1)}\Delta u_1$$
$$- (x-1)_{(0)}u_1 = 0,$$

or $\quad u_0 + x\Delta u_0 + \tfrac{1}{2}x\,(x-1)\,\Delta^2 u_0 = \tfrac{1}{2}\,(x-1)\,(x-2)\,\Delta^2 u_0$
$$+ (x-1)\,\Delta u_1 + u_1;$$

i.e. $\qquad = \tfrac{1}{2}\,(x-1)\,(x-2)\,\Delta^2 u_0 + (x-2)\,\Delta u_1 + u_2,$

the same result as before.

21. Application of the hexagon diagram.

The above example gives a formula for u_2 in terms of u_0, Δu_0, $\Delta^2 u_0$ and Δu_1, and if we put $x=2$ we have a well-known identity. A similar process will give a formula for u_n, and since we may take various routes a number of different expansions of u_n will arise, all giving exact expressions for u_n. It should be further observed that when an nth difference has been reached by travelling along the upper route the terms other than u_n in the lower route will be zero, and it follows that by travelling round any circuit we obtain expressions involving an initial term u_n and terms of lower degree than n. This is seen to be so by considering $\Delta^n u_0$: all the coefficients along the lower route will contain $(x-n)$ as a factor and will therefore vanish when $x=n$.

We have therefore from the diagram the following expansions:

(i) $u_n = u_0 + n_{(1)}\Delta u_0 + n_{(2)}\Delta^2 u_0 + n_{(3)}\Delta^3 u_0 + \ldots$ (Newton's formula).

(ii) $u_n = u_0 + n_{(1)}\Delta u_0 + n_{(2)}\Delta^2 u_{-1} + (n+1)_{(3)}\Delta^3 u_{-1}$
$\qquad\qquad + (n+1)_{(4)}\Delta^4 u_{-2} + \ldots$ (Gauss's forward formula).

(iii) $u_n = u_0 + n_{(1)}\Delta u_{-1} + (n+1)_{(2)}\Delta^2 u_{-1} + (n+1)_{(3)}\Delta^3 u_{-2} + \ldots$
$\qquad\qquad\qquad\qquad\qquad\qquad$ (Gauss's backward formula).

(iv) $u_n = u_1 + (n-1)_{(1)}\Delta u_0 + n_{(2)}\Delta^2 u_0 + n_{(3)}\Delta^3 u_{-1}$
$\qquad\qquad\qquad\qquad + (n+1)_{(4)}\Delta^4 u_{-2} + \ldots$.

The mean of (ii) and (iii) gives Stirling's formula, and the mean of (iii) and (iv) can be arranged to give either Bessel's or Everett's form.

22. Mr Fraser has shown that the hexagon diagram can be used for divided differences in a similar manner to that given above for differences at equal intervals. (D. C. Fraser, *Newton and Interpolation*—a Memorial volume issued by the Mathematical Association, 1927.)

A typical hexagon involving divided differences is

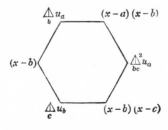

and the construction of the system follows closely the lines of that for ordinary differences.

The Δ diagram is a special case of the $\triangle$ diagram, since ordinary differences are themselves divided differences when the given values correspond to successive integral values of the argument. The results in the preceding paragraph could therefore be obtained by a consideration of the hexagon diagram for $\triangle$, the modifications necessary to produce the simpler forms of the central difference formulae being introduced at the last stage.

OTHER SYMBOLS OF OPERATION

*23. It has already been shown when considering the common operations of finite differences, Δu, Eu, Σu, that the symbols denoting the operations can, within limits, be treated as obeying the ordinary algebraic laws. By omitting the function u the various processes can be applied to the operators alone, with a resultant simplification of procedure. For example, the method can be adapted to the needs of the infinitesimal calculus, and Dr Aitken's introduction of his θ operator has produced an interpolation formula of extreme generality (see Chap. VIII). Other operators have been devised for special purposes connected with finite differences, and an interesting example is given below.

*24. The operator ∇.

In Chapter IV attention was drawn to certain symbols of operation which may be considered as supplementary to the Δ and E which are the basic operators in finite differences. These symbols —namely δ and μ—may also be assumed to follow the normal algebraic laws (with the usual limitations), and the method of separation of symbols may be applied to them equally with Δ, E and Σ. A further symbol has been introduced connecting u_x with the next lower value u_{x-1} instead of with the more usual value u_{x+1}. This symbol is ∇, and ∇u_x is defined as $u_x - u_{x-1}$.

Corresponding to $\qquad \Delta u_x = (E - 1)\, u_x,$

we have therefore $\qquad \nabla u_x = (1 - E^{-1})\, u_x.$

Thus, for example,

$$\nabla^n u_x = (1 - E^{-1})^n u_x$$

$$= u_x - n_{(1)} u_{x-1} + n_{(2)} u_{x-2} - n_{(3)} u_{x-3} + \ldots.$$

In addition to the familiar

$$\Delta x^{(m)} = m x^{(m-1)},$$

there is a similar relation

$$\nabla x^{(-m)} = m x^{(-m+1)},$$

where $x^{(-m)} \equiv (-1)^m (-x)^{(m)}$ and not the inverse factorial defined on p. 19; and if we denote the product

$$x \left(x + \tfrac{1}{2}n - 1\right) \left(x + \tfrac{1}{2}n - 2\right) \ldots \left(x - \tfrac{1}{2}n + 1\right)$$

by $x^{[n]}$ it is easy to show that

$$\delta x^{[m]} = m x^{[m-1]}$$

(Steffensen, *Interpolation*, pp. 8, 9).

No new principle is involved in dealing with these further symbols of operation; their introduction simply enables us to develop expansions and to write down formulae for interpolation with a minimum of labour.

OSCULATORY INTERPOLATION

*25. It may happen that we know the values of u_x at intervals of a unit, and that we wish to calculate a complete table of values with smaller intervals. For example it is a common practice to calculate every fifth value in a life-table, and to complete the table by interpolation: here the unit interval for the preliminary calculations is five years.

If we decide to use a third difference formula then every interpolation involves four of the given values. For the interval 0 to 1 the best course is to base the formula on the four values u_{-1}, u_0, u_1, u_2, thus giving equal weight to values on either side of the interval. An appropriate formula is Bessel's formula, namely,

$$u_x = \tfrac{1}{2}(u_0 + u_1) + (x - \tfrac{1}{2}) \Delta u_0 + \frac{x(x-1)}{2!} \frac{\Delta^2 u_0 + \Delta^2 u_{-1}}{2}$$

$$+ \frac{(x - \tfrac{1}{2}) x (x-1)}{3!} \Delta^3 u_{-1}. \quad \ldots\ldots(\text{i})$$

This is the formula for the interval 0 to 1. For the interval 1 to 2 we should use the corresponding formula based on the four given values u_0, u_1, u_2, u_3.

Thus for the two intervals 0 to 1 and 1 to 2, the two interpolation curves have a common ordinate when $x=1$; they may not necessarily have a common tangent. Two neighbouring interpolation curves will usually cut one another at the point of junction, and while there will be a smooth run of values within each unit interval the values will not run smoothly with those in the next interval.

We are led therefore to enquire whether we can find a series of curves of interpolation which shall have common tangents as well as common ordinates at the points of junction. Such curves are said to have *contact of the first order* at the points where they join, and the necessary condition for this contact is evidently that u_x and $\dfrac{du_x}{dx}$ must have the same values at these points on the one curve as on the other.

The interpolation curve given by Bessel's formula (i) for the interval 0 to 1 was based on the conditions that it should have u_{-1}, u_0, u_1, u_2 as ordinates. We retain the condition that u_0 and u_1 should be ordinates and abandon the condition that u_{-1} and u_2 should be ordinates. Instead, we shall stipulate that the differential coefficients of u_x when $x=0$ and when $x=1$ have known values. To fix these values we shall proceed as follows:

The interpolation curves for the two intervals -1 to 0 and 0 to 1 are to have the same tangent when $x=0$ as the curve of second degree which has u_{-1}, u_0 and u_1 for ordinates. The equation to this curve may be written

$$F_x\left(-1,\,0,\,1\right)=\tfrac{1}{2}\left(u_0+u_1\right)+\left(x-\tfrac{1}{2}\right)\Delta u_0+\tfrac{1}{2}x\left(x-1\right)\Delta^2 u_{-1}. \quad \text{...(ii)}$$

The interpolation curves for the two intervals 0 to 1 and 1 to 2 are to have the same tangent when $x=1$ as the curve of the second degree which has u_0, u_1 and u_2 for ordinates. In a similar manner to the above the equation to this curve may be written

$$F_x\left(0,\,1,\,2\right)=\tfrac{1}{2}\left(u_0+u_1\right)+\left(x-\tfrac{1}{2}\right)\Delta u_0+\tfrac{1}{2}x\left(x-1\right)\Delta^2 u_0. \quad \text{...(iii)}$$

It will be noticed that the forms which we have chosen for the equations (ii) and (iii) differ only in the last term.

Differentiating (ii),

$$F_x{}' (-1, 0, 1) = \Delta u_0 + (x - \tfrac{1}{2}) \, \Delta^2 u_{-1},$$

so that $\qquad F_0{}' (-1, 0, 1) = \Delta u_0 - \tfrac{1}{2} \Delta^2 u_{-1}.$ $\qquad$ ......(iv)

Differentiating (iii),

$$F_x{}' (0, 1, 2) = \Delta u_0 + (x - \tfrac{1}{2}) \, \Delta^2 u_0,$$

and $\qquad F_1{}' (0, 1, 2) = \Delta u_0 + \tfrac{1}{2} \Delta^2 u_0.$ $\qquad$ ......(v)

The values of $F_0{}' (-1, 0, 1)$ and $F_1{}' (0, 1, 2)$ in (iv) and (v) are to be values of the differential coefficients of the required interpolation curve for the interval 0 to 1.

Let v_x be that curve, so that its ordinates when $x = -1, 0, 1, 2$ form the basis for an ordinary interpolation formula of the third degree:

$$v_x = \tfrac{1}{2} (v_0 + v_1) + (x - \tfrac{1}{2}) \, \Delta v_0 + \frac{x (x-1)}{2!} \frac{\Delta^2 v_0 + \Delta^2 v_{-1}}{2}$$
$$+ \frac{(x - \tfrac{1}{2}) \, x \, (x-1)}{3!} \Delta^3 v_{-1}. \quad ......(vi)$$

The tangents to this curve are given by the equation

$$v_x{}' = \Delta v_0 + (x - \tfrac{1}{2}) \frac{\Delta^2 v_0 + \Delta^2 v_{-1}}{2} + \frac{3x^2 - 3x + \tfrac{1}{2}}{6} \Delta^3 v_{-1}. \quad ...(vii)$$

The conditions to be satisfied are:

$$v_0 = u_0,$$
$$v_1 = u_1,$$
$$v_0{}' = F_0{}' (-1, 0, 1) = \Delta u_0 - \tfrac{1}{2} \Delta^2 u_{-1},$$
$$v_1{}' = F_1{}' (0, 1, 2) = \Delta u_0 + \tfrac{1}{2} \Delta^2 u_0. \qquad ......(viii)$$

We have at once $\tfrac{1}{2} (v_0 + v_1) = \tfrac{1}{2} (u_0 + u_1)$, and $\Delta v_0 = \Delta u_0$; these determine the first and second terms in (vi).

From (vii), $\quad v_0{}' = \Delta v_0 - \dfrac{1}{2} \dfrac{\Delta^2 v_0 + \Delta^2 v_{-1}}{2} + \dfrac{1}{12} \Delta^3 v_{-1},$

$$v_1{}' = \Delta v_0 + \dfrac{1}{2} \dfrac{\Delta^2 v_0 + \Delta^2 v_{-1}}{2} + \dfrac{1}{12} \Delta^3 v_{-1},$$

and therefore
$$v_0' + v_1' = 2\Delta v_0 + \tfrac{1}{6}\Delta^3 v_{-1},$$
$$v_1' - v_0' = \tfrac{1}{2}(\Delta^2 v_0 + \Delta^2 v_{-1}).$$

But, from (viii),
$$v_0' + v_1' = 2\Delta u_0 + \tfrac{1}{2}\Delta^3 u_{-1},$$
$$v_1' - v_0' = \tfrac{1}{2}(\Delta^2 u_0 + \Delta^2 u_{-1}).$$

Comparing the two expressions for $v_0' + v_1'$ we have at once
$$\Delta^3 v_{-1} = 3\Delta^3 u_{-1} \ (\text{since } \Delta v_0 = \Delta u_0),$$
and from the two expressions for $v_1' - v_0'$
$$\tfrac{1}{2}(\Delta^2 v_0 + \Delta^2 v_{-1}) = \tfrac{1}{2}(\Delta^2 u_0 + \Delta^2 u_{-1}).$$

We have now found the values of all four terms of the formula (vi), and we can write the formula in terms of u's as follows:

$$v_x = \tfrac{1}{2}(u_0 + u_1) + (x - \tfrac{1}{2})\Delta u_0 + \frac{x(x-1)}{2}\frac{\Delta^2 u_0 + \Delta^2 u_{-1}}{2}$$
$$+ \frac{x(x-1)(x-\tfrac{1}{2})}{2}\Delta^3 u_{-1}. \quad \dots\dots (\text{ix})$$

This result is a formula of *osculatory interpolation*, and differs from the ordinary central difference formula (i) only in the last term.

The difference is

$$v_x - u_x = \frac{x(x-1)(x-\tfrac{1}{2})}{3}\Delta^3 u_{-1} = \frac{x(x-1)(2x-1)}{6}\Delta^3 u_{-1}.$$

*26. The problem of osculatory interpolation has been a fruitful source of discussion by eminent actuarial authorities. The method was devised by Dr Sprague (see *J.I.A.* vol. XXII, p. 270) and was subsequently developed by Prof. Karup, Mr George King and Dr Buchanan. An elementary demonstration of the method, depending upon advancing differences, is given by Mr King in the Supplement to the *75th Annual Report of the Registrar-General*.

The following modification of Sprague's method, using King's approach, has been suggested by Mr P. G. Neal.

Consider the four values of u_x: u_{-1}, u_0, u_1 and u_2.

The second degree curve through u_{-1}, u_0 and u_1 is

$$u_x = u_{-1} + (1+x)\,\Delta u_{-1} + \frac{(1+x)\,x}{2}\,\Delta^2 u_{-1}$$

$$= u_0 + x\Delta u_0 + \frac{x\,(x-1)}{2}\,\Delta^2 u_{-1};$$

$$\therefore\ u_x' = \Delta u_0 + x\Delta^2 u_{-1} - \tfrac{1}{2}\Delta^2 u_{-1}$$

so that
$$[u_x']_{x=0} = \Delta u_0 - \tfrac{1}{2}\Delta^2 u_{-1}. \qquad \ldots\ldots(1)$$

The second degree curve through u_0, u_1 and u_2 is

$$u_x = u_0 + x\Delta u_0 + \frac{x\,(x-1)}{2}\,\Delta^2 u_0;$$

$$\therefore\ u_x' = \Delta u_0 + x\Delta^2 u_0 - \tfrac{1}{2}\Delta^2 u_0$$

$$[u_x']_{x=1} = \Delta u_0 + \tfrac{1}{2}\Delta^2 u_0. \qquad \ldots\ldots(2)$$

Let the third degree curve through u_{-1}, u_0, u_1 and u_2 be

$$u_x = u_0 + ax + bx^2 + cx^3.$$

Then
$$u_x' = a + 2bx + 3cx^2,$$

$$a + b + c = u_1 - u_0 = \Delta u_0. \qquad \ldots\ldots(3)$$

From (1)
$$a = \Delta u_0 - \tfrac{1}{2}\Delta^2 u_{-1}. \qquad \ldots\ldots(4)$$

From (2)
$$a + 2b + 3c = \Delta u_0 + \tfrac{1}{2}\Delta^2 u_0. \qquad \ldots\ldots(5)$$

Whence, solving equations (3), (4) and (5),

$$a = \Delta u_0 - \tfrac{1}{2}\Delta^2 u_0 + \tfrac{1}{2}\Delta^3 u_{-1},$$

$$b = \tfrac{1}{2}\Delta^2 u_0 - \Delta^3 u_{-1},$$

$$c = \tfrac{1}{2}\Delta^3 u_{-1}.$$

$$\therefore\ u_x = u_0 + x\left(\Delta u_0 - \tfrac{1}{2}\Delta^2 u_0 + \tfrac{1}{2}\Delta^3 u_{-1}\right) + x^2\left(\tfrac{1}{2}\Delta^2 u_0 - \Delta^3 u_{-1}\right) + x^3\tfrac{1}{2}\Delta^3 u_{-1}$$

$$= u_0 + x\Delta u_0 + \tfrac{1}{2}x\,(x-1)\,\Delta^2 u_0 + \tfrac{1}{2}x\,(x-1)\,(x-1)\,\Delta^3 u_{-1}$$

(where, it should be noted, the last term replaces

$$\frac{x\,(x-1)\,(x-2)}{6}\,\Delta^3 u_0$$

in the ordinary advancing difference formula).

Putting $\Delta u_0 = \Delta u_{-1} + \Delta^2 u_{-1}$ and $\Delta^2 u_0 = \Delta^2 u_{-1} + \Delta^3 u_{-1}$ we obtain easily

$$u_x = u_0 + x\Delta u_{-1} + \tfrac{1}{2}(x^2 + x)\,\Delta^2 u_{-1} - \tfrac{1}{2}(x^2 - x^3)\,\Delta^3 u_{-1}$$

or

$$u_{1+x} = u_1 + x\Delta u_0 + \tfrac{1}{2}(x^2 + x)\,\Delta^2 u_0 - \tfrac{1}{2}(x^2 - x^3)\,\Delta^3 u_0,$$

which is the form given by King.

*27. The proof in paragraph 25 above is due to Mr D. C. Fraser, and depends on Bessel's formula. The ordinary interpolation formula ending with the term $\Delta^3 u_{-1}$ can be written in many different forms, all giving identical results, and the addition of the expression $\dfrac{x(x-1)(2x-1)}{6}\,\Delta^3 u_{-1}$ produces an osculatory formula.

Suppose, for example, that we take the descending difference formula

$$u_x = u_{-1} + (x+1)\,\Delta u_{-1} + \frac{x(x+1)}{2}\,\Delta^2 u_{-1} + \frac{x(x^2-1)}{6}\,\Delta^3 u_{-1}.$$

Adding the term $\dfrac{x(x-1)(2x-1)}{6}\,\Delta^3 u_{-1}$ we have

$$v_x = u_{-1} + (x+1)\,\Delta u_{-1} + x(x+1)\,\Delta^2 u_{-1}$$
$$+ \left\{\frac{x(x^2-1)}{2} + \frac{x(x-1)(2x-1)}{6}\right\}\Delta^3 u_{-1}$$
$$= u_0 + x\Delta u_{-1} + \frac{x(x+1)}{2}\,\Delta^2 u_{-1} + \frac{x^2(x-1)}{2}\,\Delta^3 u_{-1},$$

which is the form obtained in Lidstone's proof appended to Dr Buchanan's paper, *J.I.A.* vol. XLII, p. 394.

An interesting Note on the application of a graphic scheme to formulae of osculatory interpolation appears in the *Actuarial Students' Magazine*, No. 3 (Edinburgh, 1930). By treating osculatory interpolation as a particular case of divided differences, Mr Fraser shows that a diagram similar to the hexagon diagram for ordinary differences can be employed to obtain the various forms of osculatory interpolation formulae.

*28. Many writers, notably American and Scandinavian actuaries, have from time to time turned their attention to the construction of formulae of osculatory interpolation. In a paper read by Dr

Buchanan before the Faculty of Actuaries in 1929 there is an extremely interesting account of the development of the subject up to that date (*T.F.A.* vol. XII, pp. 117–56 and 277–82). Of the numerous formulae given in that paper those of Mr R. Henderson and Mr W. A. Jenkins are of particular interest.

Henderson's formula is

$$u_x = \xi u_0 + \tfrac{1}{6}\xi \, (\xi^2 - 1) \, (\delta^2 u_0 - \tfrac{1}{6}\delta^4 u_0)$$
$$+ x u_1 + \tfrac{1}{6}x \, (x^2 - 1) \, (\delta^2 u_1 - \tfrac{1}{6}\delta^4 u_1),$$

where $\xi = 1 - x$ and the δ's are central difference operators in Sheppard's notation.

It will be seen that this is Everett's formula with fourth difference adjustments.

Jenkins's formulae are also based on Everett's formula. His earlier one is

$$u_x = \xi u_0 + \tfrac{1}{6}\xi \, (\xi^2 - 1) \, \delta^2 u_0 - \tfrac{1}{12}\xi^3 \, (\xi - 1) \, \delta^4 u_0$$
$$+ x u_1 + \tfrac{1}{6}x \, (x^2 - 1) \, \delta^2 u_1 - \tfrac{1}{12}x^3 \, (x - 1) \, \delta^4 u_1,$$

where, as above, $\xi = 1 - x$; while his "modified" osculatory interpolation formula (which, in many respects, possesses advantages over existing formulae) is

$$u_x = \xi u_0 + \tfrac{1}{6}\xi \, (\xi^2 - 1) \, \delta^2 u_0 - \tfrac{1}{36}\xi^3\delta^4 u_0$$
$$+ x u_1 + \tfrac{1}{6}x \, (x^2 - 1) \, \delta^2 u_1 - \tfrac{1}{36}x^3\delta^4 u_1.$$

It should be noted that, in general, Henderson's and Jenkins's curves do not, as do Sprague's and King's, pass through the given points. They thus involve an element of adjustment as well as interpolation.

The student who wishes to pursue the subject further would be well advised to read this paper, with special reference to Buchanan's demonstration of Jenkins's modified formula and the derivation of the formula from first principles given by Mr D. C. Fraser in the discussion which followed the paper.

A comprehensive study of the methods adopted by the latest writers on osculatory interpolation will be found in an illuminating article by Mr J. E. Kerrich in *J.I.A.* vol. LXVI (pp. 88–124). The methods of

American and English actuaries differ from those of the Scandinavian authorities, and in his paper Mr Kerrich discusses the differences between these methods and gives a general procedure for the derivation of the various formulae that have been evolved.

EXAMPLES 7

1. Show that $\Delta^m x^n = 0$ or $n!$ according as $m >$ or $= n$.

Hence prove that if n and r are positive integers

$$n^r - n_{(1)}(n-1)^r + n_{(2)}(n-2)^r - n_{(3)}(n-3)^r + \ldots = 0 \text{ or } n!$$

according as $r <$ or $= n$.

2. Use differences of zero to find $(2\cdot75)^3$ and $(-\tfrac{1}{4})^3$.

3. Prove that $\Delta^n 0^{n+1} = \tfrac{1}{2}n(n+1)\Delta^n 0^n$.

4. Prove the identity

$$\Delta^m 0^n + n_{(1)}\Delta^m 0^{n-1} + n_{(2)}\Delta^m 0^{n-2} + \ldots + \frac{n!}{(n-m)!} = \frac{\Delta^{m+1} 0^{n+1}}{m+1}.$$

5. Show that $\quad (n+1)\Delta^n 0^n = 2\left[\Delta^{n-1} 0^n + \Delta^n 0^n\right].$

6. If $\delta u, \delta^2 u, \delta^3 u, \ldots$ represent differences for intervals of $1/m$ and $\Delta u, \Delta^2 u, \Delta^3 u, \ldots$ differences for unit intervals, then if fifth differences are constant, prove that

$$\delta^4 u_0 = \frac{\Delta^4 0^4}{4!}\cdot\frac{\Delta^4 u_0}{m^4} - \frac{10m\Delta^4 0^4 - \Delta^4 0^5}{5!}\cdot\frac{\Delta^5 u_0}{m^5}.$$

7. Show that $f(E^n) 0^m = n^m f(E) 0^m$.

8. If x be any quantity less than unity, prove that the limit of the series $1^n + 2^n x + 3^n x^2 + \ldots$ to infinity

$$= \frac{1}{(1-x)^2}\left\{\Delta 0^n + \frac{x}{1-x}\Delta^2 0^n + \left(\frac{x}{1-x}\right)^2 \Delta^3 0^n + \ldots\right\}.$$

9. Prove that the differential coefficient of $f(n)$ with respect to n is approximately equal to

$$\tfrac{2}{3}\{f(n+1) - f(n-1)\} - \tfrac{1}{12}\{f(n+2) - f(n-2)\}.$$

10. Find the first three differential coefficients of $\sqrt[3]{x}$, when $x = 50$, given the following cube roots:

$$\sqrt[3]{50} = 3\cdot6840; \quad \sqrt[3]{51} = 3\cdot7084; \quad \sqrt[3]{52} = 3\cdot7325; \quad \sqrt[3]{53} = 3\cdot7563;$$
$$\sqrt[3]{54} = 3\cdot7798; \quad \sqrt[3]{55} = 3\cdot8030; \quad \sqrt[3]{56} = 3\cdot8259.$$

11. $\qquad u_6 = 1{\cdot}556, \quad u_7 = 1{\cdot}690, \quad u_9 = 1{\cdot}908, \quad u_{12} = 2{\cdot}158.$

Find the value of $\dfrac{du_x}{dx}$, when $x = 8$, by using divided differences.

12. Prove that

$$\frac{du_x}{dx} = \frac{1}{h}\left(u_{x+h} - u_{x-h}\right) - \frac{1}{2h}\left(u_{x+2h} - u_{x-2h}\right) + \frac{1}{3h}\left(u_{x+3h} - u_{x-3h}\right) - \dots.$$

13. The first differences of the first differential coefficient of $\log u_x$ are in geometrical progression. Determine the form of u_x.

14. Show that $\dfrac{d^3 f(x)}{dx^3} = \Delta^3 f\left(x - \tfrac{3}{2}\right)$ approximately.

By considering the function $f(x) = a + bx + c^x$ and using the above relation, prove that $\log c = c^{\frac{1}{2}} - c^{-\frac{1}{2}}$ approximately, where c is a small quantity.

15. Given that $u_0 = 5$, $u_1 = 15$ and $u_2 = 57$, and that the value of $\dfrac{du_x}{dx}$ is 4 when $x = 0$ and 72 when $x = 2$, find the values of $\Delta^3 u_0$ and $\Delta^4 u_0$.

16. Show that $(1 + \log E)^r \, o^m = \dfrac{r!}{(r-m)!}$, when $r > m$.

17. If $\delta u_x = u_{x+\frac{1}{2}} - u_{x-\frac{1}{2}}$, prove that

$$\frac{du_x}{dx} = \delta u_x - \frac{1}{24}\,\delta^3 u_x + \frac{3}{640}\,\delta^5 u_x - \dots.$$

18. Prove that

$$\Sigma u_x v_x = u_{x-1}\Sigma v_x - \Delta u_{x-2}\Sigma^2 v_x + \Delta^2 u_{x-3}\Sigma^3 v_x - \dots.$$

19. Given

$u_{20:15} = 6{\cdot}004$	$u_{20:20} = 4{\cdot}304$	$u_{20:25} = 3{\cdot}325$
$u_{25:15} = 6{\cdot}029$	$u_{25:20} = 4{\cdot}346$	
$u_{30:15} = 6{\cdot}075$		

find $u_{23:17}$ as accurately as possible.

20. Obtain a Lagrange formula for $u_{x:y}$, given $u_{0:0}, u_{1:0}, u_{0:1}, u_{1:1}$.

21. Show that if $u_{0:1} = u_{1:0}$ and $u_{0:2} = u_{2:0}$, then

$$u_{x:y} = u_{0:0} + (x+y)\left[\Delta_x + \frac{x+y-1}{2}\Delta_x^2\right]u_{0:0} + xy\left[u_{1:1} - u_{2:0}\right].$$

22.

$a_{40:45} = 13{\cdot}133$	$a_{40:50} = 12{\cdot}450$	$a_{45:40} = 12{\cdot}880$
$a_{50:40} = 11{\cdot}898$	$a_{45:45} = 12{\cdot}432$	

Find $a_{42:43}$.

23. Given the following premiums for endowment assurances, obtain as accurately as possible the premium for age 23, term 17 years:

Age	Premiums		
	Term 15 years	Term 20 years	Term 25 years
20	5·947	4·418	3·547
25	6·046	4·530	
30	6·144		

24. Find $u_{27:34}$, given

$$u_{20:20} = 3\cdot1000 \qquad u_{25:30} = 3\cdot6875$$

$$u_{20:25} = 3\cdot2625 \qquad u_{25:35} = 3\cdot9542$$

$$u_{20:30} = 3\cdot5042 \qquad u_{30:30} = 3\cdot9333$$

$$u_{20:35} = 3\cdot8458 \qquad u_{30:35} = 4\cdot1417$$

$$u_{25:25} = 3\cdot5000 \qquad u_{35:35} = 4\cdot5500$$

25. The following values of $f(x, y)$ are given:

$$f(35, 55) = 10\cdot020, \quad f(35, 50) = 11\cdot196, \quad f(35, 45) = 12\cdot019,$$
$$f(40, 55) = 9\cdot796, \quad f(40, 50) = 10\cdot894, \quad f(40, 45) = 11\cdot641,$$
$$f(45, 55) = 9\cdot583, \quad f(45, 50) = 10\cdot591, \quad f(45, 45) = 11\cdot243.$$

(i) Using only six of the above values, find $f(42, 52)$.

(ii) Making use of all the data, calculate $f(44, 51)$.

26. Prove that $\Delta(u_x v_x w_x)$ can be expressed in either of the two following forms:

(a) $u_{x+1} v_{x+1} \Delta w_x + u_{x+1} w_x \Delta v_x + v_x w_x \Delta u_x$.

(b) $\Delta u_x \Delta v_x \Delta w_x + u_x v_x \Delta w_x + \text{two similar terms}$
$$+ u_x \Delta v_x \Delta w_x + \text{two similar terms.}$$

*27. If $\qquad \nabla f(x) = f(x) - f(x-1)$,

prove that

$$\nabla^n f(x) = f(x) - n_{(1)} f(x-1) + n_{(2)} f(x-2) - \ldots + (-1)^n f(x-n).$$

*28. Prove that

$$E^x u_0 = [1 + x_{(1)} \nabla + (x+1)_{(2)} \nabla^2 + (x+2)_{(3)} \nabla^3 + \ldots$$
$$+ (x+n)_{(n+1)} \nabla^{n+1} + \ldots] u_0.$$

29. If $\qquad x^{[n]} = x \left(x + \tfrac{1}{2}n - 1\right)^{(n-1)},$

prove that $\qquad x^{[2n]} = x^2 \left(x^2 - 1^2\right) \left(x^2 - 2^2\right) \dots \left(x^2 - \overline{n-1}^2\right)$

and $\qquad x^{[2n+1]} = x \left(x^2 - \tfrac{1}{4}\right) \left(x^2 - \tfrac{9}{4}\right) \dots \left[x^2 - \tfrac{1}{4} \left(2n-1\right)^2\right].$

30. Show that

$$f(x) = f(0) + \frac{x^{[1]}}{1!} \, \delta f(0) + \frac{x^{[2]}}{2!} \, \delta^2 f(0) + \dots + \frac{x^{[n]}}{n!} \, \delta^n f(0) + \dots,$$

where $x^{[n]}$ has the same meaning as in Qu. 29, and

$$\delta f(x) = f\left(x + \tfrac{1}{2}\right) - f\left(x - \tfrac{1}{2}\right).$$

CHAPTER VIII

MODERN EXTENSIONS AND SPECIAL DEVICES

*1. In this chapter we shall deal briefly with certain modern methods of interpolation and summation. The proofs and applications are not intended to be exhaustive, and for further information on any of the theorems or methods a study of the original papers or notes is recommended.

AITKEN'S THEOREM FOR POLYNOMIAL INTERPOLATION

*2. Dr A. C. Aitken has devised a remarkable general theorem for polynomial interpolation which covers a very wide field, embracing all the ordinary formulae as particular cases. The basis of the theorem is that when a difference operator is applied to a given polynomial u_x of the nth degree in x, the result is a polynomial of the $(n-1)$th degree, and when performed on a constant the result is zero. This obviously holds when the operator is Δ. Similarly, when u_x is differentiated with respect to x, a polynomial of one degree less in x is produced; and if A is a constant, then dA/dx is o. In this case the operator is D.

The general operators are θ and Θ. Θ denotes that form of inverse operation θ^{-1} which produces a polynomial divisible by x, so that constants (of integration, etc.) do not enter into the inverse processes, which are therefore perfectly definite.

It is evident, in the first place, that whatever operation is represented by θ, Θ 1 is x, and the effect of operating with Θ, or a succession of Θ's, gives a multiple of x.

From the definition, since u_0 is the constant part of u_x, which is removed by the operation θ,

$$\Theta\theta u_x = u_x - u_0$$

so that

$$u_x = u_0 + \Theta\theta u_x.$$

If for example $\theta \equiv \Delta$ and the interval of differencing is unity, then

$$\Theta \, \mathrm{I} = x_{(1)}, \quad \Theta x_{(1)} = x_{(2)}, \quad \Theta x_{(2)} = x_{(3)} \ldots$$

and generally

$$\Theta x_{(n-1)} = x_{(n)}.$$

Again, since $\quad \Delta \, (x - \mathrm{I})_{(n)} = (x - \mathrm{I})_{(n-1)}$

$$\Theta \, (x - \mathrm{I})_{(n-1)} = \Theta \theta \, (x - \mathrm{I})_{(n)} = (x - \mathrm{I})_{(n)} \pm \mathrm{I},$$

according as n is odd or even.

Similarly, if $\theta \equiv D$, it can easily be shown that

$$\Theta \, \frac{(x - \mathrm{I})^{n-1}}{(n-1)!} = \Theta \theta \, \frac{(x - \mathrm{I})^{n}}{n!} = \frac{(x - \mathrm{I})^{n} - (-\mathrm{I})^{n}}{n!}.$$

*3. The general formula for determining the polynomial $P_n(x)$, being given values when $x = 0$ of u_x and of all such results as $\ldots \theta_r \ldots \theta_2 \theta_1 u_x$, is

$$u_x = u_0 + (\theta_1 u_0) \, \Theta_1 \, \mathrm{I} + (\theta_2 \theta_1 u_0) \, \Theta_1 \Theta_2 \, \mathrm{I} + \ldots$$
$$+ (\theta_n \ldots \theta_2 \theta_1 u_0) \, \Theta_1 \Theta_2 \ldots \Theta_n \, \mathrm{I},$$

where the expressions in brackets are numerical values, and the expressions following them, such as $\Theta_1 \mathrm{I}$, $\Theta_1 \Theta_2 \mathrm{I}$, $\ldots$, are functions of x. It will be understood that, in each term, the first operator is the one that stands next to the operand u or I, and that the remaining operators are taken in their order from right to left; in this order the subscripts of θ increase and those of Θ decrease.

It should be noted also that the θ's are not necessarily all the same operation, nor need they be commutative. The following proof is due substantially to Mr G. J. Lidstone.

First, let u_x be a cubic in x and $= ax^3 + bx^2 + cx + d$.

Then since u_x is of the third degree, $\theta_1 u_x$ is of the second degree, $\theta_2 \theta_1 u_x$ is of the first degree, and $\theta_3 \theta_2 \theta_1 u_x$ is a constant.

Now $\qquad\qquad u_x = u_0 + \Theta_1 \theta_1 u_x.$

Hence, putting $\theta_1 u_x$ for u_x, $\Theta_2 \theta_2$ for $\Theta_1 \theta_1$ and similarly,

$$\theta_1 u_x = \theta_1 u_0 + \Theta_2 \theta_2 \theta_1 u_x,$$
$$\theta_2 \theta_1 u_x = \theta_2 \theta_1 u_0 + \Theta_3 \theta_3 \theta_2 \theta_1 u_x,$$
$$\theta_3 \theta_2 \theta_1 u_x = \theta_3 \theta_2 \theta_1 u_0 = \text{a constant}.$$

There is no term in Θ in the last identity because the process has been continued until x disappears.

From the last line above, operating with Θ_3,

$$\Theta_3\theta_3\theta_2\theta_1 u_x = \Theta_3\theta_3\theta_2\theta_1 u_0$$

and since $\theta_3\theta_2\theta_1 u_0$ is constant we may write this line as

$$\Theta_3\theta_3\theta_2\theta_1 u_x = (\theta_3\theta_2\theta_1 u_0)\,\Theta_3 \mathrm{I}.$$

Substitute this result in the third line:

$$\theta_2\theta_1 u_x = \theta_2\theta_1 u_0 + (\theta_3\theta_2\theta_1 u_0)\,\Theta_3 \mathrm{I}.$$

Operate on this with Θ_2 and substitute in the second line:

$$\theta_1 u_x = \theta_1 u_0 + (\theta_2\theta_1 u_0)\,\Theta_2 \mathrm{I} + (\theta_3\theta_2\theta_1 u_0)\,\Theta_2\Theta_3 \mathrm{I}.$$

Finally, operate on this with Θ_1 and substitute in the first line:

$$u_x = u_0 + (\theta_1 u_0)\,\Theta_1 \mathrm{I} + (\theta_2\theta_1 u_0)\,\Theta_1\Theta_2 \mathrm{I} + (\theta_3\theta_2\theta_1 u_0)\,\Theta_1\Theta_2\Theta_3 \mathrm{I}.$$

This process can evidently be extended to the general case, so that we arrive at the general formula:

$$u_x = u_0 + (\theta_1 u_0)\,\Theta_1 \mathrm{I} + (\theta_2\theta_1 u_0)\,\Theta_1\Theta_2 \mathrm{I} + \ldots$$
$$+ (\theta_n \ldots \theta_2\theta_1 u_0)\,\Theta_1\Theta_2 \ldots \Theta_n \mathrm{I},$$

which is Aitken's formula.

It will be observed that the proof is exactly analogous to that of the divided difference formula (Chap. III, p. 44).

*4. By replacing the θ's by more familiar operators various well-known formulae can easily be obtained:

(i) If $\theta_1 \equiv \theta_2 \equiv \theta_3 \equiv \ldots \equiv \Delta$, then as shown above, $\Theta_1 \mathrm{I} = x_{(1)}$, $\Theta_1\Theta_2 \mathrm{I} = x_{(2)} \ldots$, and the formula in paragraph 3 becomes

$$u_x = u_0 + \Delta u_0 x_{(1)} + \Delta^2 u_0 x_{(2)} + \Delta^3 u_0 x_{(3)} + \ldots$$

which is the ordinary advancing difference formula.

(ii) If the θ's are all equivalent to the operator D, we have

$$u_x = u_0 + D u_0 x + D^2 u_0 \frac{x^2}{2!} + D^3 u_0 \frac{x^3}{3!} + \ldots$$

which is Maclaurin's series.

(iii) Let $\theta_1 u_x = (u_x - u_a)/(x-a)$ so that $\theta_1 \equiv \underset{a}{\triangle}$, $\theta_1 \theta_2 \equiv \underset{ba}{\triangle^2}$, and so on; then it can easily be shown that the formula reproduces

$$u_x = u_a + (x-a) \underset{b}{\triangle} u_a + (x-a)(x-b) \underset{bc}{\triangle^2} u_a + \dots,$$

Newton's divided difference formula.

*5. These paragraphs are based on the note by Dr Aitken in *J.I.A.* vol. LXI, pp. 107 *et seq.* In the same volume appears a note on Lidstone's extension of the theorem to interpolation in Everett's form. In thus extending Aitken's theorem, Mr Lidstone has introduced an operator, λ, which reduces the degree of a polynomial by 2, and not by 1, as in the general form, and the corresponding inverse operator $\Lambda \equiv \lambda^{-1}$. This ingenious modification results in some very interesting identities and renders the development of Everett's series a comparatively simple matter. (*Ibid.* pp. 113–16 and the original paper cited therein.)

The student who desires further information on the subject of Aitken's formula is advised to read Dr Aitken's original paper, *Proc. Edin. Math. Soc.*, Series II, vol. I (1929), pp. 203 *et seq.*

FINITE INTEGRATION BY PARTS

*6. A formula for the finite integration of a function which is the product of two other functions is

$$\Sigma u_x v_x = u_x \Sigma v_x - \Sigma (\Delta u_x \Sigma v_{x+1}).$$

An extension of the formula (Chap. VII, paragraph 12) is

$$\Sigma u_x v_x = u_x \Sigma v_x - \Delta u_x \Sigma^2 v_{x+1} + \Delta^2 u_x \Sigma^3 v_{x+2} - \dots \quad \dots (a)$$

If u_x is a polynomial of the nth degree in x, differences of a higher order than n will vanish, and the last term in the series above will be

$$(-1)^n \Delta^n u_x \Sigma^{n+1} v_{x+n}.$$

The series can however be terminated at any stage with a remainder term.

For example,

$$\Delta\,(u_x \Sigma v_x) = u_x v_x + \Delta u_x \Sigma v_{x+1}$$

so that $\qquad u_x v_x = \Delta\,(u_x \Sigma v_x) - \Delta u_x \Sigma v_{x+1}$

or $\qquad \Sigma u_x v_x = u_x \Sigma v_x - \Sigma\,(\Delta u_x \Sigma v_{x+1}).\qquad ......(b)$

If in place of u_x and v_x we write $-\Delta u_x$ and Σv_{x+1} respectively, we have

$$-\Sigma\,(\Delta u_x \Sigma v_{x+1}) = -\Delta u_x \Sigma^2 v_{x+1} + \Sigma\,(\Delta^2 u_x \Sigma^2 v_{x+2}).$$

Identity (b) then becomes

$$\Sigma u_x v_x = u_x \Sigma v_x - \Delta u_x \Sigma^2 v_{x+1} + \Sigma\,(\Delta^2 u_x \Sigma^2 v_{x+2}).\qquad ......(c)$$

By substituting $\Delta^2 u_x$ and $\Sigma^2 v_{x+2}$ for u_x and v_x respectively in (c) it can easily be seen that the remainder term after $(-1)^n\,\Delta^n u_x \Sigma^{n+1} v_{x+n}$ will be

$$(-1)^{n+1}\,\Sigma\,(\Delta^{n+1} u_x \Sigma^{n+1} v_{x+n+1}).$$

(See G. J. Lidstone, *J.I.A.* vol. LXIV, pp. 160 *et seq.*)

7. If in formula (a) we replace u_x by Δu_x and v_x by 1, and insert the limits x and 0, we have

$$\sum_0^x\,(\Delta u_x\,.\,1) = \Delta u_x x_{(1)} - \Delta^2 u_x\,(x+1)_{(2)} + \Delta^3 u_x\,(x+2)_{(3)} - ....$$

But $\quad \Sigma\,(\Delta u_x) = u_x - C$, where C is a constant

$$= u_x - u_0, \text{ say};$$

$$\therefore\quad u_x - u_0 = x_{(1)}\,\Delta u_x - (x+1)_{(2)}\,\Delta^2 u_x + (x+2)_{(3)}\,\Delta^3 u_x - ...$$

or $\qquad u_0 = u_x - x_{(1)}\,\Delta u_x + (x+1)_{(2)}\,\Delta^2 u_x - (x+2)_{(3)}\,\Delta^3 u_x + ...$

which is the ordinary advancing formula for u_0 in terms of u_x and its differences. An alternative form for $\Sigma u_x v_x$ is

$$\Sigma u_x v_x = u_{x-1}\Sigma v_x - \Delta u_{x-2}\Sigma^2 v_x + \Delta^2 u_{x-3}\Sigma^3 v_x - ....\qquad ......(d)$$

(See Examples VII, No. 18.) If we make the same substitutions as above, we shall have

$$u_x - u_0 = x_{(1)}\,\Delta u_{x-1} - x_{(2)}\,\Delta^2 u_{x-2} + x_{(3)}\,\Delta^3 u_{x-3} - ...$$

or $\qquad u_0 = u_x - x_{(1)}\,\Delta u_{x-1} + x_{(2)}\,\Delta^2 u_{x-2} - x_{(3)}\,\Delta^3 u_{x-3} + ...,$

an interpolation formula involving backward differences.

To distinguish between the two expansions for $\Sigma u_x v_x$ we shall therefore refer to formula (*a*) as the "forward difference" summation formula and formula (*d*) as the "backward difference" summation formula.

*8. These formulae can be adapted to the problem of calculation of $\Sigma u_x v_x$ when numerical values of u_x and v_x are available. Mr G. J. Lidstone has shown that by making some simple substitutions the arithmetical work is reduced to a minimum.

The proof below follows Lidstone's proof in *J.I.A.* vol. LXX.

Let S_x denote the *indefinite* finite integral of $u_x v_x$. Then S_x can be expressed in either the forward or backward form as given above. If we wish to find the sum of *n* terms we must calculate $S_n - S_0$, and if in the formula we make either S_n or S_0 vanish by so arranging the summations as to give zero values to the particular values of the sums Σv, Σv^2, Σv^3, ..., we reduce the definite sum to a single expression, S_n or $-S_0$. Further, from the zero values we can build up the whole table of sums by using the fundamental relation $\Delta \Sigma^n \equiv \Sigma^{n-1}$.

Since in either the forward difference or backward difference summation formula we may choose our values so that S_n or S_0 is zero, there will be four forms of tabulation. For the purposes of illustrating the process it will be sufficient to use one of these forms: they are all illustrated in Lidstone's paper, *loc. cit.*

*9. Consider the simple case in which the following values are given:

x	0		2	3
u_x	27	64	125	216
v_x	1	3	7	5

Here *n* is 4. By simple arithmetic

$$\Sigma u_x v_x = 27 + 192 + 875 + 1080 = 2174.$$

(In this example u_x has been taken as $(x+3)^3$ so that third differences will be constant: the values of v_x are quite arbitrary.)

The difference table is

x	u_x	Δu_x	$\Delta^2 u_x$	$\Delta^3 u_x$
0	27			
		37		
1	64		24	
		61		6
2	125		30	
		91		
3	216			

We will use the backward form, making $S_0 = 0$.

Thus, to use u_{n-1} (the last term—in this case u_3) and its backward differences, we make $0 = \Sigma v_x = \Sigma^2 v_x = \dots$ for $x = 0$; and in that case

$$\sum_0^{n-1} u_x v_x = S_n = u_{n-1} \Sigma v_n - \Delta u_{n-2} \Sigma^2 v_n + \dots.$$

Construct the following table, where the sums of v_x are taken downwards and stepped down one line at a time:

	x	v_x	Σv_x	$\Sigma^2 v_x$	$\Sigma^3 v_x$	$\Sigma^4 v_x$
	0	1	0	0	0	0
	1	3	1	0	0	0
	2	7	4	1	0	0
$(n-1)$	3	5	11	5	1	0
(n)	4	—	16	16	6	1

Then, substituting in the formula for $\sum_0^{n-1} u_x v_x$, the required sum is

$$
\begin{aligned}
+216 \times 16 &= +3456 \\
- 91 \times 16 &= -1456 \\
+ 30 \times 6 &= + 180 \\
- 6 \times 1 &= - 6 \\
\hline
&+2174
\end{aligned}
$$

which agrees with the result found by direct calculation.

*10. The methods adopted in taking any of the other forms are similar, and the student will find it instructive to use these other forms in further examples of the same type.

It should be noted that, by combining two forms, we may take the sums from some convenient central point and so reduce the figures involved in the summations.

These formulae and methods are of great use in forming statistical "moments" of the form $\Sigma x^m u_{a+x}$.

INTERPOLATION BY CROSS-MEANS

*11. The divided difference formula is

$$u_x = u_a + (x-a) \underset{b}{\triangle} u_a + (x-a)(x-b) \underset{bc}{\triangle^2} u_a + \dots.$$

If we are given only two values of u_x, namely u_a and u_b, then

$$u_x = u_a + (x-a) \underset{b}{\triangle} u_a$$

$$= u_a + (x-a)(u_b - u_a)/(b-a)$$

$$= \frac{b-x}{b-a} u_a + \frac{x-a}{b-a} u_b$$

$$= \begin{vmatrix} u_a & a-x \\ u_b & b-x \end{vmatrix} \div b - a.$$

This is a blend of u_a and u_b in the proportions $(b-x)/(b-a)$ and $(x-a)/(b-a)$ and, from the determinant form, we may note that a first difference approximation to u_x is in fact a cross-product divided by the difference between the two given arguments. This is called a *linear cross-mean*.

*12. Dr A. C. Aitken has evolved a method of interpolation by cross-means which enables simple arithmetical processes to be used without the need for either a formula or differences.

The following is an elementary description of the method.

If in the general divided difference formula we substitute successively a, b, c, ... for x giving one, two, three ... terms, we may write down the following table:

No. of terms		Parts
One	$u_a = u_a$	$a-x$
Two	$u_b = u_a + (b-a)\underset{b}{\triangle}u_a$	$b-x$
Three	$u_c = u_a + (c-a)\underset{b}{\triangle}u_a + (c-a)(c-b)\underset{bc}{\triangle^2}u_a$	$c-x$
Four	$u_d = u_a + (d-a)\underset{b}{\triangle}u_a + (d-a)(d-b)\underset{bc}{\triangle^2}u_a$	
	$\qquad + (d-a)(d-b)(d-c)\underset{bcd}{\triangle^3}u_a$	$d-x$

....

where the column headed "parts" represents the factors to be used later.

The first step in the process is to find first difference approximations based on u_a and u_b, u_a and u_c, u_a and u_d ... as in paragraph 11. These may be denoted by $u_x(a, b)$, $u_x(a, c)$, $u_x(a, d)$ .... In order to obtain these approximations we use the parts in the last column above, and it is evident that the first two terms of the general formula (i.e. $u_a + (x-a)\underset{b}{\triangle}u_a$) appear in all the approximations.

Thus
$$u_x(a, d) = \begin{vmatrix} u_a & a-x \\ u_d & d-x \end{vmatrix} \div (d-a).$$

The first difference results are therefore of the form
$$u_a + (x-a)\underset{b}{\triangle}u_a + (x-a)\,k_1,$$

where k_1 represents the multipliers of the common factor $(x-a)$ in $u_x(a, b)$, $u_x(a, c)$, $u_x(a, d)$ ....

We may construct a table similar to that above, the expressions in the middle columns giving the various values of k_1:

$u_x(a, b)$	$0 . \underset{bc}{\triangle^2}u_a$	$b-x$
$u_x(a, c)$	$(c-b)\underset{bc}{\triangle^2}u_a$	$c-x$
$u_x(a, d)$	$(d-b)\underset{bc}{\triangle^2}u_a + (d-b)(d-c)\underset{bcd}{\triangle^3}u_a$	$d-x$
$u_x(a, e)$	$(e-b)\underset{bc}{\triangle^2}u_a + (e-b)(e-c)\underset{bcd}{\triangle^3}u_a$	
	$\qquad + (e-b)(e-c)(e-d)\underset{bcde}{\triangle^4}u_a$	$e-x$

The second difference approximations are found in the same way by the use of the parts as stated, and the results are of the form

$$u_x = \{u_a + (x-a) \underset{b}{\triangle} u_a + (x-a)(x-b) \underset{bc}{\triangle^2} u_a\} + (x-a)(x-b) k_2,$$

the first three terms being common to all the values, and the respective values of k_2 being those in the middle column below:

$u_x(a, b, c)$	$0 . \underset{bcd}{\triangle^3} u_a$	$c - x$
$u_x(a, b, d)$	$(d-c) \underset{bcd}{\triangle^3} u_a$	$d - x$
$u_x(a, b, e)$	$(e-c) \underset{bcd}{\triangle^3} u_a + (e-c)(e-d) \underset{bcde}{\triangle^4} u_a$	$e - x$
	....	

and so on.

*13. An example will make the method clear. In order to simplify the arithmetic equidistant intervals have been used, but the processes are, of course, perfectly general.

Example 1.

Find u_x when $x = \cdot 7352$ from the following data:

x	-2	-1	0	1	2
u_x	15849	16218	16596	16982	17378

We require the following table:

a	u_a			
b	u_b	$u_x(a, b)$		
c	u_c	$u_x(a, c)$	$u_x(a, b, c)$	
d	u_d	$u_x(a, d)$	$u_x(a, b, d)$	$u_x(a, b, c, d)$
e	u_e	$u_x(a, e)$	$u_x(a, b, e)$	$u_x(a, b, c, e)$ ...

where the parts are $-2 \cdot 7352, \ -1 \cdot 7352, \ - \cdot 7352, \ \cdot 2648, \ 1 \cdot 2648.$

Now
$$u_x(a, b) = \frac{b-x}{b-a} u_a + \frac{x-a}{b-a} u_b,$$

where
$$b - x = -1 \cdot 7352,$$
$$a - x = -2 \cdot 7352,$$
$$u_a = 15849,$$
$$u_b = 16218,$$

and
$$b - a = 1.$$

$$\therefore \quad u_x\,(a,\,b) = 15849 \times -1 \cdot 7352 - (16218 \times -2 \cdot 7352)$$
$$= 16858 \cdot 3.$$

The calculation is performed very quickly by the aid of an arithmometer.

Similarly,

$$u_x\,(a,\,c) = \tfrac{1}{2}\,[(15849 \times -\cdot 7352) - (16596 \times -2 \cdot 7352)],$$

since $\quad c - a = 2,$

$$= 16870 \cdot 6$$

and so on.

Again, $\qquad u_x\,(a,\,b,\,c) = \dfrac{c-x}{b-a}\,u_x\,(a,\,b) + \dfrac{x-b}{b-a}\,u_x\,(a,\,c),$

where

$$c - x = -\cdot 7352,$$
$$b - x = -1 \cdot 7352,$$
$$u_x\,(a,\,b) = 16858 \cdot 3,$$
$$u_x\,(a,\,c) = 16870 \cdot 6,$$

and

$$b - a = 1\,;$$
$$\therefore \quad u_x\,(a,\,b,\,c) = 16879 \cdot 6.$$

The completed table is as under.

x	u_x							
-2	15849							
-1	16218	16	858·3					
0	16596		870·6	87	9·6			
1	16982		882·0		8·9	9	·1	
2	17378		894·3		9·1		·4	

In practice, work is saved by omitting common figures in the columns, as in the calculations of the cross-means these figures will merely be repeated.

The final result is 16879.

The gradual closing-up of the approximation is clearly seen. It is best to arrange the u's in the order in which they come into Gauss's formula, namely, u_0, u_1, u_{-1}, u_2 .... In this way quicker convergence is secured.

*14. A further adaptation of this method is by the use of *quadratic cross-means*. Here the values of u_x are taken in the order u_{-a}, u_a,

u_{-b}, u_b ... and the divided difference formula becomes

$$u_x = u_{-a} + (x+a) \underset{a}{\triangle} u_{-a} + (x^2 - a^2) \underset{a,-b}{\triangle^2} u_{-a}$$
$$+ (x^2 - a^2)(x+b) \underset{a,-b,b}{\triangle^3} u_{-a} + \dots.$$

The first stage in the calculations is interpolation to first differences by linear cross-means as before; at each subsequent stage, by an arithmetically similar process, two further differences are allowed for simultaneously.

Dr Aitken's method of application is as follows:

$$u_x(a, -a) = [(a+x) u_a + (a-x) u_{-a}]/2a.$$

Since this expression is unaltered by substituting $-a$ for a, it is an even polynomial in a, say $v_x(a^2)$.

By letting $a = x$ in $u_x(a, -a)$, we have $u_x(x, -x)$, which is $v_x(x^2)$.

The problem is therefore reduced to interpolating for $v_x(x^2)$, given $v_x(a^2)$, $v_x(b^2)$, $v_x(c^2)$ .... The repeated cross-means are therefore available, beginning with

$$v_x(a^2, b^2) = [(b^2 - x^2) v_x(a^2) - (a^2 - x^2) v_x(b^2)]/(b^2 - a^2)$$

and similarly for $v_x(a^2, c^2)$ ....

Again,

$$v_x(a^2, b^2, c^2) = \frac{(c^2 - x^2) v_x(a^2, b^2) - (b^2 - x^2) v_x(a^2, c^2)}{c^2 - b^2}$$

and so on.

It is evident now that by interpolating on variables of the form r^2 we are moving by two orders of differences at a time, which improves the convergence to a marked degree. Further, with a central origin a, b, c ... are ·5, 1·5, 2·5 ... and the factors $a^2 - x^2$, $b^2 - x^2$, $c^2 - x^2$ ... all have the same decimal part. Also, the divisors $b^2 - a^2$, $c^2 - a^2$, $c^2 - b^2$ ... are all even integers, which enables *halved* cross-multipliers and divisors to be used. Where the arguments are ·5, 1·5, 2·5 ... these halved divisors become 1, 3, 6, 10 ..., the coefficients in the ordinary binomial expansion.

Finally, for these arguments the first multiplier is $\frac{1}{2}(\frac{1}{4} - x^2)$ of $\frac{1}{2}(\frac{1}{2} - x)(\frac{1}{2} + x)$, which is one-half the product of the multipliers used in the first linear cross-mean for $v(\frac{1}{4})$.

An example will help to explain the method.

Example 2.

Using the data in Example 1, together with $u_3 = 17773$, interpolate to find $u_{.7352}$.

The extra value is required, as in the quadratic method we need an even number of terms.

The working is as follows:

The decimal part of the multiplier is

$$\tfrac{1}{2}\,(\cdot 7352 \times \cdot 2648) = \cdot 0973405.$$

The v's are

$$\cdot 7352 \times 16982 + \ \cdot 2648 \times 16596 = 16879 \cdot 8$$

$$1 \cdot 7352 \times 17378 + 1 \cdot 2648 \times 16218 = 16888 \cdot 9$$

$$2 \cdot 7352 \times 17773 + 2 \cdot 2648 \times 15849 = 16901 \cdot 5$$

The next steps are

$$879 \cdot 8 \times 1 \cdot 0973405 - 888 \cdot 9 \times \cdot 0973405 = 878 \cdot 9$$

$$879 \cdot 8 \times 3 \cdot 0973405 - 901 \cdot 5 \times \cdot 0973405 = 879 \cdot 1$$

Further values of v are unnecessary, and the table, similar to that for linear cross-means interpolations, is

16	879·8			·0973405
	888·9	87	8·9	1·0973405
	901·5		9·1	3·0973405

Hence $u_{.7352} = 16879$, as before.

*15. The cross-means methods possess particular advantages. No interpolation formula and no differences are required and we may stop the calculation at any point, so that any required degree of accuracy may be attained. For equidistant intervals the quadratic method is much to be preferred. When the intervals are unequal the linear process has considerable practical value; it is, in fact, one of the most direct and effective methods for inverse interpolation.

Generally, the quadratic method is very advantageous for direct interpolation. It can also be readily adapted to inverse interpolation. When the arguments are equally spaced and the calculations can be effected by the aid of an arithmometer this device enables interpolated results to be obtained much more rapidly than by any other method. For instance, in Example 2, after the multiplier has been calculated, the successive values of v can be obtained on an arithmometer without clearing the machine after each operation. After the method has been mastered simple interpolations can be obtained in a very few minutes.

16. This part of the chapter is based largely on the note by Mr G. J. Lidstone, "Aitken's new processes for direct and inverse interpolation" in *J.I.A.* vol. LXVIII, pp. 272–86. In this note there is a full and lucid description of the methods of interpolation by cross-means with a number of fully-worked examples, and the student will find it instructive to compare the advantages and disadvantages of interpolation by difference formulae and the methods of cross-means, by working out actual numerical questions.

COMRIE'S "THROW-BACK" DEVICE

17. In the same paper (*loc. cit.* pp. 286–93), Mr Lidstone gives a comprehensive account (with references) of the *throw-back* device of Dr L. J. Comrie, based on Bessel's or Everett's formula. This process is of great advantage when the interpolation is to be taken beyond third differences, as it shortens the work and reduces the number of differences to be recorded in the Tables. The nature of the process is indicated in the next paragraph; for a fuller account reference may be made to the paper mentioned above and to Comrie's papers cited therein.

18. In Bessel's formula (Chap. IV, paragraph 6), let the coefficients of the odd differences be called $B^{\mathrm{I}}u$, $B^{\mathrm{III}}u$, $B^{\mathrm{V}}u$ ..., and the coefficients of the mean even differences $B^{\mathrm{II}}u$, $B^{\mathrm{IV}}u$, $B^{\mathrm{VI}}u$ .... Then for the practical range of interpolation $x=0$ to $x=1$, it is found that the ratios

$$\frac{B^{\mathrm{III}}u}{B^{\mathrm{I}}u}, \quad \frac{B^{\mathrm{V}}u}{B^{\mathrm{I}}u}, \dots$$

and

$$\frac{B^{\mathrm{IV}}u}{B^{\mathrm{II}}u}, \quad \frac{B^{\mathrm{VI}}u}{B^{\mathrm{II}}u}, \dots$$

change so slightly with x that they may, with sufficient accuracy, be assigned constant mean values provided that higher differences are not too large.

Adopting these values the formula takes the convenient form

$$u_x = u_0 + x\Delta u_0 + \frac{x(x-1)}{2!} \left[\bar{\Delta}^2 - \cdot 184\bar{\Delta}^4 + \cdot 038\bar{\Delta}^6 \dots\right] u_0$$

$$+ \frac{x(x-1)(x-\frac{1}{2})}{3!} \left[\Delta^3 - \cdot 108\Delta^5 + \cdot 016\Delta^7 \dots\right] u_0,$$

where Δu, $\Delta^3 u$, $\Delta^5 u$ ... represent the odd central differences and $\bar{\Delta}^2 u$, $\bar{\Delta}^4 u$, $\bar{\Delta}^6 u$ ... the mean even central differences.

The quantities in the square brackets are evidently independent of x and may therefore be tabulated.

The throw-back device may be used with great advantage in double-entry tables (i.e. functions of x and y). Its use curtails very considerably the complicated interpolation formulae otherwise required when even moderately high orders of differences are involved.

The device is also very useful for inverse interpolation, since it enables differences beyond the third to be included by a direct process without increasing the degree of the equation to be solved. Further, the last coefficient, $B^{\text{iii}}u$, is very small and changes slowly, so that allowance is easily made for the last term in the formula given above.

CHAPTER IX

APPROXIMATE INTEGRATION

1. In order to obtain the area of a curve by the methods of the integral calculus two conditions must necessarily hold. These conditions are

- (i) the equation of the curve must be known; and in that event
- (ii) the function $y = u_x$ representing the equation of the curve must be integrable.

In the theory of life contingencies these conditions are rarely satisfied. Rates of mortality, marriage, etc. are generally obtained from actual observations and the functions derived from these rates are seldom capable of expression in the form of a mathematical expansion. For example, if l_x be the number of persons attaining exact age x in any year of time, the number living between ages x and $x + 1$ is given by

$$L_x = \int_0^1 l_{x+t}\, dt,$$

where x and t are independent.

Unless l_{x+t} follows some definite mathematical law, we cannot evaluate the integral by the methods hitherto employed. By making certain assumptions, however, we can obtain approximations to the value of the integral which are accurate enough for practical purposes.

Thus, if we expand l_{x+t} in terms of l_x and differences of l_x, we have

$$l_{x+t} = (1 + \Delta)^t\, l_x$$
$$= l_x + t\Delta l_x \qquad \text{to first differences.}$$

But $\qquad \Delta l_x = l_{x+1} - l_x,$

and $l_x - l_{x+1}$ is d_x, the number out of the l_x persons who die before reaching age $x + 1$.

$$\therefore \quad L_x = \int_0^1 l_{x+t}\, dt$$

$$= \int_0^1 (l_x - t d_x)\, dt \quad \text{as far as first differences}$$

$$= \left[t l_x - \tfrac{1}{2} t^2 d_x \right]_0^1$$

$$= l_x - \tfrac{1}{2} d_x$$

$$= l_x - \tfrac{1}{2}(l_x - l_{x+1})$$

$$= \tfrac{1}{2}(l_x + l_{x+1}).$$

This is an approximate value of L_x on the assumption that l_{x+t} is a first difference function of l_x.

It is evident that a simple approximation to first differences will not be justifiable except in a limited number of instances: the construction of formulae for approximate integration will necessarily depend on the data available and on the degree of accuracy required.

2. Simpson's rule.

Suppose that we are given two values of u_x only and that we represent these two values by means of the points H and K whose co-ordinates are (a, u_a) and (b, u_b) respectively. Suppose also that we have sufficient information to justify our representing the function $y = u_x$ by a curve of small changes of slope, not affected by periodic changes. An infinite number of such mathematical curves can be drawn to pass through H and K. The simplest curve passing through the points is a straight line, and for the purpose of interpolation it is often sufficient to adopt a first difference formula, as was done for example in obtaining the approximation to L_x in the preceding paragraph. If the straight line be drawn, the area

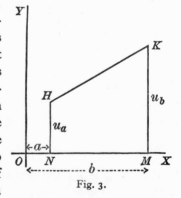

Fig. 3.

cut off by the curve, the x-axis and the ordinates $x=a$ and $x=b$ will be that of the trapezium $HNMK$. The area of the trapezium is $\frac{1}{2}(u_a+u_b)(b-a)$.

Accurately, this area is $\int_a^b u_x dx$.

A first approximation to the integral is therefore $\frac{1}{2}(u_a+u_b)(b-a)$.

If $y=u_x=l_{x+t}$ and the limits b and a are 1 and 0 respectively, we have the approximation to $\int_0^1 l_{x+t}\,dt$ given above, namely

$$\frac{1}{2}(l_x+l_{x+1}).$$

Let us now improve the approximation by introducing a third known value of u_x. In other words, suppose our data to be u_a, u_b, u_c.

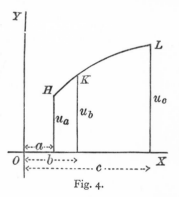

Then there is still an unlimited number of curves which can be drawn to pass through the three points H, K, L. The simplest of these curves will now no longer be a straight line, but a second difference curve. The form of this curve will be $y=A+Bx+Cx^2$, and since three points on the curve are given we are in possession of sufficient data to determine the coefficients A, B, C.

Fig. 4.

In practice the data will generally be available at equidistant intervals, and since we may choose our origin where we please, the problem is therefore reduced to one of finding the second difference curve which passes through the points $(0, u_0)$, $(1, u_1)$, $(2, u_2)$.

Having found the equation of the curve we can then find the area enclosed by the curve, the extreme ordinates and the x-axis, by integrating the function thus obtained between the limits 0 and 2.

Assume therefore that $y=u_x=a+bx+cx^2$ is the required equation.

Then, by substitution,

$$u_0 = a,$$
$$u_1 = a + b + c,$$
$$u_2 = a + 2b + 4c,$$

whence

$$a = u_0,$$
$$b = \tfrac{1}{2}\left(-u_2 + 4u_1 - 3u_0\right) = \Delta u_0 - \tfrac{1}{2}\Delta^2 u_0,$$
$$c = \tfrac{1}{2}\left(u_2 - 2u_1 + u_0\right) = \tfrac{1}{2}\Delta^2 u_0.$$

Also

$$\int_0^2 u_x\,dx = \int_0^2 \left(a + bx + cx^2\right)\,dx$$

$$= \left[ax + \tfrac{1}{2}bx^2 + \tfrac{1}{3}cx^3\right]_0^2$$

$$= 2a + 2b + \tfrac{8}{3}c$$

$$= \tfrac{1}{3}\left(u_0 + 4u_1 + u_2\right),$$

on substituting for a, b and c.

This is *Simpson's rule* for approximate integration.

We can obtain this formula by alternative methods.

For example, let

$$u_x = (1 + \Delta)^x\, u_0 = u_0 + x\Delta u_0 + \tfrac{1}{2}x\,(x - 1)\,\Delta^2 u_0$$

as far as second differences.

Then

$$\int_0^2 u_x\,dx = \int_0^2 \left\{u_0 + x\Delta u_0 + \tfrac{1}{2}x\,(x - 1)\,\Delta^2 u_0\right\}\,dx$$

$$= \int_0^2 \left\{u_0 + x\,(\Delta u_0 - \tfrac{1}{2}\Delta^2 u_0) + \tfrac{1}{2}x^2\Delta^2 u_0\right\}\,dx$$

$$= \left[xu_0 + \tfrac{1}{2}x^2\,(\Delta u_0 - \tfrac{1}{2}\Delta^2 u_0) + \tfrac{1}{6}x^3\Delta^2 u_0\right]_0^2$$

$$= 2u_0 + 2\,(\Delta u_0 - \tfrac{1}{2}\Delta^2 u_0) + \tfrac{4}{3}\Delta^2 u_0$$

$$= 2u_0 + 2\Delta u_0 + \tfrac{1}{3}\Delta^2 u_0,$$

and since

$$u_0 = u_0,$$
$$u_1 = u_0 + \Delta u_0,$$
$$u_2 = u_0 + 2\Delta u_0 + \Delta^2 u_0,$$

this reduces to $\tfrac{1}{3}\left(u_0 + 4u_1 + u_2\right)$ as before.

A third method is to assume that the integral can be expressed in the form

$$mu_0 + nu_1 + pu_2.$$

Then if $y = a + bx + cx^2$ we have eventually that

$$\int_0^2 u_x dx = 2a + 2b + \tfrac{8}{3}c,$$

as in the first method.

Substituting in the assumed expression for the integral:

$$ma + n(a+b+c) + p(a+2b+4c) = 2a + 2b + \tfrac{8}{3}c.$$

Whence, by equating coefficients of a, b, c and solving the resulting equations,

$$m = \tfrac{1}{3}; \quad n = \tfrac{4}{3}; \quad p = \tfrac{1}{3}.$$

3. Change of unit.

The formula $\int_0^2 u_x dx = \tfrac{1}{3}(u_0 + 4u_1 + u_2)$ is an approximate formula obtained by considering unit intervals. If we wish to transform the formula to a form in which the interval is changed to, say, n, then the given values of u_x will be u_0; u_n; u_{2n}. Our new variable is z, where $z = nx$.

$$\therefore \quad dz = n\,dx.$$

The new limits are evidently o and $2n$.

The formula is

$$\int_0^{2n} \frac{1}{n} u_z dz = \tfrac{1}{3}(u_0 + 4u_n + u_{2n}),$$

i.e.
$$\int_0^{2n} u_z dz = \tfrac{1}{3}n(u_0 + 4u_n + u_{2n}),$$

or, on changing the variable to x,

$$\int_0^{2n} u_x dx = \tfrac{1}{3}n(u_0 + 4u_n + u_{2n}).$$

This principle is of universal application and any formula of approximate integration can immediately be transferred from unit intervals to $n$thly intervals and vice versa.

For example, the approximate formula

$$\int_0^{10} u_x dx = \tfrac{5}{2}\,(u_1 + u_4 + u_6 + u_9)$$

becomes

$$\int_0^{20} u_x dx = 5\,(u_2 + u_8 + u_{12} + u_{18})$$

on doubling the interval;

and

$$\int_0^{10n} u_x dx = \frac{5n}{2}\,(u_n + u_{4n} + u_{6n} + u_{9n})$$

when the interval is n.

4. Change of origin.

Consider again Simpson's rule:

$$\int_0^2 u_x dx = \tfrac{1}{3}\,(u_0 + 4u_1 + u_2).$$

We have obtained a formula which gives in terms of u_0, u_1 and u_2 the area of the curve cut off by the ordinates $x = 0$ and $x = 2$. If we change the origin so that the point $(1, u_1)$ becomes the point $(0, v_0)$, as in Fig. 5, we shall have a formula of integration between the limits -1 and 1 in terms of v_{-1}, v_0 and v_1. The formula will be otherwise unaltered and we shall have found an approximation to the same area with reference to a new y-axis $O_1 Y_1$.

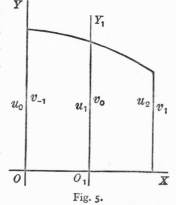

Fig. 5.

In its new form the formula becomes

$$\int_{-1}^{1} v_x dx = \tfrac{1}{3}\,(v_{-1} + 4v_0 + v_1),$$

or, changing back to u's,

$$\int_{-1}^{1} u_x dx = \tfrac{1}{3}\,(u_{-1} + 4u_0 + u_1).$$

Now when it is desired to obtain an approximate integration formula it is evident that integration between -1 and 1 (or between $-n$ and n) involves much simpler algebra than integration between 0 and 2 (or between 0 and $2n$). Thus, if

$$u_x = a + bx + cx^2,$$

then

$$u_0 = a,$$

$$u_{-1} = a - b + c,$$

$$u_1 = a + b + c,$$

and

$$\tfrac{1}{3}(u_{-1} + 4u_0 + u_1) = \tfrac{1}{3}\{4u_0 + (u_{-1} + u_1)\}$$
$$= \tfrac{1}{3}(4a + 2a + 2c)$$
$$= \tfrac{1}{3}(6a + 2c).$$

Also

$$\int_{-1}^{1} (a + bx + cx^2)\, dx = \left[ax + \tfrac{1}{2}bx^2 + \tfrac{1}{3}cx^3 \right]_{-1}^{1}$$
$$= 2a + \tfrac{2}{3}c,$$

which proves the approximation.

Again, since in this form the coefficients of odd powers of x disappear in the definite integral and also in the paired terms u_t and u_{-t}, we could equally well employ as our assumed expansion for u_x the third difference function $a + bx + cx^2 + dx^3$.

We should have

$$4u_0 + (u_{-1} + u_1) = 4a + a - b + c - d + a + b + c + d = 6a + 2c$$

as before, and

$$\left[ax + \tfrac{1}{2}bx^2 + \tfrac{1}{3}cx^3 + \tfrac{1}{4}dx^4 \right]_{-1}^{1} = 2a + \tfrac{2}{3}c.$$

This leads to the important fact that Simpson's rule is true to one more order of differences than was originally assumed, i.e. to third differences.

Generally, formulae involving $2r + 1$ terms, placed symmetrically with reference to the centre of the range, are correct to $(2r + 1)$th differences.

For the above reasons, namely

(i) for simplicity in working;

(ii) to enable us to find the true order of differences to which the approximation is correct;

it is advisable to integrate between $-n$ and n in preference to any other limits.

This can always be done by a suitable change of limits; for example, integration between $\frac{1}{2}$ and 1 can be simplified to integration between, say, 2 and 4 by increasing the interval from $\frac{1}{2}$ to 2. Then, by changing the origin, a formula can be obtained for integration between -1 and 1. To express the formula in the required form the process can then be reversed.

Example 1.

Show that $\int_{1\cdot5}^{2\cdot5} v_x dx = \frac{1}{24} (v_1 + 22v_2 + v_3)$ approximately.

$$\int_{1\cdot5}^{2\cdot5} v_x dx = \frac{1}{2} \int_{3}^{5} u_x dx \text{ (if we double the interval).}$$

This will produce a formula in u_2; u_4; u_6.

In the first place we will obtain a formula for $\int_{-1}^{1} u_x dx.$

This formula will have to be of the form $mu_{-2} + nu_0 + pu_2$, since we have moved our origin to the point where x was originally 4.

Let $\qquad\qquad u_x = a + bx + cx^2 + dx^3.$

Then $\qquad\qquad u_0 = a,$

$\qquad\qquad\qquad u_{-2} = a - 2b + 4c - 8d,$

and $\qquad\qquad u_2 = a + 2b + 4c + 8d,$

so that $\qquad \frac{1}{24} (u_{-2} + 22u_0 + u_2) = \frac{1}{24} (22a + 2a + 8c) = a + \frac{1}{3}c.$

$$\int_{-1}^{1} u_x dx = \left[ax + \frac{1}{2}bx^2 + \frac{1}{3}cx^3 + \frac{1}{4}dx^4 \right]_{-1}^{1} = 2a + \frac{2}{3}c.$$

$$\therefore \quad \frac{1}{24} (u_{-2} + 22u_0 + u_2) = \frac{1}{2} \int_{-1}^{1} u_x dx.$$

Reverting to the first origin:

$$\frac{1}{24} (u_2 + 22u_4 + u_6) = \frac{1}{2} \int_{3}^{5} u_x dx.$$

$$\therefore \quad \frac{1}{24} (v_1 + 22v_2 + v_3) = \int_{1\cdot5}^{2\cdot5} v_x dx.$$

Moreover, although only three values of v_x have been given (so that only second differences are known), the formula is true to third differences, for it is symmetrical about the middle point.

5. Some well-known approximate integration formulae.

(1) *Extension of Simpson's rule.*

We have
$$\int_0^2 u_x\, dx = \tfrac{1}{3}\left(u_0 + 4u_1 + u_2\right).$$

Therefore by changing the origin
$$\int_2^4 u_x\, dx = \tfrac{1}{3}\left(u_2 + 4u_3 + u_4\right).$$

Similarly
$$\int_4^6 u_x\, dx = \tfrac{1}{3}\left(u_4 + 4u_5 + u_6\right).$$

. . . .

In general, by addition,
$$\int_0^{2n} u_x\, dx = \tfrac{1}{3}\left(u_0 + 4u_1 + 2u_2 + 4u_3 + 2u_4 + \ldots + u_{2n}\right).$$

This is a formula for approximate integration used extensively in practical mathematics. In engineering problems, where the curve to be integrated has actually been sketched as the result of experiments, a small unit may be chosen and a large number of ordinates drawn. In that event the extended formula can be applied. This will in general give better results than the single formula
$$\int_0^{2n} u_x\, dx = \frac{n}{3}\left(u_0 + 4u_n + u_{2n}\right).$$

It should be noted that Simpson's rule, applied in sections (as above), does not assume that a smooth curve can be drawn between all the points u_0, u_1, ... u_{2n}. The method of obtaining the formula has in fact been to draw a number of disjointed curves between u_0, u_1, u_2; u_2, u_3, u_4; ... u_{2n-2}, u_{2n-1}, u_{2n}, and the curve passing through three points such as u_0, u_1, u_2 will not as a rule pass through the next series u_3 and u_4.

(2) *The "three-eighths" rule.*

The following symmetrical formula can be derived by working on the above lines, when four consecutive points are given.

If the four points were u_0, u_1, u_2, u_3 we should commonly integrate between o and 3. Change the unit and origin so that we pass firstly to the limits o and 6 and secondly to the limits -3 and 3.

We require $\int_{-3}^{3} u_x\, dx$, given u_{-3}, u_{-1}, u_1, u_3.

Let $$u_x = a + bx + cx^2 + dx^3,$$

so that $$u_{-1} + u_1 = 2\,(a+c)$$

and $$u_{-3} + u_3 = 2\,(a+9c).$$

If $$\int_{-3}^{3} u_x\, dx = m\,(u_{-1}+u_1) + n\,(u_{-3}+u_3),$$

we have

$$\left[ax + \tfrac{1}{2}bx^2 + \tfrac{1}{3}cx^3 + \tfrac{1}{4}dx^4 \right]_{-3}^{3} = m\,(u_{-1}+u_1) + n\,(u_{-3}+u_3);$$

i.e.
$$6a + 18c = m\,(u_{-1}+u_1) + n\,(u_{-3}+u_3)$$
$$= m\,(2a+2c) + n\,(2a+18c)$$
$$= a\,(2m+2n) + c\,(2m+18n),$$

from which, easily, $m = 18/8$ and $n = 6/8$.

$$\therefore \quad \int_{-3}^{3} u_x\, dx = \tfrac{3}{8}\{6\,(u_{-1}+u_1) + 2\,(u_{-3}+u_3)\},$$

i.e.
$$\int_{0}^{6} u_x\, dx = \tfrac{3}{8}\{6\,(u_2+u_4) + 2\,(u_0+u_6)\},$$

or
$$\int_{0}^{3} u_x\, dx = \tfrac{3}{8}\{3\,(u_1+u_2) + (u_0+u_3)\}$$
$$= \tfrac{3}{8}\,(u_0 + 3u_1 + 3u_2 + u_3)$$
$$= \tfrac{3}{8}\,(1+E)^3\, u_0.$$

This formula, like Simpson's rule, is correct to third differences.

(3) *Weddle's rule.*

Suppose that seven equidistant ordinates are given. In order to reduce the algebra to a minimum, we integrate between limits -3 and $+3$, and write the assumed formula for u_x thus:

$$u_x = a + bx + \frac{cx^2}{2} + \frac{dx\,(x^2-1)}{6} + \frac{ex^2\,(x^2-1)}{24} + \frac{fx\,(x^2-1)\,(x^2-4)}{120}$$
$$+ \frac{gx^2\,(x^2-1)\,(x^2-4)}{720}.$$

This is Stirling's formula with the constants a, b, c, ... g replacing the differences of u_x.

Then

$$\int_{-3}^{3} u_x dx = \left[ax + \frac{bx^2}{2} + \frac{cx^3}{6} + \frac{d}{6}\left(\frac{x^4}{4} - \frac{x^2}{2}\right) + \frac{e}{24}\left(\frac{x^5}{5} - \frac{x^3}{3}\right) \right.$$

$$\left. + \frac{f}{120}\left(\frac{x^6}{6} - \frac{5x^4}{4} + \frac{4x^2}{2}\right) + \frac{g}{720}\left(\frac{x^7}{7} - \frac{5x^5}{5} + \frac{4x^3}{3}\right) \right]_{-3}^{3}$$

$$= 6a + 54\left(\frac{c}{6} - \frac{e}{72} + \frac{g}{540}\right) + 486\left(\frac{e}{120} - \frac{g}{720}\right) + \frac{243}{280}g$$

$$= 6a + 9c + \tfrac{33}{10}e + \tfrac{41}{140}g.$$

Replacing a, c, e, g by the differences of u_x in Stirling's formula, we have

$$\int_{-3}^{3} u_x dx = 6a + 9c + \tfrac{33}{10}e + \tfrac{41}{140}g$$

$$= 6u_0 + 9\Delta^2 u_{-1} + \tfrac{33}{10}\Delta^4 u_{-2} + \tfrac{41}{140}\Delta^6 u_{-3}.$$

If now $\Delta^2 u_{-1}$, $\Delta^4 u_{-2}$ and $\Delta^6 u_{-3}$ are expressed in terms of u_{-3}, u_{-2}, ... u_2, u_3, we shall obtain a formula correct to seventh differences. It will be found, however, that the coefficients of the terms are large. This is due to the awkward fraction $\tfrac{41}{140}$ multiplying $\Delta^6 u_{-3}$. As sixth differences are usually small, the error involved in replacing $\tfrac{41}{140}\Delta^6 u_{-3}$ by $\tfrac{42}{140}\Delta^6 u_{-3}$, i.e. by $\tfrac{3}{10}\Delta^6 u_{-3}$, will, in general, be negligible. By this substitution the coefficients in the final formula will be much simplified. The modified formula will involve an error of $\tfrac{1}{140}\Delta^6 u_{-3}$ and will therefore be strictly correct to fifth differences only but virtually correct to seventh differences.

The terms in the expression thus adjusted, namely,

$$6u_0 + 9\Delta^2 u_{-1} + \tfrac{33}{10}\Delta^4 u_{-2} + \tfrac{3}{10}\Delta^6 u_{-3},$$

may be expressed in terms of the u's and collected as shown in the following table:

	u_{-3}	u_{-2}	u_{-1}	u_0	u_1	u_2	u_3
$6u_0$				6·0			
$9\Delta^2 u_{-1}$			9·0	−18·0	9·0		
$3·3\Delta^4 u_{-2}$		3·3	−13·2	19·8	−13·2	3·3	
$·3\Delta^6 u_{-3}$	·3	−1·8	4·5	− 6·0	4·5	−1·8	·3
Total ...	·3	1·5	·3	1·8	·3	1·5	·3

Therefore $\int_{-3}^{3} u_x\,dx$ is approximately equal to

$$\cdot 3u_{-3}+1\cdot 5u_{-2}+\cdot 3u_{-1}+1\cdot 8u_0+\cdot 3u_1+1\cdot 5u_2+0\cdot 3u_3$$
$$=\tfrac{3}{10}\left[(u_{-3}+u_3)+5\,(u_{-2}+u_2)+(u_{-1}+u_1)+6u_0\right]$$

or $\int_{0}^{6} u_x\,dx=\tfrac{3}{10}\left[(u_0+u_6)+5\,(u_1+u_5)+(u_2+u_4)+6u_3\right].$

This is Weddle's rule.

An alternative method of obtaining Weddle's rule is by combining a 7-ordinate Simpson's formula with a 7-ordinate three-eighths formula in the ratio $9:-4$. This method proceeds by eliminating the principal error terms in each of the two formulae involved.

(4) *Hardy's formulae.*

Certain approximate formulae due to G. F. Hardy were at one time used extensively in actuarial work.

Let $u_x=a+bx+cx^2+dx^3+ex^4+fx^5$

so that $\int_{-3}^{3} u_x\,dx=6a+18c+\tfrac{486}{5}e;$

$u_0=a;\quad u_{-2}+u_2=2a+8c+32e;\quad u_{-3}+u_3=2a+18c+162e.$

Solving for a, c and e, and substituting:

$$\int_{-3}^{3} u_x\,dx=2\cdot 2u_0+1\cdot 62\,(u_{-2}+u_2)+\cdot 28\,(u_{-3}+u_3)$$

or $\int_{0}^{6} u_x\,dx=2\cdot 2u_3+1\cdot 62\,(u_1+u_5)+\cdot 28\,(u_0+u_6)$
$$=\cdot 28\,(u_0+u_6)+1\cdot 62\,(u_1+u_5)+2\cdot 2u_3,$$

which is Hardy's "formula (37)".

If the interval of differencing be n, this becomes

$$\int_{0}^{6n} u_x\,dx=n\left\{\cdot 28\,(u_0+u_{6n})+1\cdot 62\,(u_n+u_{5n})+2\cdot 2u_{3n}\right\}.$$

Similarly

$$\int_{6n}^{12n} u_x\,dx=n\left\{\cdot 28\,(u_{6n}+u_{12n})+1\cdot 62\,(u_{7n}+u_{11n})+2\cdot 2u_{9n}\right\},$$

and so on.

Since

$$\int_0^\infty u_x\,dx = \int_0^{6n} u_x\,dx + \int_{6n}^{12n} u_x\,dx + \int_{12n}^{18n} u_x\,dx + \ldots,$$

$$\int_0^\infty u_x\,dx = n\,\{\cdot 28\,(u_0 + 2u_{6n} + 2u_{12n} + \ldots)$$
$$+\,1\cdot 62\,(u_n + u_{5n} + u_{7n} + \ldots) + 2\cdot 2\,(u_{3n} + u_{9n} + \ldots)\}.$$

This is Hardy's "formula (38)".

If we are dealing with functions derived from a mortality table, and we choose n so that $7n$ falls just within or just without the limits of the table—so that $7n$ is in fact about 100—we can write the above formula thus:

$$\int_0^\infty u_x\,dx = n\,(\cdot 28u_0 + 1\cdot 62u_n + 2\cdot 2u_{3n} + 1\cdot 62u_{5n} + \cdot 56u_{6n} + 1\cdot 62u_{7n}).$$

In this form the formula is known as Hardy's "formula (39a)".

6. (i) Since all these approximations give in effect the area of the curve bounded by u_x, the limiting ordinates and the x-axis, they are often termed "quadrature formulae", the word "quadrature" being defined as the exact or approximate calculation of the area of the square equal in area to that of the given figure.

(ii) In any of the foregoing formulae the sum of the coefficients must equal the range of integration, where this is finite. This may easily be seen by making all the u's involved equal to the same constant.

7. Practical applications of the formulae.

Integration formulae of the above type may be used to advantage in obtaining approximations to the values of certain complicated forms of integral which occur in the theory of life contingencies. Where the functions involved are such that the summation extends to the end of the life table, it is of advantage to calculate the values of the functions by Hardy's formula (39a). If, on the other hand, the upper limit is at an age-point short of the limiting age of the life table, any of the simpler integration formulae can be employed to advantage.

It is evident that we can neither integrate the function u_x nor interpolate between given values of u_x if we are absolutely without information regarding the value of the function between the ordinates. For example, in a mortality table we may integrate between, say, l_{30} and l_{31}, assuming first differences constant, for we know that in general the decrements between ages 30 and 31 are small and may be fairly considered as being evenly distributed over the interval. We could not reasonably adopt the same assumption for interpolation between l_0 and l_1, since the deaths of infants in the first year of age are not evenly distributed over the year. Again, a reliable estimate of the population of a seaside resort in June of any calendar year would not be obtained by a first difference interpolation between the population figures for January and December of the same year. In the two latter illustrations further information would be necessary before we could proceed to interpolation or integration.

In applying the formulae of approximate integration to the solution of a problem it is therefore essential that we have sufficient knowledge of the function to justify our assumptions regarding the nature of the curve passing through the given points.

When the function to be integrated is one in which the neglected differential coefficients of the curve are small between the limits of the integration, almost any of the above formulae will give satisfactory results. If these differential coefficients are not small, i.e. those of lower order are changing rapidly between the limits, there may be considerable differences between the approximate results.

Example 2.

The formula for a continuous annuity-certain is

$$\bar{a}_{\overline{m}|} = \int_0^m e^{-\delta t}\, dt,$$

where δ is the force of interest corresponding to the rate of interest i at which the annuity is valued.

By means of an approximate integration formula find the value of $\bar{a}_{\overline{6}|}$ at 4 per cent.

Since we have to evaluate $\bar{a}_{\overline{6}|}$ we shall require some or all of the values of u_t from $t=0$ to $t=6$, where $u_t = e^{-\delta t}$.

By a well-known formula in the theory of interest,

$$e^{-\delta t} = v^t, \text{ where } v = (1+i)^{-1}.$$

Values of v^t at 4 per cent. are available from any tables of interest. We have, therefore:

$$
\begin{aligned}
u_0 &= e^0 &&= 1, \\
u_1 &= e^{-\delta} = v &&= \cdot 96154, \\
u_2 &= e^{-2\delta} = v^2 &&= \cdot 92456, \\
u_3 &= e^{-3\delta} = v^3 &&= \cdot 88900, \\
u_4 &= e^{-4\delta} = v^4 &&= \cdot 85480, \\
u_5 &= e^{-5\delta} = v^5 &&= \cdot 82193, \\
u_6 &= e^{-6\delta} = v^6 &&= \cdot 79031.
\end{aligned}
$$

The following results will be obtained:

(i) Simpson's rule applied three times:

$$\tfrac{1}{3}\left(u_0 + 4u_1 + 2u_2 + 4u_3 + 2u_4 + 4u_5 + u_6\right)$$
$$= 5 \cdot 34630.$$

(ii) The three-eighths rule (with interval of differencing 2):

$$\tfrac{3}{8}\left\{2\left(u_0 + 3u_2 + 3u_4 + u_6\right)\right\}$$
$$= 5 \cdot 34629$$

(iii) Weddle's rule:

$$\cdot 3\left(u_0 + 5u_1 + u_2 + 6u_3 + u_4 + 5u_5 + u_6\right)$$
$$= 5 \cdot 34631.$$

The result obtained by integrating $\displaystyle\int_0^6 e^{-\delta t}\, dt$ will be $\left[-\dfrac{1}{\delta} e^{-\delta t}\right]_0^6$ or $\dfrac{v^0 - v^6}{\delta}$, and since the value of δ at 4 per cent. as given by an interest table is $\cdot 039220713\ldots$, the integral becomes

$$\frac{1 - \cdot 7903145257\cdots}{\cdot 039220713\cdots} = 5 \cdot 34629\ldots.$$

The three approximate formulae all give results which differ very little from this. The excellence of the approximations is due to the fact that between the limits $t=0$ and $t=6$ the higher differential coefficients of $y = u_t = e^{-\delta t}$ are very small and the range is short.

8. The Euler-Maclaurin expansion.

We have considered quadrature formulae in which the integral is expressed in terms of a number of particular ordinates. All formulae of this type can be deduced in a straightforward manner by means of Lagrange's interpolation formula, as shown at the end of this chapter. We will now proceed to investigate the problem of approximate integration more generally.

The basic formula for expressing a definite integral in terms of given ordinates, with adjustments, is the *Euler-Maclaurin expansion*. This expansion is in effect of similar form to the expressions already obtained, a greater degree of accuracy being ensured by the addition of functions, not of the ordinates themselves, but of derivatives of certain of the ordinates.

The formula may be derived by the expansion of operators, thus:

$$\sum_{x=0}^{x=n-1} f(x) = f(0) + f(1) + \dots + f(n-1)$$

$$= F(n) - F(0), \text{ where } f(x) \text{ is } \Delta F(x).$$

Since $f(x) = \Delta F(x)$,

$$F(x) = \Delta^{-1} f(x)$$

$$= (e^D - 1)^{-1} f(x) \text{ (since } 1 + \Delta \equiv e^D. \text{ Chap. VII, para. 6)}$$

$$= \left[\left(1 + D + \frac{D^2}{2!} + \frac{D^3}{3!} + \dots \right) - 1 \right]^{-1} f(x)$$

$$= D^{-1} \left[1 + \frac{D}{2!} + \frac{D^2}{3!} + \dots \right]^{-1} f(x)$$

$$= D^{-1} \left[1 - \frac{D}{2} + \frac{D^2}{12} - \frac{D^4}{720} \dots \right] f(x)$$

$$= \left[D^{-1} - \tfrac{1}{2} + \frac{D}{12} - \frac{D^3}{720} \dots \right] f(x)$$

$$= D^{-1} f(x) - \tfrac{1}{2} f(x) + \frac{D}{12} f(x) - \frac{D^3}{720} f(x) \dots$$

$$= \int f(x)\, dx - \tfrac{1}{2} f(x) + \frac{1}{12} \frac{df(x)}{dx} - \frac{1}{720} \frac{d^3 f(x)}{dx^3} \dots.$$

Between limits o and n, we have therefore

$$F(n) - F(o) = \int_0^n f(x)\, dx - \tfrac{1}{2}\{f(n) - f(o)\} + \tfrac{1}{12}\{f'(n) - f'(o)\}$$
$$- \tfrac{1}{720}\{f'''(n) - f'''(o)\} \dots.$$

For $F(n) - F(o)$ we may write

$$\sum_{x=0}^{x=n-1} f(x) \quad \text{or} \quad f(o) + f(1) + f(2) + \dots + f(n-1).$$

$$\therefore \int_0^n f(x)\, dx = f(o) + f(1) + f(2) + \dots + f(n-1) + \tfrac{1}{2}\{f(n) - f(o)\}$$
$$- \tfrac{1}{12}\{f'(n) - f'(o)\} + \tfrac{1}{720}\{f'''(n) - f'''(o)\} \dots$$
$$= \tfrac{1}{2}f(o) + f(1) + f(2) + \dots + f(n-1) + \tfrac{1}{2}f(n)$$
$$- \tfrac{1}{12}\{f'(n) - f'(o)\} + \tfrac{1}{720}\{f'''(n) - f'''(o)\} \dots.$$

This is a simple form of the Euler-Maclaurin expansion.

A more general form can be obtained by changing the origin to the point a and the unit of measurement to r, thus:

$$\frac{1}{r} \int_a^{a+nr} f(x)\, dx = \tfrac{1}{2}f(a) + f(a+r) + f(a+2r) + \dots$$

$$+ f(a + \overline{n-1}r) + \tfrac{1}{2}f(a+nr) - \frac{r}{12}\{f'(a+nr) - f'(a)\}$$

$$+ \frac{r^3}{720}\{f'''(a+nr) - f'''(a)\} \dots.$$

It will be noted that, since

$$\frac{x}{e^x - 1} = 1 - \tfrac{1}{2}x + B_1 \frac{x^2}{2!} - B_2 \frac{x^4}{4!} + B_3 \frac{x^6}{6!} - \dots$$

we can express the coefficients in $(e^D - 1)^{-1}$ in terms of Bernouilli's numbers. As, however, the resulting approximation formula is to be used for numerical computation, it is of advantage to give the coefficients their actual numerical values.

9. The following examples are illustrative of the use of the formula.

Example 3.

Evaluate $\int_0^1 \dfrac{dx}{1+x}$ to five places of decimals.

Choose a convenient unit, say 0·1. Then in the Euler-Maclaurin expansion we have

$$a = 0, \quad n = 10, \quad r = 0\cdot1, \quad \text{and} \quad u_x = \frac{1}{1+x}.$$

$$\frac{du_x}{dx} = -\frac{1}{(1+x)^2}; \quad \frac{d^3u}{dx^3} = -\frac{6}{(1+x)^4}.$$

$$\therefore \quad \frac{1}{0\cdot1}\int_0^1 \frac{dx}{1+x} = \frac{1}{2}\cdot\frac{1}{1} + \frac{1}{1\cdot1} + \frac{1}{1\cdot2} + \frac{1}{1\cdot3} + \dots + \frac{1}{1\cdot9} + \frac{1}{2}\cdot\frac{1}{2}$$

$$- \frac{0\cdot1}{12}\left[-\frac{1}{2^2}+\frac{1}{1^2}\right] + \frac{0\cdot001}{720}\left[-\frac{6}{2^4}+\frac{6}{1^4}\right] \dots$$

$$= \cdot50000 - \frac{1}{120}\cdot\frac{3}{4} + \frac{1}{720000}\cdot6\cdot\frac{15}{16}$$

$$\cdot90909$$
$$\cdot83333$$
$$\cdot76923$$
$$\cdot71429$$
$$\cdot66667$$
$$\cdot62500$$
$$\cdot58824$$
$$\cdot55556$$
$$\cdot52632$$
$$\cdot25000$$

$$\overline{\qquad\qquad}$$

$$6\cdot93773$$

$$= 6\cdot93773 - \cdot00625 + \cdot00001$$

$$= 6\cdot93149.$$

$$\therefore \quad \int_0^1 \frac{dx}{1+x} = \cdot69315 \text{ to five places of decimals.}$$

This agrees with the true result ($\log_e 2$) to the required degree of accuracy.

Example 4.

Find the sum of the fourth powers of the first n natural numbers by means of the Euler-Maclaurin formula.

In the formula

$$\frac{1}{r}\int_a^{a+nr} u_x dx = \tfrac{1}{2}u_a + u_{a+r} + u_{a+2r} + \dots$$

$$+ \tfrac{1}{2}u_{a+nr} - \frac{r}{12}(u'_{a+nr} - u'_a) + \frac{r^3}{720}(u'''_{a+nr} - u'''_a) \dots,$$

put $a=0$, $r=1$, $u_x=x^4$; then

$$\int_0^n x^4\,dx = 1^4 + 2^4 + 3^4 + \dots$$
$$+ (n-1)^4 + \frac{1}{2}n^4 - \frac{1}{12}[4x^3]_{x=n} + \frac{1}{720}[4\cdot3\cdot2x]_{x=n},$$

since higher differential coefficients of u_x than the fourth will be zero.

I.e.
$$\left[\frac{x^5}{5}\right]_0^n = \sum_{r=1}^{r=n} r^4 - \frac{1}{2}n^4 - \frac{1}{12}4n^3 + \frac{1}{720}24n.$$

$$\therefore \sum_{r=1}^{r=n} r^4 = \frac{1}{5}n^5 + \frac{1}{2}n^4 + \frac{1}{3}n^3 - \frac{1}{30}n.$$

By proceeding on the above lines it can easily be proved that the general formula for the sum of the pth powers of the first n natural numbers is

$$\sum_{r=1}^{r=n} r^p = \frac{1}{p+1}n^{p+1} + \frac{1}{2}n^p + \frac{1}{12}pn^{p-1} - \frac{1}{720}p\,(p-1)\,(p-2)\,n^{p-3}$$
$$+ \frac{p\,(p-1)\,(p-2)\,(p-3)\,(p-4)}{30,240}n^{p-5}\,\dots.$$

10. Lubbock's formula.

The previous formulae have been developed for the purpose of relating a definite integral to the sum of a number of weighted ordinates at finite distances apart. We have, in effect, obtained approximate formulae for the value of

$$\underset{h\to0}{\text{Lt}}\ h\,(u_a + u_{a+h} + u_{a+2h} + \dots + u_b).$$

In addition to formulae of this type we can find expressions which enable us to find the value of the sum of a number of ordinates at finite distances apart in terms of the ordinates at greater or less finite intervals apart. Thus, if for the curve $y=u_x$ there are m unit intervals, so that we have Σu_x from $x=0$ to $x=m-1$, we may develop a relationship between this sum and the sum when the intervals are, say, h, where $nh=1$.

In place of the sum $h\,(u_a + u_{a+h} + u_{a+2h} + \dots + u_b)$, we may consider, without loss of generality, the simpler form when the series commences with u_0.

Let there be m ordinates at unit distances apart, and let each of these unit distances be divided into n equal parts, so that the new ordinates are

$$u_0, u_{1/n}, u_{2/n}, \ldots u_{r/n}, \ldots u_{m-1/n}.$$

We have $\quad S \equiv u_0 + u_{1/n} + u_{2/n} + \ldots + u_{m-1/n}$

$$= \frac{E^m - 1}{E^{1/n} - 1} u_0 = \frac{\Delta}{E^{1/n} - 1} \cdot \frac{E^m - 1}{\Delta} u_0.$$

By ordinary algebra, putting h for $1/n$,

$$\frac{\Delta}{E^{1/n} - 1} \equiv \frac{\Delta}{(1 + \Delta)^h - 1} \equiv \frac{\Delta}{h\Delta + h_{(2)}\Delta^2 + \ldots}$$

$$\equiv \frac{1}{h} - \frac{h-1}{2h}\Delta + \frac{h^2-1}{12h}\Delta^2 - \frac{h^2-1}{24h}\Delta^3 \ldots,$$

so that the operator is

$$n + \frac{n-1}{2}\Delta - \frac{n^2-1}{12n}\Delta^2 + \frac{n^2-1}{24n}\Delta^3 \ldots.$$

To obtain S we apply this operator to

$$\frac{E^m - 1}{\Delta} u_0 = u_0 + u_1 + \ldots + u_{m-1}.$$

We note the first difference of this is

$$(E^m - 1) u_0 = u_m - u_0,$$

the second difference is $\Delta u_m - \Delta u_0$ and so on.

Thus, applying the operator,

$$S \equiv u_0 + u_{1/n} + u_{2/n} + \ldots + u_{m-1/n}$$

$$= n\,(u_0 + u_1 + \ldots + u_{m-1}) + \frac{n-1}{2}\,(u_m - u_0) - \frac{n^2-1}{12n}\,(\Delta u_m - \Delta u_0)$$

$$+ \frac{n^2-1}{24n}\,(\Delta^2 u_m - \Delta^2 u_0) \ldots.$$

This is Lubbock's formula.

The coefficients of higher differences than the second were not given by Lubbock and are cumbersome. The terms in $\Delta^3 u$ and $\Delta^4 u$ are respectively

$$- \frac{(n^2-1)\,(19n^2-1)}{720n^3}\,(\Delta^3 u_m - \Delta^3 u_0)$$

and $$\frac{(n^2-1)(9n^2-1)}{480n^3}(\Delta^4 u_m - \Delta^4 u_0).$$

If the interval of differencing be originally n instead of unity, Lubbock's formula becomes, on changing the unit,

$$u_0 + u_1 + u_2 + \ldots + u_{mn-1}$$

$$= n\left(u_0 + u_n + u_{2n} + \ldots + u_{(m-1)n}\right) + \frac{n-1}{2}\left(u_{mn} - u_0\right)$$

$$-\frac{n^2-1}{12n}\left(\Delta u_{mn} - \Delta u_0\right) + \frac{n^2-1}{24n}\left(\Delta^2 u_{mn} - \Delta^2 u_0\right)\ldots.$$

*11. Lubbock's original formula involves Δu_m, $\Delta^2 u_m$, ... and these involve u_{m+1}, u_{m+2}, ..., i.e. values of u beyond the range of summation; these u's may have to be specially calculated or may even be completely unavailable. De Morgan (*Differential and Integral Calculus*, pp. 317–18) and T. B. Sprague (*J.I.A.* vol. XVIII, pp. 309–10) transformed the formula so as to involve only $u_0 \ldots u_m$. If the numerical values (without sign) of the coefficients of the differences in Lubbock's formula be represented by C_1, C_2, ..., the transformed formula is

$$n\left(u_0 + u_1 + \ldots + u_{m-1}\right) + \frac{n-1}{2}\left(u_m - u_0\right) - C_1\left(\Delta u_{m-1} - \Delta u_0\right)$$

$$- C_2\left(\Delta^2 u_{m-2} + \Delta^2 u_0\right) - C_3\left(\Delta^3 u_{m-3} - \Delta^3 u_0\right) - C_4\left(\Delta^4 u_{m-4} + \Delta^4 u_0\right)\ldots,$$

where all C coefficients are negative and the terms involve alternately the *difference* between the terminal *odd* differences and the *sum* of the terminal *even* differences. The differences Δu_{m-1}, $\Delta^2 u_{m-2}$, $\Delta^3 u_{m-3}$, ... are the concluding differences of the scheme based on $u_0 \ldots u_m$, and lie on a diagonal sloping upwards (Sprague, *loc. cit.* p. 310).

12. Woolhouse's formula.

Although Lubbock's formula has the advantage that it may be used when the function is not capable of expression as a mathematical expansion—as for example when the data are based on a mortality table—there are disadvantages in adopting the formula. In the first place, if it is necessary to proceed further than second differences the calculations are heavy, and secondly it may happen that the differences converge slowly, so that if we stop at second or third differences we are likely to obtain a result differing considerably from the true value of the function. In the case of a mathematical function whose differential coefficients are easily evaluated an alternative summation formula can be adopted in which differential coefficients of odd order replace the finite differences in Lubbock's formula.

The formula involving differential coefficients is due to Woolhouse, and may be developed directly from the Euler-Maclaurin expansion.

The Euler-Maclaurin expansion is

$$\int_0^m u_x dx = \tfrac{1}{2}u_0 + u_1 + u_2 + \ldots + u_{m-1} + \tfrac{1}{2}u_m - \frac{1}{12}\left(u_m{}' - u_0{}'\right)$$

$$+ \frac{1}{720}\left(u_m{}''' - u_0{}'''\right) \ldots .$$

If the interval of differencing be $1/n$, the formula becomes

$$n\int_0^m u_x dx = \left(\tfrac{1}{2}u_0 + u_{1/n} + u_{2/n} + \ldots + \tfrac{1}{2}u_m\right) - \frac{1}{12n}\left(u_m{}' - u_0{}'\right)$$

$$+ \frac{1}{720n^3}\left(u_m{}''' - u_0{}'''\right) \ldots .$$

If, however, we multiply both sides of the first expression by n we have

$$n\int_0^m u_x dx = n\left(\tfrac{1}{2}u_0 + u_1 + u_2 + \ldots + \tfrac{1}{2}u_m\right) - \frac{n}{12}\left(u_m{}' - u_0{}'\right)$$

$$+ \frac{n}{720}\left(u_m{}''' - u_0{}'''\right) \ldots .$$

Equating the two values of $n\int_0^m u_x dx$:

$$\tfrac{1}{2}u_0 + u_{1/n} + u_{2/n} + \ldots + \tfrac{1}{2}u_m - \frac{1}{12n}\left(u_m{}' - u_0{}'\right) + \frac{1}{720n^3}\left(u_m{}''' - u_0{}'''\right) \ldots$$

$$= n\left(\tfrac{1}{2}u_0 + u_1 + u_2 + \ldots + \tfrac{1}{2}u_m\right) - \frac{n}{12}\left(u_m{}' - u_0{}'\right) + \frac{n}{720}\left(u_m{}''' - u_0{}'''\right) \ldots$$

or

$$u_0 + u_{1/n} + u_{2/n} + \ldots + u_m - \tfrac{1}{2}(u_0 + u_m) - \frac{1}{12n}(u_m' - u_0')$$

$$+ \frac{1}{720n^3}(u_m''' - u_0''') \ldots$$

$$= n(u_0 + u_1 + u_2 + \ldots + u_m) - \frac{n}{2}(u_0 + u_m) - \frac{n}{12}(u_m' - u_0')$$

$$+ \frac{n}{720}(u_m''' - u_0''') \ldots.$$

Re-arranging:

$$u_0 + u_{1/n} + u_{2/n} + \ldots + u_m = n(u_0 + u_1 + u_2 + \ldots + u_m)$$

$$- \frac{n-1}{2}(u_0 + u_m) - \frac{n^2 - 1}{12n}(u_m' - u_0') + \frac{n^4 - 1}{720n^3}(u_m''' - u_0''') \ldots.$$

If the unit of measurement be changed to n, we have

$$u_0 + u_1 + u_2 + \ldots + u_{mn} = n(u_0 + u_n + u_{2n} + \ldots + u_{mn})$$

$$- \frac{n-1}{2}(u_0 + u_{mn}) - \frac{n^2 - 1}{12}(u_{mn}' - u_0') + \frac{n^4 - 1}{720}(u_{mn}''' - u_0''') \ldots,$$

the usual form of Woolhouse's formula.

It should be noted that, by replacing the derivatives of u by their values in finite differences, Lubbock's formula can be obtained directly from the formula above.

In applying these formulae to certain actuarial functions the values of u, $\frac{du}{dx}$, $\frac{d^3u}{dx^3}$, ... at the end of the mortality table will disappear. Woolhouse's formula may then be written as

$$\frac{1}{n}(u_0 + u_{1/n} + u_{2/n} + \ldots)$$

$$= (u_0 + u_1 + \ldots) - \frac{n-1}{2n}u_0 + \frac{n^2 - 1}{12n^2}u_0' - \frac{n^4 - 1}{720n^4}u_0''' \ldots.$$

This is a convenient form for expressing the value of a benefit paid at $n$thly intervals in terms of the values at intervals of a year.

13. Other formulae for approximate integration.

It will have been observed that in the formulae of the type of Simpson's, Weddle's, etc., the function of the u's is symmetrical about the central value. If, however, a number of fixed ordinates be given and it is desired to obtain an approximation to the area of a curve in terms of these ordinates, the resulting form will not necessarily be symmetrical. Again, the formula for the area of the curve may be related not only to ordinates falling within the area to be measured, but to ordinates outside the area. It may be noted therefore that although standard formulae are available, it is not difficult to devise approximations to fit the particular problems under investigation. (See paragraph 15.)

Example 5.

If u_x is of the form $a + bx + cx^2$, find a formula for $\int_0^1 u_x dx$ in terms of u_0, u_1 and u_2.

The interpolation formula which involves the terms u_0, u_1 and u_2 is

$$u_x = u_0 + x\Delta u_0 + \tfrac{1}{2}x(x-1)\Delta^2 u_0.$$

$$\therefore \quad \int_0^1 u_x dx = \left[xu_0 + \tfrac{1}{2}x^2\Delta u_0 + (\tfrac{1}{6}x^3 - \tfrac{1}{4}x^2)\Delta^2 u_0 \right]_0^1$$

$$= u_0 + \tfrac{1}{2}\Delta u_0 - \tfrac{1}{12}\Delta^2 u_0$$

$$= u_0 + \tfrac{1}{2}(u_1 - u_0) - \tfrac{1}{12}(u_2 - 2u_1 + u_0)$$

$$= \tfrac{5}{12}u_0 + \tfrac{8}{12}u_1 - \tfrac{1}{12}u_2.$$

The required formula is therefore

$$\int_0^1 u_x dx = \tfrac{1}{12}(5u_0 + 8u_1 - u_2).$$

It should be noted that (i) the expression is unsymmetrical in the u's, and (ii) the ordinate u_2 falls without the area to be integrated.

Example 6.

If u_x is of the same form as in the example above, derive a formula for $\int_0^1 u_x dx$ in terms of u_{-1}, u_1 and u_2.

Let u_x be expressed in the divided difference formula, thus:

$$u_x = u_{-1} + (x+1)\underset{1}{\triangle}u_{-1} + (x+1)(x-1)\underset{1,2}{\triangle^2}u_{-1}.$$

Then
$$\int_0^1 u_x = \left[xu_{-1} + \left(\frac{x^2}{2} + x \right) \underset{1}{\triangle} u_{-1} + \left(\frac{x^3}{3} - x \right) \underset{1,2}{\triangle^2} u_{-1} \right]_0^1$$

$$= u_{-1} + \tfrac{3}{2} \underset{1}{\triangle} u_{-1} - \tfrac{2}{3} \underset{1,2}{\triangle^2} u_{-1};$$

$$\underset{1}{\triangle} u_{-1} = \frac{u_1 - u_{-1}}{2},$$

$$\underset{1,2}{\triangle^2} u_{-1} = \left\{ \frac{u_2 - u_1}{1} - \frac{u_1 - u_{-1}}{2} \right\} \bigg/ \{2 - (-1)\}.$$

On reduction, the integral is easily found to be

$$\tfrac{1}{36} (5u_{-1} + 39u_1 - 8u_2).$$

It is obviously impossible to quote all the formulae that are in current use. Further examples and illustrations of various approximation integration formulae will be found in the following sources: Whittaker and Robinson's *Calculus of Observations*, Chap. VII; C. H. Wickens, *J.I.A.* vol. LIV, pp. 209–13; A. E. King, *T.F.A.* vol. IX, pp. 218–31; Elderton's *Frequency Curves and Correlation*, 3rd ed., pp. 26–8; J. Buchanan, *J.I.A.* vol. XXXVII, p. 384.

14. Alternative methods of proof of the formulae.

It has been stated above that the Euler-Maclaurin expansion can be used as the basic quadrature formula. It will be instructive to develop Simpson's formula from this expansion.

$$\int_0^{2mn} u_x dx = n \left(\tfrac{1}{2} u_0 + u_n + u_{2n} + \dots + u_{(2m-1)n} + \tfrac{1}{2} u_{2mn} \right) - \frac{n^2}{12} \left(u'_{2mn} - u_0' \right)$$

approximately.

Writing $2n$ for n, but preserving the same range 0 to $2mn$,

$$\int_0^{2mn} u_x dx = 2n \left(\tfrac{1}{2} u_0 + u_{2n} + u_{4n} + \dots + u_{(2m-2)n} + \tfrac{1}{2} u_{2mn} \right)$$
$$- \frac{4n^2}{12} \left(u'_{2mn} - u_0' \right).$$

Subtracting this from four times the first:

$$3 \int_0^{2mn} u_x dx = 2n \left(\tfrac{1}{2} u_0 + 2u_n + u_{2n} + 2u_{3n} + \dots + u_{(2m-2)n} \right.$$
$$\left. + 2u_{(2m-1)n} + \tfrac{1}{2} u_{2mn} \right);$$

i.e.

$$\int_0^{2mn} u_x dx = \frac{n}{3} \left(u_0 + 4u_n + 2u_{2n} + 4u_{3n} + \ldots + 2u_{(2m-2)n} \right.$$
$$\left. + 4u_{(2m-1)n} + u_{2mn} \right),$$

which is the extended Simpson's formula.

15. Proofs by Lagrange's formula.

We have shown in paragraph 2 (p. 176) that we may adopt the expression for u_x in terms of u_0 and differences of u_0 as the assumed form of function. Since Lagrange's formula is based on the same assumption it is evident that, given selected ordinates, at either equal or unequal intervals, we can obtain any approximate formula by the use of the Lagrange formula.

For example, given u_0, u_1, u_2,

$$u_x = u_0 \frac{(x-1)(x-2)}{(-1)(-2)} + u_1 \frac{x(x-2)}{1.(-1)} + u_2 \frac{x(x-1)}{2.1}$$
$$= \tfrac{1}{2} u_0 (x^2 - 3x + 2) + u_1 (2x - x^2) + \tfrac{1}{2} u_2 (x^2 - x),$$

so that

$$\int_0^2 u_x dx = \left[u_0 \left(\frac{x^3}{6} - \frac{3x^2}{4} + x \right) + u_1 \left(x^2 - \frac{x^3}{3} \right) + u_2 \left(\frac{x^3}{6} - \frac{x^2}{4} \right) \right]_0^2$$
$$= \tfrac{1}{3} (u_0 + 4u_1 + u_2), \text{ which is Simpson's rule.}$$

If we integrate between 0 and 1 we shall obtain

$$\int_0^1 u_x dx = \tfrac{1}{12} (5u_0 + 8u_1 - u_2),$$

the formula given in Example 5.

By this method it is easy and straightforward to deduce special formulae for particular cases.

*16. Remainder terms.

It is known (Chap. III, paragraph 17) that if an interpolation formula is used to find u_x from n values u_a, u_b, ... u_k, the error involved, or remainder term, is of the form

$$(x-a)(x-b) \ldots (x-k) \frac{d^n}{dx^n} u_\xi,$$

where ξ is an unknown number falling in the range which includes $x, a, b \ldots k$. By means of this result, expressions in similar form have been found for the errors or remainder terms of the principal quadrature formulae.

For example, if the range of integration is a to b, the remainder term in Simpson's formula is

$$-\cdot00035\,(b-a)^5\,\frac{d^4}{dx^4}\,u_\xi$$

and that of the three-eighths rule is

$$-\cdot00016\,(b-a)^5\,\frac{d^4}{dx^4}\,u_\xi.$$

We cannot usually find ξ, but if the maximum value of the differential coefficient can be found the expression gives an upper limit for the error.

For further information on this point the student is referred to Steffensen, *Interpolation*, Sections 12–16, and Milne-Thomson, *Calculus of Finite Differences*, Chap. VII.

EXAMPLES 9

1. Prove that

$$\int_0^{2a} u_x\,dx = \int_0^a (u_x + u_{2a-x})\,dx,$$

and illustrate the result geometrically.

2. If $u_x = a + bx + cx^2$, prove that

$$\int_1^3 u_x\,dx = 2u_2 + \tfrac{1}{12}(u_0 - 2u_2 + u_4),$$

and hence find an approximate value for

$$\int_{-\frac{1}{2}}^{\frac{1}{2}} e^{-\frac{x^2}{10}}\,dx.$$

3. Show that $\int_0^1 u_x\,dx = \tfrac{1}{12}(5u_1 + 8u_0 - u_{-1})$ approximately.

Find the approximate mileage travelled between 12.0 and 12.30 by use of the above formula, from the following:

Time	Speed (m.p.h.)
11.50	24·2
12.0	35·0
12.10	41·3
12.20	42·8
12.30	39·2

4. Prove that, if u_x is a rational integral function of x, then

$$\int e^{\frac{x}{a}} u_x\, dx = ae^{\frac{x}{a}} \left(1 - aD + a^2D^2 - a^3D^3 + \ldots\right) u_x,$$

where $D \equiv \dfrac{d}{dx}$.

5. Show that the area of a curve, divided into n parts by $n+1$ equidistant ordinates $u_0, u_1, \ldots u_n$, is given approximately by the series

$$nu_0 + \frac{n^2}{2}\Delta u_0 + \left\{\frac{n^3}{3} - \frac{n^2}{2}\right\}\frac{\Delta^2 u_0}{1.2} + \left\{\frac{n^4}{4} - n^3 + n^2\right\}\frac{\Delta^3 u_0}{1.2.3} \ldots$$

to $n+1$ terms.

6. Between the limits $x=0$ and $x=n$ the functions u_x and du_x/dx are continuously increasing.

Show that $\displaystyle\int_0^n u_x\, dx$ is less than $\frac{1}{2}u_0 + \displaystyle\sum_1^{n-1} u_x + \frac{1}{2}u_n$.

7. Obtain the approximate formula

$$\int_{-1}^1 u_x\, dx = \frac{13\,(u_1 + u_{-1}) - (u_3 + u_{-3})}{12},$$

showing up to what order of differences it holds.

8. Assuming u_x to be of the fourth degree in x, express $\displaystyle\int_0^5 u_x\, dx$ in terms of u_0, u_1, u_2, u_3 and u_4.

9. A plane area is bounded by a curve, the axis of x, and two ordinates. The area is divided into five figures by equidistant ordinates 2 inches apart, the lengths of the ordinates being 21·65, 21·04, 20·35, 19·61, 18·75 and 17·80 inches respectively. Apply the method of integration to obtain an approximate value of the area.

10. Prove the approximate formula

$$\int_0^{10} u_x\, dx = 2·5\,(u_1 + u_4 + u_6 + u_9),$$

and show that the formula involves a small second difference error.

11. Find the value of $\int_0^6 (1+x)^{-2}\,dx$.

Obtain approximations to the value by applying

(i) Weddle's rule:

$$\int_0^6 u_x\,dx = 0\cdot3\,(u_0 + 5u_1 + u_2 + 6u_3 + u_4 + 5u_5 + u_6),$$

(ii) Simpson's rule:

$$\int_0^2 u_x\,dx = \tfrac{1}{3}\,(u_0 + 4u_1 + u_2),\ \text{applied three times.}$$

12. Which of the two following formulae would you expect to give the better approximation for $\int_0^4 u_x\,dx$?

(a) $\tfrac{1}{9}\{5\,(u_0 + u_4) + 4\,(u_1 + u_3) + 18u_2\}$,

(b) $\tfrac{2}{15}\{2\,(u_0 + u_2 + u_4) + 12\,(u_1 + u_3)\}$.

13. Prove the approximate integration formula:

$$\int_0^n u_x\,dx = n\,\{\tfrac{3}{8}u_0 + \tfrac{1}{24}\,(19u_n - 5u_{2n} + u_{3n})\},$$

and hence find $\int_0^1 u_x\,dx$ given the following table:

x	0	1	2	3
u_x	27,650	31,252	35,154	39,368

14. Prove that

$$\int_{-\frac{1}{2}}^{\frac{1}{2}} f(x)\,dx = \tfrac{1}{2}\,\{f(-\tfrac{1}{2}) + f(\tfrac{1}{2})\} + \tfrac{1}{24}\,\{\Delta f(-\tfrac{3}{2}) - \Delta f(\tfrac{1}{2})\}\ \text{approximately.}$$

Hence find $\int_1^3 f(x)\,dx$, when $f(0) = 105$, $f(1) = 212$, $f(2) = 421$, $f(3) = 749$ and $f(4) = 1050$.

15. If u_x either increases continually or decreases continually as x increases, prove that $\int_1^n u_x\,dx$ differs from $\overset{n-1}{\underset{1}{\Sigma}}\,u_x$ by less than the difference between u_1 and u_n.

Prove that the difference between $\log n$ and

$$1 + \tfrac{1}{2} + \tfrac{1}{3} + \dots + 1/(n-1) < 1,$$

however great n may be.

16. If third differences are constant, prove that

$$\int_0^2 u_x dx = \tfrac{1}{24}(u_{-\frac{1}{2}} + 23u_{\frac{1}{2}} + 23u_{\frac{3}{2}} + u_{\frac{5}{2}}).$$

Adapt this formula to find the approximate value of $\log_e 2$ from the integral $\int_a^{2a} \dfrac{dx}{x}$.

17. Prove that, approximately,

$$\int_{-3}^3 u_x dx = 0.3\,(1.1u_{-3} + 4.4u_{-2} + 2.5u_{-1} + 4u_0 + 2.5u_1 + 4.4u_2 + 1.1u_3).$$

18. $f(x)$ is a rational integral function of the fifth degree in x. Prove that

$$\int_{-1}^1 f(x)\,dx = \tfrac{8}{9}f(0) + \tfrac{5}{9}\{f(\sqrt{0.6}) + f(-\sqrt{0.6})\}.$$

19. Use Simpson's rule to prove that $\log_e 7$ is approximately 1.95.

20. Apply the Euler-Maclaurin formula to find a formula for the sum of the fifth powers of the first n natural numbers.

21. Obtain Shovelton's integration formula:

$$\int_0^{10} u_x dx = \tfrac{5}{126}\{8\,(u_0 + u_{10}) + 35\,(u_1 + u_3 + u_7 + u_9)$$
$$+ 15\,(u_2 + u_4 + u_6 + u_8) + 36u_5\}.$$

22. By means of Hardy's formula

$$\int_0^6 u_x dx = .28u_0 + 1.62u_1 + 2.2u_3 + 1.62u_5 + .28u_6,$$

calculate the value of

$$\int_0^{\frac{1}{2}} (1 - x^2)^{-\frac{1}{2}}\,dx$$

correct to four places of decimals.

23. If $f(x)$ be a function of the third degree in x, and if

$$u_{-1} = \int_{-3t}^{-t} f(x)\,dx, \quad u_0 = \int_{-t}^t f(x)\,dx, \quad u_1 = \int_t^{3t} f(x)\,dx,$$

show that $$f(0) = \frac{1}{2t}\left\{u_0 - \frac{\Delta^2 u_{-1}}{24}\right\}.$$

24. AB is the base of a semicircle, centre O and radius unity. The points P and Q bisect OA and OB respectively. The area between the

semicircle, the base PQ and the ordinates at P and Q is $\dfrac{\pi}{6}+\dfrac{\sqrt{3}}{4}$. Use Weddle's rule that

$$\int_0^6 f(x)\,dx = 0\cdot3\,\{f(0)+5f(1)+f(2)+6f(3)+f(4)+5f(5)+f(6)\}$$

to find an approximate value of π to three places of decimals.

25. The following values of u_x are given:

x	0	1	2	3	4	5	6
u_x	·146	·161	·176	·190	·204	·217	·230

Use an approximate integration formula to find the value of $\displaystyle\int_0^6 u_x\,dx$.

It is found that, for the values given, $y=\log_{10}(\cdot05x+1\cdot4)$ fits the data. Verify that this is so by integrating $\log_{10}(\cdot05x+1\cdot4)$ between the limits 0 and 6. ($\log_{10} e = \cdot4343$; $\log_{10} 1\cdot7 = \cdot2304$; $\log_{10} 1\cdot4 = \cdot1461$.)

26. If u_x is a function whose fifth differences are constant, $\displaystyle\int_{-1}^1 u_x\,dx$ can be expressed in the form

$$pu_{-\alpha}+qu_0+pu_\alpha.$$

Find the values of p, q and α.

Use this formula, after making the necessary changes in the origin and scale, to find the value of $\log_e 2$ to four places of decimals from the equation

$$\int_0^1 \frac{1}{1+x}\,dx = \log_e 2.$$

27. Prove that, if $a=0$,

$$\int_a^{a+r} u_x\,dx = \tfrac12 u_0+u_1+u_2+\ldots+u_{r-1}+\tfrac12 u_r-\tfrac{1}{12}\,(\Delta u_{r-1}-\Delta u_0)$$
$$-\tfrac{1}{24}\,(\Delta^2 u_{r-2}+\Delta^2 u_0)-\tfrac{19}{720}\,(\Delta^3 u_{r-3}-\Delta^3 u_0)$$
$$-\tfrac{3}{160}\,(\Delta^4 u_{r-4}+\Delta^4 u_0)\ldots.$$

If u_x be the function $(1+x^2)^{-1}$ find an approximate value for π.

28. Obtain an approximate formula for $\displaystyle\int_{-3}^3 u_x\,dx$ in the form

$$a\,(u_{-2}+u_2)+b\,(u_{-3}+u_3)$$

and find the values of a and b.

29. Use Lagrange's formula to show that

$$\int_{-\frac12}^{\frac12} y_x\,dx = \tfrac{1}{5760}\,[5178y_0+308\,(y_{-1}+y_1)-17\,(y_{-2}+y_2)].$$

MISCELLANEOUS EXAMPLES

1. Find the sum of n terms of the series 1, 2, 4, 9, 19, 36, 62.

2. Given $u_0 = 1027$, $u_6 = 1212$, $u_{12} = 1469$, $u_{18} = 2014$, explain

   (i) how you would complete the series from u_0 to u_6;

   (ii) how you would proceed if you were asked to complete the series from u_6 to u_{12} supposing that it were unnecessary to find u_1, u_2, u_3, u_4 and u_5.

3. From the following data find the values of u_2 and u_{10}:

$$u_0 = 2000, \ u_4 = 1592, \ u_6 = 1462, \ u_8 = 1356 \text{ and } u_{12} = 1164.$$

4. Find the tenth term of the series:

   (a) 1, 4, 13, 36, 97, 268, 765, ...;

   (b) 2, 12, 36, 98, 270, 768, ...

5. Show that $\Delta u_x v_x = v_x \Delta u_x + u_{x+1} \Delta v_x$ and hence prove by mathematical induction that

$$\Delta^n u_x v_x = v_x \Delta^n u_x + n_{(1)} \Delta v_x \Delta^{n-1} u_{x+1} + n_{(2)} \Delta^2 v_x \Delta^{n-2} u_{x+2} \\ + n_{(3)} \Delta^3 v_x \Delta^{n-3} u_{x+3} + \dots.$$

6. u_x is a polynomial of the third degree in x. $u_0 = 13$, $u_1 + u_2 + u_3 = 214$, $u_4 + u_5 + u_6 = 844$ and $u_7 + u_8 + u_9 = 2149$. Find u_9.

7. Prove that in the process of obtaining divided differences of the function u_x, given u_a, u_b, u_c, ..., the last divided difference is numerically the same whatever the order of the arguments and the corresponding u's.

8. Show that

$$(1) \ \Sigma x^m = C + \frac{x^{(2)}}{2!} \Delta o^m + \frac{x^{(3)}}{3!} \Delta^2 o^m + \dots;$$

$$(2) \ \Sigma u_x = C + x^{(1)} u_0 + \frac{x^{(2)}}{2!} \Delta u_0 + \frac{x^{(3)}}{3!} \Delta^2 u_0 + \dots.$$

9. Given $u_{20} = 8820$, $u_{21} = 9240$, $u_{22} = 9684$, $u_{23} = 10{,}158$ and $u_{24} = 10{,}668$, find that value of x lying between 22 and 23 for which $u_x = 10{,}000$ by

   (i) the method of successive approximation,

   (ii) the method of elimination of third differences.

10. If u_0, u_5, u_{10}, u_{15} be four values of a function at equidistant points, find expressions true to third differences for u_6 and u_8, solely in terms of u_0, u_5, u_{10} and u_{15}.

11. Show that the series whose nth term is

$$\frac{(-1)^{n-1}}{8^{n-1}}\frac{1.3.5\ldots(2n-3)}{(n-1)!}\Delta^{2(n-1)}u_{x-n+\frac{1}{2}}$$

is equivalent to

$$2\left(u_x - u_{x+1} + u_{x+2} - u_{x+3} + \ldots\right).$$

12. If $u_0 = 21$, $u_2 = 29$, $u_3 = 66$ and $u_6 = 597$, find by divided differences the value of $\dfrac{du_x}{dx}$ when $x = 2$.

13. Obtain the approximate quadrature formula

$$\int_{-\frac{1}{2}}^{1\frac{1}{2}} u_x\,dx = \tfrac{1}{24}\left(27u_0 + 17u_1 + 5u_2 - u_3\right).$$

14. Given that u_x is a function of x of the third degree, obtain an expression in as simple a form as possible for u_0 in terms of $[3]\,u_0$, $[7]\,u_0$ and $[9]\,u_0$.

15. Find the sum to n terms of each of the following series:

(i) $1^2.2.3 + 2^2.3.4 + 3^2.4.5 + \ldots$.

(ii) $\dfrac{2}{1.3.4} + \dfrac{3}{2.4.5} + \dfrac{4}{3.5.6} + \ldots$.

16. Show that $\Delta^2 \sin x = -2\left(1 - \cos h\right)\sin\left(x+h\right)$ and hence prove that if n is a positive integer

$$\frac{\Delta^{2n}\sin x}{\Delta^{2n}\cos x} = \tan\left(x+nh\right),$$

where h is the interval of differencing.

17. Given $f(-5) = 192$, $f(-1) = 52$, $f(2) = 10$ and $f(9) = 1102$, construct a divided difference table for $f(x)$ and hence find the minimum value of $f(x)$ in this range, assuming that it is a polynomial in x of the third degree.

18. Prove that

$$\Delta^n o^m = n^m - n_{(1)} (n-1)^m + n_{(2)} (n-2)^m - \ldots,$$

and hence, or otherwise, find the sum to infinity of the series

$$\frac{1^4}{2} + \frac{2^4}{2.4} + \frac{3^4}{2.4.6} + \frac{4^4}{2.4.6.8} + \ldots.$$

19. Prove that $\sum_{x=0}^{n-1} (u_x \Delta v_x) = (u_n v_n - u_0 v_0) - \sum_{x=0}^{n-1} (v_{x+1} \Delta u_x)$ and find the value of $\sum_{x=0}^{n-1} x^2$ by means of this formula.

20. If $\sum_{x=a}^{a+x} u_x = w_a$ for all integral values of a, prove that, to the third order of differences,

$$u_7 = \cdot 2 w_5 - \cdot 008 (w_{10} - 2 w_5 + w_0).$$

Given the following table, find u_7, u_{12} and u_{17}:

a	0	5	10	15	20
$\sum_{x=a}^{a+4}$	·0427	·1467	·2459	·3408	·4317

21. Given that u_x is a polynomial in x of the third degree and that $u_0 = 0$, $u_1 = 30$, $u_5 = 330$ and $u_8 = 1080$, use Lagrange's interpolation formula to find the form of u_x.

Hence, or otherwise, find values of x for which $\Delta u_x = 2 \Delta^2 u_x$.

22. The equation $10x^3 + 3 = 15x$ has a root between 1 and 2. Obtain it to three places of decimals by inverse interpolation.

23. The following formulae for approximate integration are correct to third differences:

$$\int_{-3}^{+3} u_x dx = \tfrac{3}{4} (3u_{-2} + 2u_0 + 3u_2),$$

$$\int_{-3}^{+3} u_x dx = u_{-3} + 4u_0 + u_3.$$

Prove that if these formulae are applied to a function whose fifth differences are constant, the respective errors involved in the approximations are in the ratio 7:18, and are in opposite directions.

By a combination of the two formulae obtain an expression, correct to fifth differences, for $\int_{-3}^{+3} u_x dx$.

24. Develop Stirling's formula

$$u_x = u_0 + x \cdot \tfrac{1}{2}(\Delta u_0 + \Delta u_{-1}) + \frac{x^2}{2!}\Delta^2 u_{-1} + \frac{x(x^2-1)}{3!} \cdot \tfrac{1}{2}(\Delta^3 u_{-1} + \Delta^3 u_{-2}) + \dots$$

from Gauss's formula.

Hence, if n is an integer, prove that, neglecting third and higher differences,

$$u_{-x} = \frac{x(x+n)}{2n^2} u_{-n} - \frac{x^2-n^2}{n^2} u_0 + \frac{x(x-n)}{2n^2} u_n.$$

25. (i) If third differences of u_n are constant express u_n in terms of u_0, Δu_1, $\Delta^2 u_2$ and $\Delta^3 u_3$.

(ii) Prove that

$$(u_1 - u_0) - x(u_2 - u_1) + x^2(u_3 - u_2) - x^3(u_4 - u_3) + \dots$$
$$= \frac{\Delta u_0}{1+x} - \frac{x\Delta^2 u_0}{(1+x)^2} + \frac{x^2\Delta^3 u_0}{(1+x)^3} - \dots.$$

The series may be assumed to be convergent.

26. Given that $f(0) = 1 \cdot 00$, $f(1) = \cdot 96$, $f(4) = \cdot 84$ and $f(9) = \cdot 67$, calculate $f(6)$ by means of Lagrange's formula.

Check your result by altering the scale of the argument in $f(x)$ so that a value for $f(6)$ may be obtained directly by means of the advancing difference formula.

27. If $f(x) = u_x + u_{x+1}$, show that

$$u_{x+\frac{1}{2}} = \frac{1}{2}\left[f(x) - \frac{1}{8}\Delta^2 f(x-1) + \frac{1 \cdot 3}{8 \cdot 16}\Delta^4 f(x-2) \right.$$
$$\left. - \frac{1 \cdot 3 \cdot 5}{8 \cdot 16 \cdot 24}\Delta^6 f(x-3) + \dots \right].$$

28. Explain Sheppard's rules and use them to obtain any two central difference formulae as far as fourth differences.

Use either of these formulae to find $u_{17 \cdot 4}$ correct to two decimal places from the following data:

$$u_{12} = 49 \cdot 00; \; u_{14} = 54 \cdot 84; \; u_{16} = 59 \cdot 04; \; u_{18} = 62 \cdot 02; \; u_{20} = 64 \cdot 04.$$

29. Using finite difference methods, sum to n terms:

(i) $3 \cdot 2^2 + 5 \cdot 5^2 + 7 \cdot 8^2 + 9 \cdot 11^2 + \dots$

(ii) $\dfrac{8}{1 \cdot 7 \cdot 10} + \dfrac{11}{4 \cdot 10 \cdot 13} + \dfrac{14}{7 \cdot 13 \cdot 16} + \dfrac{17}{10 \cdot 16 \cdot 19} + \dots$

30. (i) Obtain an approximate formula for $\displaystyle\int_0^{10} u_x \, dx$ in terms of u_0, u_3, u_6 and u_9, and state to what order of difference the formula is true.

(ii) Prove that $\displaystyle\int_0^6 u_x \, dx = \tfrac{3}{10} \left[(u_0 + u_6) + 5(u_1 + u_5) + (u_2 + u_4) + 6u_3 \right]$ approximately. Show that the formula is true to fifth differences and find the sixth difference error.

31. Find an expression, correct to fourth differences, for the value of du_x/dx when $x = 1$, in terms of u_{-2}, u_{-1}, u_0, u_1, u_2.

32. Show that, if fourth differences of u are constant,

$$\left(\tfrac{1}{5}\,[5] - 1 \right)(u_{n+2} - u_2) = \Delta^2 u_{n+1} - \Delta^2 u_1.$$

33. Prove that

$$\int_0^1 \frac{dx}{1 + x^2} = \frac{1}{4a} \left(1 + \frac{1}{6a} \right) + \sum_{x=1}^{x=a} \frac{a}{a^2 + x^2}$$

approximately, where a is a positive integer.

By putting $a = 3$, obtain the value of π to three places of decimals.

34. Find the sum to n terms of the series

$$1, \ 4, \ 13, \ 30, \ 59, \ \dots,$$

(i) assuming fourth differences constant, and

(ii) assuming third differences increase in geometrical progression.

Compare the two answers where $n = 6$.

35. By means of the formula (taking $n = 10$)

$$\sum_{x=0}^{x=mn} u_{a+x} = n \sum_{x=0}^{x=m} u_{a+nx} - \frac{n-1}{2} (u_{a+mn} + u_a)$$

$$- \frac{n^2 - 1}{12} \left[\left(\frac{du_x}{dx} \right)_{x=a+mn} - \left(\frac{du_x}{dx} \right)_{x=a} \right] \text{ approx.,}$$

find the approximate value of $\log_{10} \dfrac{50!}{9!}$, given that $\log_{10} 2 = \cdot 3010$, $\log_{10} 3 = \cdot 4771$, $\log_{10} e = \cdot 4343$.

36. If $u_{x:y}$ is a function of the two independent variables x and y, develop the advancing difference formula for $u_{x:x}$ in terms of $u_{0:0}$ and differences of $u_{0:0}$ up to the third order.

Hence show that to second differences

$$u_{x:-x} = \tfrac{1}{2} (x-1)(x-2) u_{0:0} - x(x-2) u_{1:-1} + \tfrac{1}{2} x(x-1) u_{2:-2},$$

and also derive the formula from the advancing difference formula with a single variable.

37. Express E in terms of ascending powers of δ, where $\delta \equiv \Delta E^{-\frac{1}{2}}$ and where $E \equiv 1 + \Delta$.

Hence obtain an expression for u_x, correct to third differences, in terms of u_0, $\Delta u_{-\frac{1}{2}}$, $\Delta^2 u_{-1}$ and $\Delta^3 u_{-1\frac{1}{2}}$.

38. u_x is a polynomial of the third degree in x. Find u_4 and u_5 given that $u_0 = 16$, $\sum\limits_{x=0}^{2} u_x = 80$, $\sum\limits_{x=0}^{5} u_x = 346$ and $\sum\limits_{x=0}^{9} u_x = 1375$.

39. Calculate u_{11} by means of advancing differences given the following values of u_x: $u_2 = 1 \cdot 0$, $u_4 = 1 \cdot 2$, $u_6 = 1 \cdot 3$, $u_{13} = 1 \cdot 5$.

Check your result by means of divided differences.

40. (i) Prove that, if u_x is a function of x whose fourth differences are constant,

$$\frac{du_x}{dx} = \tfrac{2}{3} (u_{x+1} - u_{x-1}) - \tfrac{1}{12} (u_{x+2} - u_{x-2}).$$

Obtain an expression for $\dfrac{d^2 u_x}{dx^2}$ in a similar manner.

(ii) Show that

$$\frac{d^3 u_x}{dx^3} = \frac{1}{2h^3} (\Delta^3 u_{x-h} + \Delta^3 u_{x-2h}) \text{ approximately.}$$

41. A school contains 330 children, all of whom were born in the eleven years 1940–50. Four times the total number of children born in any group of five consecutive years is equal to five times the number born in the first and last years of the group *plus* ten times the number

born in the middle year of the group. The total number of children born in 1944, 1945 and 1946 is three less than three times the number born in 1945. Find the number born in 1945.

42. Given the function $f(x) = 3x^2 - 6x + 2$, what are the largest equal intervals of x at which $f(x)$ may be tabulated so that, within any interval, values of $f(x)$ can be found by first difference interpolation with an error numerically less than 0·05?

43. Establish Hardy's formula 39 a; and use a Hardy formula to find the value of $\int_0^1 (1 + x^2)^{-1} dx$ correct to four places of decimals.

44. Using finite difference methods find an expression for the sum to n terms of the series whose xth term is
$$(3x - 4)(3x - 1)(3x + 2)(3x + 5) - (2x - 1)(2x)(2x + 1).$$
(You are not required to reduce the expression to its simplest form.)

45. Prove that $u_1 - u_2 + u_3 - \ldots = \frac{1}{2}u_1 - (\frac{1}{2})^2\Delta u_1 + (\frac{1}{2})^3\Delta^2 u_1 - \ldots$, where u_n is a real positive quantity which diminishes as n increases and $\underset{n \to \infty}{\mathrm{Lt}} \ u_n = 0$.

In the series $1 - \frac{1}{3} + \frac{1}{5} - \frac{1}{7} + \ldots$ find the value of $\Delta^r u_n$ and prove that this series is equivalent to the series
$$\frac{1}{2}\left[1 + \frac{1}{3} + \frac{1 \cdot 2}{3 \cdot 5} + \frac{1 \cdot 2 \cdot 3}{3 \cdot 5 \cdot 7} + \ldots\right].$$

46. Use the conception of finite differences to prove that the general term in the recurring series $u_0 + u_1 x + u_2 x^2 + u_3 x^3 + \ldots$ (scale of relation $1 - px - qx^2$) is of the form $Aa^n + Bb^n$, where a and b are functions of p and q, and A and B are constants.

Prove that every series whose coefficients form an arithmetical progression is a recurring series, and that the generating function is
$$\frac{a + (d - a)x}{(1 - x)^2},$$
where a is the first term and d the common difference of the progression.

47. If u_x is a rational integral function of the third degree in x prove that
$$u_x = -\tfrac{1}{6}(x^2 - \tfrac{1}{4})(x - \tfrac{3}{2})u_{-\frac{3}{2}} + \tfrac{1}{2}(x - \tfrac{1}{2})(x^2 - \tfrac{9}{4})u_{-\frac{1}{2}}$$
$$- \tfrac{1}{2}(x + \tfrac{1}{2})(x^2 - \tfrac{9}{4})u_{\frac{1}{2}} + \tfrac{1}{6}(x^2 - \tfrac{1}{4})(x + \tfrac{3}{2})u_{\frac{3}{2}}$$
and hence find an approximate formula for $\int_0^1 u_x dx$ in terms of $u_{-\frac{1}{2}}$, $u_{\frac{1}{2}}$ and $u_{\frac{3}{2}}$.

48. Obtain a formula for the finite integration of any rational integral function of x and apply it to find the sum to n terms of the series whose rth term is $(r^2 + 1)(r - 2)$.

49. $a_{25:30} = 16\cdot311$; $a_{30:30} = 15\cdot784$; $a_{25:35} = 15\cdot660$;

   $a_{35:30} = 14\cdot420$; $a_{25:40} = 14\cdot824$; $a_{30:35} = 15\cdot209$.

Find as accurately as possible $a_{27:32}$.

50. Discuss the relative advantages of central difference formulae and advancing difference formulae with regard to accuracy and convenience.

From Gauss's "forward" and "backward" formulae deduce the most common form of Everett's formula.

51. By successive approximations based on the values of $x^3 - 5x + 3$ when $x = 0$, 1, 2 and 3, find to two places of decimals the smallest positive root of the equation $x^3 - 5x + 3 = 0$.

52. Prove the following approximate six-point formula:

$$u_{x:y} = u_{0:0} + \tfrac{1}{2}x\,(u_{1:0} - u_{-1:0}) + \tfrac{1}{2}y\,(u_{0:1} - u_{0:-1})$$
$$+ \tfrac{1}{2}x^2\,(u_{1:0} - 2u_{0:0} + u_{-1:0}) + xy\,(u_{1:1} - u_{1:0} - u_{0:1} + u_{0:0})$$
$$+ \tfrac{1}{2}y^2\,(u_{0:1} - 2u_{0:0} + u_{0:-1})$$

and state to what order of differences this formula is correct.

Use this formula to calculate the value of $u_{44:11}$ from six suitable values selected from the following values of $u_{x:y}$:

x	y			
	0	5	10	15
30	6	13	30	93
40	16	34	97	309
50	38	98	299	454
60	107	299	443	602

53. Given that u_x is a function of the third degree in x, show by a finite difference method that

$$\frac{16v_x}{x - 1} = (15v_3 - 5v_5 + v_7) - (x - 2)(7v_3 - 5v_5 + v_7)$$
$$+ \frac{(x - 2)(x - 3)}{3}(3v_3 - 3v_5 + v_7),$$

where $v_x = u_x - u_1$.

54. Complete the series u_5 to u_{15} by means of Everett's formula:

x	-5	0	5	10	15	20	25
u_x	61·0	91·4	113·6	134·2	179·4	238·0	296·2

55. Prove that $\Delta^n 0^m = n\,(\Delta^{n-1} 0^{m-1} + \Delta^n 0^{m-1})$ and by using the properties of the differences of zero find the value of

$$n^2 + (n-1)^2\,n + (n-2)^2\,\frac{n(n-1)}{2!} + (n-3)^2\,\frac{n(n-1)(n-2)}{3!} + \dots,$$

where n is a positive integer.

56. Obtain an expression for $\dfrac{d^n u_x}{dx^n}$ in terms of the differences of u_x up to and including differences of the $(n+2)$th order.

57. Prove the following approximate formulae:

(i) $\dfrac{1}{n} \displaystyle\int_0^n u_x\,dx = \dfrac{9u_0 + 19u_n - 5u_{2n} + u_{3n}}{24}.$

(ii) $\displaystyle\int_0^3 u_x\,d_x = \tfrac{3}{8}\,(u_0 + 3u_1 + 3u_2 + u_3).$

Use formula (ii) to determine an approximate value for $\log_e 2$.

58. (i) $f(x) = (x^3 + 3x^2 - 10)\,[x(x+1)(x+2)(x+5)]^{-1}$. Find $\Delta f(x)$.

(ii) $u_x = \dfrac{x^3 + x + 5}{x^4 + 10x^3 + 35x^2 + 50x + 4}$. Express the function as the sum of a number of inverse factorials and hence find $\Delta^2 u_x$.

59. Four variables x, y, z and u are connected by the equations

$$100y = 1 + 9x^3,$$
$$10z = 2 + 7y^2,$$
$$u = 3 + 5z.$$

If you were told to construct a table showing the value of u (but not the values of y and z) corresponding to each integral value of x from 1 to 20, how many values of u would it be necessary for you to compute by means of the above equations before you could fill in the remaining values by a finite difference method?

Write down the formula by which you would calculate these remaining values.

60. In an examination the numbers of candidates who obtained marks between certain limits were as follows:

Number of marks	Number of candidates
0–19	41
20–39	62
40–59	65
60–79	50
80–99	17

Estimate the number of candidates who obtained fewer than 70 marks.

61. Use Sheppard's rules to express u_x in terms of

(i) $u_0, \Delta u_0, \Delta^2 u_{-1}, \Delta^3 u_{-2}, \Delta^4 u_{-3}, \Delta^5 u_{-3}, \Delta^6 u_{-3}$;

(ii) $u_0, \Delta u_{-1}, \Delta^2 u_{-1}, \Delta^3 u_{-1}, \Delta^4 u_{-1}, \Delta^5 u_{-2}, \Delta^6 u_{-2}$.

62. Prove the formula

$$\Sigma u_x v_x = u_{x-1} \Sigma v_x - \Delta u_{x-2} \Sigma^2 v_x + \Delta^2 u_{x-3} \Sigma^3 v_x - \dots$$

and use it to find an expression for $\Sigma x^2 e^{2x}$.

63. Prove that

$$u_0 + n_{(2)} u_2 + n_{(4)} u_4 + n_{(6)} u_6 + \dots$$
$$= n\Delta^{n-1} u_0 + 2n_{(2)} \Delta^{n-2} u_0 + 4n_{(3)} \Delta^{n-3} u_0 + 8n_{(4)} \Delta^{n-4} u_0 + \dots$$

where n is an odd positive integer.

64. Find the values of the constants A, α and β if the formula

$$\int_0^{3+\sqrt{3}} u_x \, dx = A(u_\alpha + u_\beta)$$

is to be correct to second differences and show that for these values of the constants it is also correct to third differences. Hence or otherwise show that

$$\int_0^{19} u_x \, dx = \tfrac{19}{2} (u_4 + u_{15}) \text{ approximately.}$$

65. (i) If u_a, u_b, u_c ... denote the values of a function u_x at the n points a, b, c, ... and if $f_n(x, a, b, c, \dots)$ denotes the polynomial of lowest degree in x which coincides with u_x at these points, show by Newton's divided difference formula, or otherwise, that

$$(d-c) f_4(x, a, b, c, d) = (d-x) f_3(x, a, b, c) - (c-x) f_3(x, a, b, d).$$

15

(ii) If M is an operator such that

$$Mu_x = \tfrac{1}{3}\,(u_x + u_{x+h} + u_{x+2h}),$$

show that

$$\delta^n M^n u_x = \Delta^n u_x / 3^n,$$

where δ operates on u_x at intervals of h and Δ operates on u_x at intervals of $3h$.

66. Show that $[n]\, u_0 = nu_0 + \dfrac{n^3 - n}{24}\,\Delta^2 u_{-1}$ as far as third differences when n is odd.

Hence prove that, to the same degree of approximation,

$$6\,(-u_1 + 3u_0 - u_{-1}) = \{[3]\,[5] + [5]^2 + [3]\,[7] + 3\,[5] - 10\,[7]\}\,u_0.$$

67. Show that

$$\tfrac{1}{4}u_x + \tfrac{1}{8}u_{x+1} + \tfrac{1}{16}u_{x+2} + \tfrac{1}{32}u_{x+3} + \ldots$$

$$= \tfrac{1}{2}u_{x-1} + \Delta u_{x-3} + \frac{1\cdot 3}{2!}\,2\Delta^2 u_{x-5} + \frac{1\cdot 3\cdot 5}{3!}\,4\Delta^3 u_{x-7}$$

$$+ \frac{1\cdot 3\cdot 5\cdot 7}{4!}\,8\Delta^4 u_{x-9} + \ldots$$

for those values of u_x which make these series convergent.

68. (i) Prove that

$$e^x = \left(\frac{\Delta^2}{E}\right) e^x \cdot \frac{E\,e^x}{\Delta^2 e^x}$$

(interval of differencing h).

(ii) If u_x be a function of the form

$$b_1 x + b_2 x^2 + b_3 x^3 + \ldots \text{ to infinity,}$$

show that it can be expressed in the form

$$u_x = \frac{b_1 x}{1 - x} + \frac{\Delta b_1 x^2}{(1 - x)^2} + \frac{\Delta^2 b_1 x^3}{(1 - x)^3} + \ldots.$$

69. On 1 March a plant 6 inches high was put into a greenhouse. On 8 March its height was found to be 10 inches and on 29 March 14 inches. Estimate its height on 12 April (i) assuming that the height (h) is a rational integral function of the time (t); (ii) assuming that h and t are connected by a relation of the form $h = a + bt^n$; and explain why one method should give a better answer than the other in this particular case.

70. The following data are available:

Age x	32	37	42	47	52	57
e_x	35·36	33·25	30·72	27·23	23·16	19·11

It is desired to obtain $e_{57\frac{1}{2}}$ with as little labour as possible, and it is suggested that 18·71 would be a reasonable approximation. Do you agree with this? Give reasons.

From the above data, obtain a value for e_s.

71. Prove that

(i) $\Delta u_x = \Delta u_0 + x\Delta^2 u_0 + x_{(2)}\Delta^3 u_{-1} + (x+1)_{(3)}\Delta^4 u_{-1} \dots$

(ii) $u_x - \Delta u_x + \Delta^3 u_x - \Delta^4 u_x + \Delta^6 u_x - \Delta^7 u_x + \dots$
$$= u_{x-1} - \Delta^2 u_{x-2} + \Delta^4 u_{x-3} - \Delta^6 u_{x-4} + \dots.$$

72. If u_x be a function whose differences, when the increment of x is unity, are denoted by δu_x, $\delta^2 u_x$, $\delta^3 u_x$, ... and by Δu_x, $\Delta^2 u_x$, $\Delta^3 u_x$, ... when the increment of x is n; then if $\delta^2 u_x$, $\delta^2 u_{x+1}$, ... are in geometric progression with common ratio q, show that

$$\frac{\Delta u_x - n\delta u_x}{(q^n - 1) - n(q - 1)} = \frac{\delta^2 u_x}{(q-1)^2}.$$

73. Prove that, approximately,

$$125 u_0 = [5]^3 (u_0 + \Delta u_{-2} - \Delta u_1).$$

74. Obtain a Lagrange formula for $u_{x:y}$ given $u_{0:0}$, $u_{0:1}$, $u_{1:0}$, $u_{1:1}$, and by means of the formula find $u_{31:43}$ from the data below:

$$u_{30:40} = 28·90,$$
$$u_{35:40} = 28·10,$$
$$u_{30:45} = 27·30,$$
$$u_{35:45} = 26·62.$$

75. Given that

$$f(0) = 12, \quad f(2) = 31, \quad f(5) = 45, \quad f(8) = 67, \quad f(10) = 84,$$

calculate the value of $\int_0^{10} f(x)\,dx$ as accurately as you can and state to what order of differences the formula used is true.

76. If

$$u_0 = 6,$$
$$u_{10} = 27,$$
$$u_{20} = 62,$$
$$u_{30} = 111,$$

find the value of x satisfying the equation

$$u_x + u_{10+x} + u_{20+x} = (u_{10-x} + u_{20-x} + u_{30-x}) - 42.$$

77. Given that $u_1 = 9$, $u_2 = 18$, $u_3 = 37$, $u_4 = 78$, $u_5 = 165$, $u_6 = 346$, $u_7 = 717$, find a general expression for $\sum\limits_1^n u_x$.

78. Find $u_{2:2}$ from the following table of $u_{x:y}$, using all the values given:

$$x$$

		0	1	2
	0	16·25	15·08	13·49
y	1	15·55	14·58	13·15
	2	14·48	13·74	

79. Show that

(i) $u_x - \frac{1}{8}\Delta^2 u_{x-1} + \frac{1\cdot 3}{8\cdot 16}\Delta^4 u_{x-2} - \frac{1\cdot 3\cdot 5}{8\cdot 16\cdot 24}\Delta^6 u_{x-3} + \ldots$

$$= u_{x+\frac{1}{2}} - \frac{1}{2}\Delta u_{x+\frac{1}{2}} + \frac{1}{4}\Delta^2 u_{x+\frac{1}{2}} - \frac{1}{8}\Delta^3 u_{x+\frac{1}{2}} + \ldots$$

(ii) $\Sigma u_x v_x = u_x \Sigma v_x - \Delta u_x \Sigma^2 v_{x+1} + \Delta^2 u_x \Sigma^3 v_{x+2} - \ldots$.

80. Given that u_x is a rational integral function of the second degree in x and that

$$\sum_{x=1}^{20} u_x = 470,$$
$$2u_7 = u_6 + u_{11},$$
$$\sum_{x=4}^{7} u_x = u_{14} + u_{15},$$

construct the table of values u_1 to u_6.

81. If u_x is a rational integral function of the fourth degree in x, and if $u_0 = u_2 = u_1 + u_3 = u_1 u_3 + 1 = u_4 + 2u_1 = 0$ and u_1 is negative, find for what values of n greater than 4

$$6(n-2)\sum_{x=0}^{n-1} u_x = (n-1)(n-4)u_n.$$

82. If $f(x)$ is a rational integral function of the third degree in x, and $\phi(x) = f(x) + f(t-x)$, show that $\int_0^t f(x)\,dx$ can be expressed in the form $\sum\limits_{x=0}^{t} f(x) + a\phi(0) + b\phi(1) + c\phi(2)$, where a, b and c are independent of t, and find the values of these constants.

83. (i) Sum to n terms $26 + 66 + 132 + 230 + 366 + 546 + \dots$.

(ii) Find the value of

$$n(n+1) + n.(n-1)n + \frac{n(n+1)}{1.2}.(n-2)(n-1) + \dots$$

84. Find $a_{44:51}$, given that $a_{40:50} = 10\cdot894$, $a_{40:55} = 9\cdot796$, $a_{40:60} = 8\cdot553$, $a_{45:50} = 10\cdot591$, $a_{45:55} = 9\cdot583$ and $a_{50:50} = 10\cdot059$

85. It is required to calculate numerical values of the function u_x for all integral values of x from 1 to n, given that $u_3 = 3$ and that $\Delta^r u_1 = r(r-1)$ for all positive integral values of r. Find in its simplest form an expression for u_x, in terms of x, that can be used for calculating the required values.

86. (i) Prove that

$$\int_{-3}^{3} u_x\,dx = 6u_0 + 9\Delta^2 u_{-1} + \tfrac{33}{10}\Delta^4 u_{-2} + \tfrac{41}{140}\Delta^6 u_{-3},$$

where u_x is a function of the sixth degree in x.

(ii) Obtain a formula for $\int_1^5 f(x)\,dx$ in terms of $f(0), f(1), f(2)$ and $f(3)$, where $f(x)$ is a function of the third degree in x.

87. Find the values of a, b, c and d for which

$$u_0 = [3]\,[5]\,\{au_0 + bu_1 + cu_2 + du_3\}$$

assuming third differences constant.

88. Prove Lubbock's formula

$$u_0 + u_{1/n} + u_{2/n} + \dots + u_{m-1/n}$$
$$= n(u_0 + u_1 + \dots + u_{m-1}) + \frac{n-1}{2}(u_m - u_0) - \frac{n^2-1}{12n}(\Delta u_m - \Delta u_0)$$
$$+ \frac{n^2-1}{24n}(\Delta^2 u_m - \Delta^2 u_0) \dots$$

and use it to find $\overset{50}{\underset{x=10}{\Sigma}} x^2 (x-3)$ by calculating values of $x^2 (x-3)$ when x

is 10, 20, 30, 40 and 50.

89. If interpolated values are found in the interval $x=0$ to $x=1$ from the values u_{-1}, u_0, u_1, u_2, by means of the formula

$$u_x = \xi u_0 + \frac{\xi^2 (\xi - 1)}{2} \Delta^2 u_{-1}$$

$$+ x u_1 + \frac{x^2 (x-1)}{2} \Delta^2 u_0 \quad \text{(where } \xi = 1 - x),$$

and in the next interval $x=1$ to $x=2$ by the corresponding formula based on the values u_0, u_1, u_2 and u_3, show that:

(1) The given values u_0, u_1 and u_2 will be reproduced by the interpolation.

(2) The two interpolation curves have the same differential coefficient when $x=1$.

(3) The interpolated values for $u_{\frac{1}{2}}$ and $u_{\frac{3}{2}}$ agree with those given by the ordinary third difference interpolation formula based on the same values of u_x.

Given the following values:

$$u_{-5} = 1000, \qquad u_{10} = 2609,$$
$$u_0 = 1403, \qquad u_{15} = 3487,$$
$$u_5 = 1931,$$

complete the table for unit intervals from u_0 to u_{10} by the above formulae and calculate the value of the differential coefficient of the interpolated curves when $x=5$.

90. (i) Prove that

$$\frac{d^2 u_x}{dx^2} = \overset{\infty}{\underset{r=2}{\Sigma}} 2 (-1)^r \left\{ 1 + \tfrac{1}{2} + \tfrac{1}{3} + \dots + \frac{1}{r-1} \right\} \frac{\Delta^r u_x}{r}.$$

(ii) Hence, or otherwise, given the series $f(1) = 8$, $f(2) = 6$, $f(3) = 42$, $f(4) = 134$, $f(5) = 300$ and $f(6) = 558$, construct a series of values for $d^2 f(x)/dx^2$ for integral values of x from 1 to 6.

91. Having given the present value of £1 per annum at the end of 20 years at the undermentioned rates of interest per cent.:

Rate per cent.	Present value of £1 per annum
2	16·351433
$2\frac{1}{2}$	15·589162
3	14·877475
$3\frac{1}{2}$	14·212403
4	13·590326
$4\frac{1}{2}$	13·007936

use Everett's formula of interpolation to find the present value of £1 per annum at the end of 20 years at 3·2 per cent. per annum.

92. Find, to four decimal places, the real root of the equation $x^3 + x - 1 = 0$ by whichever of the following methods you consider most suitable, stating briefly the reasons for your choice:

(a) divided differences applied inversely,

(b) successive approximation,

(c) elimination of third differences.

93. Given

$$u_0 + u_1 + u_2 = 11\cdot3,$$
$$u_3 + u_4 + u_5 = 37\cdot7,$$
$$u_6 + u_7 + u_8 = 93\cdot8,$$
$$3u_0 + u_1 = u_{10} - u_9 - 3\cdot7,$$

find the form of u_x, assuming that it is a function of the third degree in x.

94. Find

$$\Delta^{-1} \frac{(-1)^{x+1}\, x!}{(a-1)(a-2)\dots(a-x)},$$

when a is a constant, and hence show that, except when a is a positive integer less than $n+1$,

$$\frac{1}{a-1} - \frac{2!}{(a-1)(a-2)} + \frac{3!}{(a-1)(a-2)(a-3)} - \dots$$
$$+ \frac{(-1)^{n+1}\, n!}{(a-1)(a-2)\dots(a-n)} = \frac{1}{a+1}\left[1 + \frac{(-1)^{n+1}(n+1)!}{(a-1)(a-2)\dots(a-n)}\right].$$

95. Prove that, to third differences,

$$\frac{1}{m}\sum_{n=1}^{m}\left(\frac{[1][2][3]\dots[n]}{n!}u_0\right) = u_0 + \frac{1}{288}(m^2-1)(m+4)\,\Delta^2 u_{-1}.$$

96. The xth term of the series 1, 2, 17, 72, 243, 754 ... is of the form $a + bx + c^x + d^x$. Determine a, b, c, d and find the sum of n terms of the series.

97. Find $\Delta\left(a^{(x)}/b^{(x)}\right)$ where a and b are constants, and prove that, if m is a positive integer and b is not a positive integer less than m,

$$1 - m_{(1)}\frac{a}{b} + m_{(2)}\frac{a(a-1)}{b(b-1)} - m_{(3)}\frac{a(a-1)(a-2)}{b(b-1)(b-2)} + \cdots$$

$$= \left(1 - \frac{a}{b}\right)\left(1 - \frac{a}{b-1}\right)\cdots\left(1 - \frac{a}{b-m+1}\right).$$

98. Prove that

$$\Delta \sin(ax+b) = 2 \sin\frac{a}{2}\sin\left(ax + b + \frac{a+\pi}{2}\right)$$

where the interval of differencing is unity, and deduce an expression for $\Delta^n \sin(ax+b)$.

Hence, or otherwise, show that

$$\sin^n \pi x \frac{\Delta^n \sin \pi x}{E^n \sin \pi x} = \left(\frac{\Delta}{E}\sin \pi x\right)^n,$$

given that $\sin \pi x$ is not zero.

99. If $\displaystyle\int_0^m f(x)\,dx = a_1 f(x_1) + a_2 f(x_2) + \cdots + a_n f(x_n)$, where $f(x)$ is a polynomial in x of the $(n-1)$th degree $(n > 2)$, prove that

$$3\sum_{r=1}^{n} a_r x_r^2 = m^3.$$

Hence, or otherwise, obtain a formula correct to third differences for $\displaystyle\int_0^7 u_x\,dx$ in terms of u_1, u_3, u_4 and u_6.

100. If
$$\begin{aligned}
w_{-1} &= u_{-7} + u_{-6} + u_{-5} + u_{-4} + u_{-3},\\
w_0 &= u_{-2} + u_{-1} + u_0 + u_1 + u_2,\\
w_1 &= u_3 + u_4 + u_5 + u_6 + u_7,\\
w_2 &= u_8 + u_9 + u_{10} + u_{11} + u_{12},
\end{aligned}$$

prove that
$$u_2 + u_3 = \cdot 2\,(w_0 + w_1) - \cdot 032\,(\Delta^2 w_{-1} + \Delta^2 w_0).$$

ANSWERS TO THE EXAMPLES

Examples 1.

1. 58.   **2.** 30, 42.   **3.** 15.

4. 1·9.   **5.** 1110.   **8.** $6ah^3$.

9. $\frac{1}{6}(-11x^3 + 252x^2 - 1051x + 1344)$.   **10.** $abcd.10!$.

11. $ab^{cx}(b^c - 1)$; $ab^{cx}(b^c - 1)^2$; $ab^{cx}\dfrac{(b^c - 1)\,[(b^c - 1)^{10} - 1]}{b^c - 2}$.

12. (i) $\frac{1}{2}x(x-1) + k$,   (ii) $c^x/(c-1) + k$,

(iii) $3x(x-1)(x-2) + \frac{9}{2}x(x-1) + 3x + k$, where k is a constant.

13. $-\dfrac{2}{(x+2)(x+3)} - \dfrac{3}{(x+3)(x+4)}$;

$\dfrac{4}{(x+2)(x+3)(x+4)} + \dfrac{6}{(x+3)(x+4)(x+5)}$.

14. $\dfrac{2}{x(x-1)(x-2)}$.   **15.** -2 or 109.

16. (1) $an!$;   (2) $e^{ax+b}(e^a - 1)^n$.   **18.** 55.   **19.** $a^{2x} + (a^2 + 1)^2\,a^{4x}$.

20. $\frac{1}{4}x(x-1)(x-2)(x-3) + 2x(x-1)(x-2) + \frac{9}{2}x(x-1) + 12x + k$.

21. 2225.   **22.** 20.   **23.** -161.   **24.** 229.   **25.** 1261.

28. $x^{(4)} - 6x^{(3)} + 13x^{(2)} + x^{(1)} + 9$; $4x^{(3)} - 18x^{(2)} + 26x^{(1)} + 1$;

$12x^{(2)} - 36x^{(1)} + 26$; $24x^{(1)} - 36$;   24.

29. (i) $(m+1)\,m\,(m-1)\,\ldots\,(m-n+2)\,a^{m+1}\,(b/a + x + m)^{(m-n+1)}$;

(ii) $(-1)^n\,(m+1)\,(m+2)\,\ldots\,(m+n)\,a^{-\overline{m+1}}\,(b/a - 1 + x)^{(-m+n+1)}$.

30. $2\cos(x + \frac{1}{2}\alpha)\sin\frac{1}{2}\alpha$; $\sin\alpha/\{\cos(x+\alpha)\cos x\}$; $\alpha - 2\sin(x + \frac{1}{2}\alpha)\sin\frac{1}{2}\alpha$.

31. $6x$; $6/(x+1)^2$.   **42.** $\gamma^2 + 4\alpha\gamma = \beta^2$.   **43.** $2(x-2)^n - 2(x-3)^n$.

Examples 2.

1. 465.   **2.** 441; 653.   **3.** 300.

4. 182; 343.   **5.** 5414.   **6.** 89,920; 89,073.

7. 128.   **8.** 94; 396; 662.   **9.** 194·3; 279·9.

10. 97,357.   **11.** 844; 746.   **12.** ·98127.

13. 69,215.   **14.** 2·37223.   **15.** −·432; −·338; −·196.

16. 30; 0.   **17.** 14·73658.   **18.** 3·708; 3·711.

19. 5281; 6504.   **20.** ·5479.   **21.** 2153; 1705.

22. 2459; 2424; 2359; 2268; 2153; 2018; 1868; 1705; 1534; 1357; 1180.

23. ·017; ·035; ·052; ·070; ·087; ·104; ·122; ·139; ·157.

24. 23·1234; 23·2039; 23·2914; 23·3865; 23·4898; 23·6019; 23·7234.

26. 1·000.　　　**27.** ·020660; ·020625; ·020628.　　　**28.** 58,835.

29. 1; 2·10; 3·31; 4·64; 6·11; 7·73; 9·51; 11·47; 13·62; 15·97.

31. 117·7; 114·2; 110·5; 106·7; 102·7; 98·6; 94·3; 89·8; 85·2; 80·3; 75·4.

32. ·24928.　　　**33.** Third degree: 275.　　　**34.** 459.

35. $u_2 = 218$; $u_4 = 0$; $u_5 = -19$; $u_x = 1876 - 1429x + 360x^2 - 30x^3$.

Examples 3.

1. 5745.　**2.** 47,983.　**3.** 2·8169.　**4.** 1·7243.　**5.** 2300.　**6.** 460.

7. $-\dfrac{l+m}{l^2m^2}$; $\dfrac{lm+mn+nl}{l^2m^2n^2}$; $-\dfrac{lmn+mnp+npl+plm}{l^2m^2n^2p^2}$.

8. 13·18.　　　**9.** 14·942.　　　**10.** 20·43.　　　**11.** 162.

12. $659 + 22\frac{1}{4}x + \frac{29}{12}x^2 - \frac{1}{12}x^3$.　　　**13.** 32.　　　**16.** 1; 25.

18. 33 and 67 to the nearest integer.　　　**19.** 37·2.

20. 7·37.　　　**21.** 130,326.

23. $(x-4)$; $(x-3)(x-4)$; $(x-3)(x-4)(x-7)$; $x(x-3)(x-4)(x-7)$.

24. The $\triangle u$'s are $\underset{3}{\triangle}u_4$; $\underset{3,0}{\triangle^2}u_4$; $\underset{4,3,0}{\triangle^3}u_7$; $\underset{4,3,0,11}{\triangle^4}u_7$.

Examples 4.

1. 33.　　**2.** 6.　　**3.** 47,692.　　**4.** 3251.　　**5.** 16·9216.

6. 2·85805; 2·86305; 2·86157; 2·86155.　　**7.** 2017.

8. 3·5283.　　　**9.** 2196, 2108, 2022, 1939; 1786, 1718, 1657, 1604.

10. ·01625.　　　**11.** ·3165.　　　**12.** 2290·1.　　　**14.** 4·034.

Examples 5.

1. 471·5; 2·7.　　**2.** 13·3.　　　**3.** 2·019...; 2·018....

4. 43·1.　　　**5.** 8·34.　　　**6.** 2·751.　　　**7.** 16·9.

8. 1·1576....　　**9.** 1·2134.　　**10.** 45·70.　　**11.** 1·85.

12. 3·091.　　　**13.** 3·667 per cent.　　　**14.** 1·3713.　　　**15.** 37·2.

Examples 6.

1. $\frac{1}{6}n(-2n^2+27n+17)$.　　　**2.** $\frac{-1}{12}n(n+1)(3n^2+7n+2)$.

3. -4195.　　**4.** $2^{21}+628$.　　　**5.** $3^{n+1}+\frac{1}{2}(n^2+7n-6)$.

6. $\frac{1}{8}\{\frac{1}{2}(3^n-1)+5n+\frac{1}{3}n(n+1)(2n+1)\}$.

7. $2^{2k+1}-2-\frac{1}{3}k(2k+1)(4k+1)$.　　　**8.** $\frac{1}{3}(n^4-10n^3+29n^2+10n)$.

9. $2n^4 + 16n^3 + 47n^2 + 60n.$ **10.** $2^{19} - 2095.$

11. $\frac{1}{4}(n+3)(n+4)(n+5)(n+6) - 90.$

12. $\frac{1}{4}n(n+1)(n+4)(n+5).$

13. $\frac{1}{12}\{(3n-2)(3n+1)(3n+4)(3n+7) + 56\}.$

14. $\frac{1}{12}n(n+1)(n+2)(3n+13).$

15. $\frac{1}{30}n(n+1)(n+2)(6n^2 + 57n + 137).$

16. $\frac{1}{10}\{(2n+3)(2n+5)(2n+7)(2n+9)(2n+11) - 10395\}.$

17. $\dfrac{n}{4(n+4)}.$ **18.** $\dfrac{n(5n+13)}{12(n+2)(n+3)}.$ **19.** $\dfrac{n(n+1)}{6(n+3)(n+4)}.$

20. $\dfrac{n(3n+5)}{8(3n+1)(3n+4)}.$ **21.** $\dfrac{n(5n+11)}{4(n+1)(n+2)}.$

22. $\frac{16}{15}n(n+1)(n+2)(3n^2 + 36n + 101).$

23. $\dfrac{19}{168} - \dfrac{12n^2 + 33n + 19}{6(3n+1)(3n+4)(3n+7)};\ \dfrac{19}{168}.$

24. $\frac{1}{12}n(n+1)(3n^2 + 31n + 74).$

25. $\frac{1}{4}(n+3)(n+2)(n+1)n;\ \frac{1}{4}n(n-1)(n-2)(n-3).$

26. $3^n - 1 - n.$ **27.** $\dfrac{a^x}{a-1}\left\{x^2 - \dfrac{2ax}{a-1} + \dfrac{a(a+1)}{(a-1)^2}\right\} + C.$

28. $1 - 3(n+1)! + (n+2)!.$

29. $\frac{1}{15}\{(3n-1)(3n+2)(3n+5)(3n+8)(3n+11) + 880\}.$

30. $\frac{1}{8}n(6n^3 + 16n^2 + 9n - 4).$ **31.** $\frac{1}{24}n(7n^3 - 34n^2 + 89n - 254).$

33. $\frac{1}{12}n(n+1)(9n^2 + 17n + 4);\ \{2^{n+1}(n^3 - 3n^2 + 10n - 14)\} + 28.$

34. $\dfrac{2}{3} + \dfrac{4^{n+1}}{3}\left\{\dfrac{n-1}{n+2}\right\}.$ **35.** $\dfrac{11}{768}.$ **36.** $34 - (4n^2 + 12n + 17)/2^{n-1}.$

37. $(x-2)3^x.$ **38.** $\frac{5}{2}(3^n - 1) + \frac{1}{12}(42n + 17n^2 + n^4).$

39. $\dfrac{(n+2)x^n - 2}{x-1} - \dfrac{x^{n+1} - x}{(x-1)^2}.$ **40.** $C - \dfrac{12x^3 + 36x^2 + 28x + 3}{12x(x+1)(x+2)(x+3)}.$

42. $\dfrac{1}{54}\left\{\dfrac{39}{10} - \dfrac{36n + 39}{(3n+2)(3n+5)}\right\}.$ **43.** $23.$ **44.** $n^2 2^{n+1}.$

45. $\dfrac{2 - (n+1)(n+2)x^n}{1-x} + \dfrac{2x}{(1-x)^2}\{2 - (n+2)x^n\} + \dfrac{2x^2}{(1-x)^3}(1 - x^n).$

46. $C - 2^{x-2}\dfrac{(x-1)!}{(2x-1)!}.$

47. $\frac{5}{4} + \frac{1}{60}(2n-1)(2n+1)(2n+3)(24n^2 + 54n + 25).$

48. $\frac{1}{4}ax^4 - (\frac{1}{2}a - \frac{1}{3}b)x^3 + (\frac{1}{4}a - \frac{1}{2}b + \frac{1}{2}c)x^2 + (\frac{1}{6}b - \frac{1}{2}c + d)x + C.$

49. $(1-x)^{r+1}.$ **52.** $\dfrac{1}{a-1}\left\{1 - \dfrac{(n+1)!}{(a+1)(a+2)\ldots(a+n)}\right\}.$

53. $2^{n-4}n(n+1)(n^2 + 5n - 2).$

Examples 7.

2. $20 \cdot 796875$; $-\frac{1}{64}$.   **10.** $\cdot 02455$; $-\cdot 0003$; o.

11. $\cdot 109$.   **13.** $ke^{ax+\lambda cx}$.   **15.** 48; 24.

19. $5 \cdot 254$.   **22.** $13 \cdot 094$.   **23.** $5 \cdot 319$.

24. $3 \cdot 9634$.   **25.** $10 \cdot 389$; $10 \cdot 475$.

Examples 9.

2. $\cdot 9921$.   **3.** $20 \cdot 4$ miles.

8. $\frac{1}{144}(95u_0 - 50u_1 + 600u_2 - 350u_3 + 425u_4)$.

9. 200 square inches.   **11.** $\cdot 8571\ldots$; (i) $\cdot 8806\ldots$; (ii) $\cdot 8946\ldots$

12. The second.   **13.** $29,426$.   **14.** 888.   **16.** $\cdot 6942$.

22. $\cdot 5236$.   **24.** $3 \cdot 142\ldots$ **25.** $1 \cdot 1358\ldots$

26. $\cdot 6931\ldots$ **27.** $3 \cdot 142\ldots$

Miscellaneous Examples

1. $\dfrac{n}{12}(n^3 - 4n^2 + 11n + 4)$.   **3.** 1764, 1260.

4. (a) $19,764$; (b) 59, 156.   **6.** 913.   **9.** $22 \cdot 674$.

12. 18.

15. (i) $\frac{1}{20}n(n+1)(n+2)(n+3)(4n+1)$;

     (ii) $\frac{1}{6}n\left[\dfrac{1}{n+1} + \dfrac{1}{2(n+2)} + \dfrac{4}{3(n+3)}\right]$.

17. 6.   **18.** $\frac{49}{16}e^{\frac{1}{4}}$.   **20.** $\cdot 0294$; $\cdot 0492$; $\cdot 0682$.

22. $1 \cdot 109$.   **28.** $60 \cdot 72$.

29. $\dfrac{n}{2}[9n^3 + 16n^2 + 2n - 3]$; $\dfrac{n}{56} \cdot \dfrac{261n^2 + 876n + 655}{(3n+1)(3n+4)(3n+7)}$.

34. $\dfrac{n}{60}[n^4 - 5n^3 + 65n^2 - 85n + 84]$; $2^{n+1} - 2 + \dfrac{n}{6}[4n^2 - 9n - 1]$;

     213; 215.

35. $58 \cdot 9321\ldots$ **38.** 86; 121.   **41.** 45.

43. $\cdot 7854$.   **49.** $15 \cdot 975$.   **51.** $\cdot 66$.

52. $187 \cdot 52$.

54. $113 \cdot 6$, $117 \cdot 0$, $120 \cdot 4$, $124 \cdot 2$, $128 \cdot 8$, $134 \cdot 2$, $141 \cdot 4$, $149 \cdot 4$, $158 \cdot 6$, $168 \cdot 6$, $179 \cdot 4$.

55. $2^{n-2}n(n+1)$.   **60.** 196.

69. (i) 10 in.; (ii) $15 \cdot 8$ in.   **70.** $29 \cdot 08$.   **74.** $27 \cdot 80$.

76. 3.   **77.** $6 \cdot 2^{n+1} - 12 - \dfrac{n}{6}[2n^2 + 3n + 13]$.   **78.** $12 \cdot 50$.

80. 90, 65, 43, 24, 8, -5.   **81.** 7, 13.

82. $a = -\frac{5}{8}$, $b = \frac{1}{6}$, $c = -\frac{1}{24}$.

83. (i) $\dfrac{n}{12}[3n^3 + 34n^2 + 117n + 158]$; (ii) $\dfrac{2(2n+1)!}{(n+2)!(n-1)!}$.

84. 10·476.

89. 1403, 1498, 1598, 1703, 1814, 1931, 2054, 2182, 2316, 2458, 2609; 120·6.

91. 14·606063. 92. ·6823.

96. $\frac{1}{2}[2^{n+2} + 3^{n+1} - 7n^2 - n - 7]$.

INDEX

The numbers refer to the pages